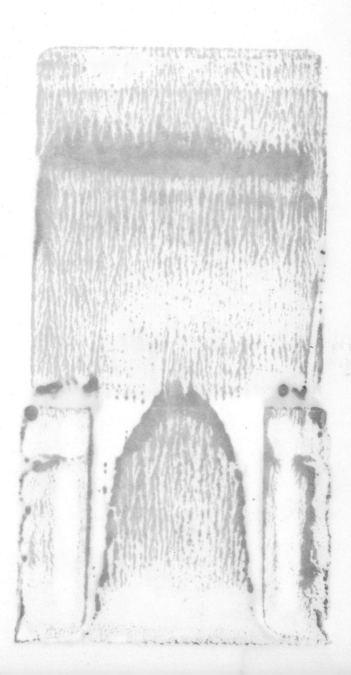

MOLECULAR BIOCHEMISTRY

McGRAW-HILL SERIES IN ADVANCED CHEMISTRY

Bair   *Introduction to Chemical Instrumentation*
Benson   *The Foundations of Chemical Kinetics*
Davidson   *Statistical Mechanics*
Davydov (TRANS. *Kasha and Oppenheimer*) *Theory of Molecular Excitons*
Dean   *Flame Photometry*
Djerassi   *Optical Rotatory Dispersion*
Eliel   *Stereochemistry of Carbon Compounds*
Fitts   *Nonequilibrium Thermodynamics*
Helfferich   *Ion Exchange*
Hill   *Statistical Mechanics*
Hine   *Physical Organic Chemistry*
Kirkwood and Oppenheim   *Chemical Thermodynamics*
Kosower   *Molecular Biochemistry*
Laitinen   *Chemical Analysis*
Pitzer and Brewer   (REVISION OF *Lewis and Randall*) *Thermodynamics*
Pople, Schneider, and Bernstein   *High-resolution Nuclear Magnetic Resonance*
Pryor   *Mechanisms of Sulfur Reactions*
Roberts   *Nuclear Magnetic Resonance*
Rossotti and Rossotti   *The Determination of Stability Constants*
Wiberg   *Laboratory Technique in Organic Chemistry*

MOLECULAR
BIOCHEMISTRY

EDWARD M. KOSOWER

Department of Chemistry
State University of New York
Long Island Center
Stony Brook, New York

New York
San Francisco
Toronto
London

McGRAW-HILL BOOK COMPANY, INC. 1962

MOLECULAR BIOCHEMISTRY

35320

II

This book is dedicated to my wife, Nechama, for her unfailing affection and patience at all times.

PREFACE

One of the most challenging frontiers to human inquiry lies within the domain of molecular biology, the explanation of biological processes and phenomena in molecular terms. In areas as diverse as genetics, medicine, and pharmacology, the relationship between molecular occurrence and visible result is being eagerly sought.

In many cases, the molecular occurrences are or result from chemical transformations. For example, the medically identified condition of galactosemia has been traced to a deficiency of the enzyme galactose-1-phosphate uridyl transferase, which catalyzes the conversion of UDP-galactose to UDP-glucose.

During the last fifty years, enormous effort on the part of biochemists has led to a fairly complete understanding of the stoichiometry of intermediary metabolism, that is, a description of the sequences of compounds through which a molecule of, say, glucose is converted into carbon dioxide and water.

Over the same time period, vigorous research into the mechanisms of reaction of organic compounds (physical-organic chemistry) had led to a considerable clarification of the pathways by which one organic compound is converted into another.

In the past few years, a new research area has emerged from the application of the physical-organic approach to the problems in chemical transformation found in biochemistry. We choose to call this area *molecular biochemistry*, and delimit it as the study of the detailed chemical mechanisms of the chemical transformations in biology, usually as they are described in biochemistry.

The present book is an attempt to survey and organize the area in such a way as to indicate the numerous lacunas which exist as well as to point out some of the exciting new avenues of research with implications for molecular biochemistry. The level at which the book is written is roughly that of a second-year graduate student in chemistry or biochemistry, but it could be read with profit by research workers in both fields, or by younger students with a good background in organic mechanisms.

The book is divided into three rather unequal parts: the first, a survey and classification of many of the reactions of intermediary metabolism; the second, a discussion of the mechanisms of many of these reactions, with the relationship to the enzymatic reaction shown where possible; and the third, a brief discussion of one of the central problems of molecular biochemistry, the "active site." To a large extent, the distribution of topics has been dictated by such objective factors as the frequency of occurrence of certain reaction types as outlined in the first part, and the availability of material which could be discussed within the context of this book. In some cases, e.g., decarboxylation, an organization of the subject matter from organic chemistry was deemed worthwhile, and in others, i.e., ester and amide hydrolysis, the discussion is shortened because of the extensive review material which can be readily obtained.

The special interests of the author are no doubt visible in the section on pyridine nucleotides, but it should be emphasized that detailed chemical inquiries into biologically important reactions of molecules, apart from their intrinsic chemical value, often have serendipitous consequences.

A number of simplifying conventions have been adopted in the presentation of the figures, as follows: Enzymatic reactions are almost always written as proceeding in one direction, whereas they are, in fact, reversible. Formulas are written with full bonds, even though these do not always reflect the correct charge distributions (as in carboxylate, phosphate, etc.). The state of ionization is usually that which probably exists at physiological pH.

The author is indebted to the Alfred P. Sloan Foundation for a fellowship which released him to a great extent from the burden of other duties and accelerated the completion of the book. He also owes a considerable amount to friendly critics, especially Prof. Edward L. King, of the Department of Chemistry, and Prof. Helmut Beinert, of the Enzyme Institute, both of the University of Wisconsin. For stimulating conversations on many aspects of the subject, he would like to thank Dr. Leonard Peller and Dr. David Lemal, of the Department of Chemistry, University of Wisconsin, and many other students and colleagues, among whom might be mentioned Sue Brown; Jon Brodie; Prof. S. Wakil, of Duke University; Prof. Y. Hatefi, Prof. D. E. Green; Prof. H. Khorana; Dr. W. Lee, of the Enzyme Institute; and Dr. H. Abrash.

Edward M. Kosower

ACKNOWLEDGMENTS

The author is grateful for permission to publish excerpts from the following:

"The Dissolution," by John Donne, in "The Complete Poetry and Selected Prose of John Donne and the Complete Poetry of William Blake," p. 44.   Copyright 1941 by Random House, Inc., New York.

"Écoutez la Chanson Bien Douce," by Paul Verlaine, in "Verlaine et Les Poètes Symbolistes," with notes by A. Micha, p. 29.   Copyright by Editions Messein, Paris.

"Tartuffe," by Molière, p. 30.   Copyright 1941 by Librairie Larousse, Paris.

"Die Lorelei," by Heinrich Heine, in "The Penguin Book of German Verse," introduced and edited by Leonard Forster, p. 329.   Copyright by Penguin Books, Ltd., London.

"Du Maître D'Astres et de Navigation" in "Amers," by St.-John Perse, p. 40.   Copyright 1958 by Bollingen Foundation, Inc., New York. Reproduced by permission of Bollingen Foundation, New York.

"The Waste Land, I.   The Burial of the Dead" in "Collected Poems 1909–1935 by T. S. Eliot."   Copyright 1936 by Harcourt, Brace, and World, Inc., New York.

"La Cantatrice Chauve," by E. Ionesco.   Copyright 1954 by Librairie Gallimard, Paris.

"Ciba Foundation Symposium on the Biosynthesis of Terpenes and Sterols," 1959.   Copyright 1959 by J. and A. Churchill, Ltd., London.

ix

"Veglia," by Guiseppi Ungaretti, in "Penguin Book of Italian Verse," edited by George Kay, p. 366. Copyright by Arnoldo Mondadori Editore, Milan.

"Antoine et Cléopâtre" by José-María de Heredia, in "Penguin Book of French Verse," vol. 3, "The Nineteenth Century," p. 184. Copyright by Penguin Books, Ltd., London.

"Gulliver's Travels," by Jonathan Swift. Copyright 1940 by Heritage Press, New York.

"Klage," by Rainer Maria Rilke, in "Selected Poems" by R. M. Rilke. Copyright 1941 by Insel-Verlag, Wiesbaden.

"The Backbone Flute," by Vladimir Mayakovsky, in "The Bedbug and Selected Poetry," edited by Patricia Blake. Copyright 1960 by Meridian Books, Inc., New York.

"Japanese Haiku," by Shusen, p. 21. Copyright 1955–1956 by Peter Pauper Press, Mount Vernon, N.Y.

"Expectation," by Thomas Stanley, in "The Centuries' Poetry 2: Donne to Dryden," p. 132. Copyright by Penguin Books, Ltd., London.

"Bitter Lemons," by Lawrence Durrell, p. 38. Copyright by E. P. Dutton and Co., Inc., New York.

"The Old Familiar Faces," by Charles Lamb, in "The Centuries' Poetry 3." Copyright by Penguin Books, Ltd., London.

"Sueño," by Juan Ramón Jiménez, in "The Penguin Book of Spanish Verse," edited by J. M. Cohen, p. 354. Copyright by Penguin Books, Ltd., London.

"Canto notturno di un pastore errante dell'Asia," by G. Leopardi, in "The Penguin Book of Italian Verse," edited by G. R. Kay, p. 279. Copyright by Penguin Books, Ltd., London.

"Hard, Ain't It Hard," words and music by Woody Guthrie. Copyright 1952 by Ludlow Music, Inc., New York, N.Y. Used by permission.

CONTENTS

PART 1
BIOCHEMICAL PATTERNS

1.0. INTRODUCTION

Shee is dead; And all which die
To their first elements resolve. . . .
John Donne

Life is the resultant of a complex set of chemical and physical processes. Driven by urges with both idealistic and practical roots, man is now engaged in a vigorous effort to understand the molecular basis of life. One should perhaps be a bit shy of repeating an optimistic statement of the early part of the century, "Nothing indicates, however, at present that the artificial production of living matter is beyond the possibilities of science . . . ,"[1] but few scientists would assert that such an accomplishment is impossible.

The complexity of physical phenomena has led to fragmentation of scientific studies. To appreciate the relationship of molecular biochemistry to other disciplines concerned with life, a hierarchy of sciences can be constructed, in which it can be remarked that particle size is a determinant factor in position (Table 1.0-1).

Sciences in the same or neighboring levels are those which are most enriched by interdisciplinary cooperation, because of the ease in hybridizing intellectual and experimental techniques. Thus, biochemistry and organic chemistry possess a relationship appropriate to the

---

[1] J. Loeb, "The Mechanistic Conception of Life," p. 5, University of Chicago Press, Chicago, 1912.

1

exchange of ideas and experience in the form of the area of *molecular biochemistry.*

The ultimate source of energy for life on this planet is the radiation of the sun. Systems present in certain varieties of life can utilize radiation to convert one set of molecules into another (*photosynthesis*), and by this means a fair proportion of the incident radiation within a certain wavelength range is trapped. The most important sequence of this type results in the formation of carbohydrates and oxygen from carbon dioxide

TABLE 1.0-1. HIERARCHY OF SCIENCES

Level	Science
Abstract	Mathematics
Subnucleonic	High-energy physics
Subatomic	Nuclear physics
Atomic	Spectroscopy
Polyatomic (low number)	Theoretical chemistry
	Molecular, solid-state physics
	Physical chemistry
	Organic chemistry
Polyatomic (high number)	MOLECULAR·BIOCHEMISTRY
	Polymer chemistry
	Biochemistry
Subcellular	Colloids
	Genetics
	Virology
	Immunology
Cellular	Cytology
	Bacteriology
Polycellular	Physiology
	Neurology
Organism	Medicine
Polyorganism	Psychology
	Sociology

and water. Evolution has also led to mobile organisms that consume energy at a higher rate than would be available through photosynthesis, and these depend parasitically upon the organisms which utilize radiation directly.

Early in the evolutionary process, a large number of intermediate steps were introduced into the pathways from stored energy to oxidation products so as to gain the most effective use of the energy available. The basic reaction sequences are common to many kinds of living systems and are summarized in a general way in Fig. 1.0.

The primary nutrients for highly organized living systems are carbohydrate, lipid, and protein; these are converted through many simpler compounds to carbon dioxide, water, and nitrogen compounds by means

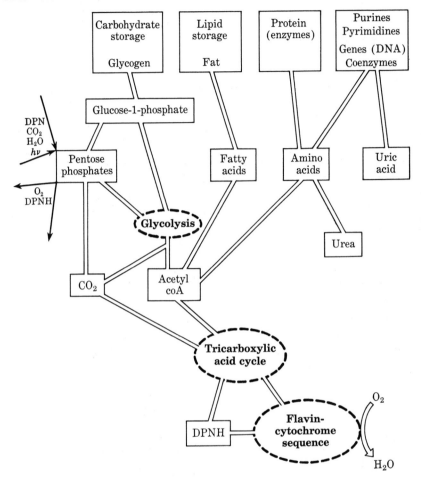

FIG. 1.0. Basic pathways in intermediary metabolism.

of reactions catalyzed by enzymes. Much of the metabolic "traffic" proceeds through the intermediate, acetyl coenzyme A, which is then introduced into the "tricarboxylic acid cycle." A reduction product of that "cycle," DPNH (reduced diphosphopyridine nucleotide), is reoxidized by the "terminal oxidation sequence," which, in turn, reduces oxygen to water. These relationships, illustrated in Fig. 1.0, provide the background for the detailed discussions of Part 1 of this book.

1.1. GLYCOLYSIS

Écoutez la chanson bien douce
Qui ne pleure que pour vous plaire,
Elle est discrète, elle est légère:
Un frisson d'eau sur de la mousse!
Paul Verlaine

It will be noted in this section and others that the arrows in the reaction schemes are accompanied by symbols.   These are intended to indicate the reaction type or types occurring in the transformation.   For example, GH signifies that a carbon-hydrogen bond has been formed or broken,

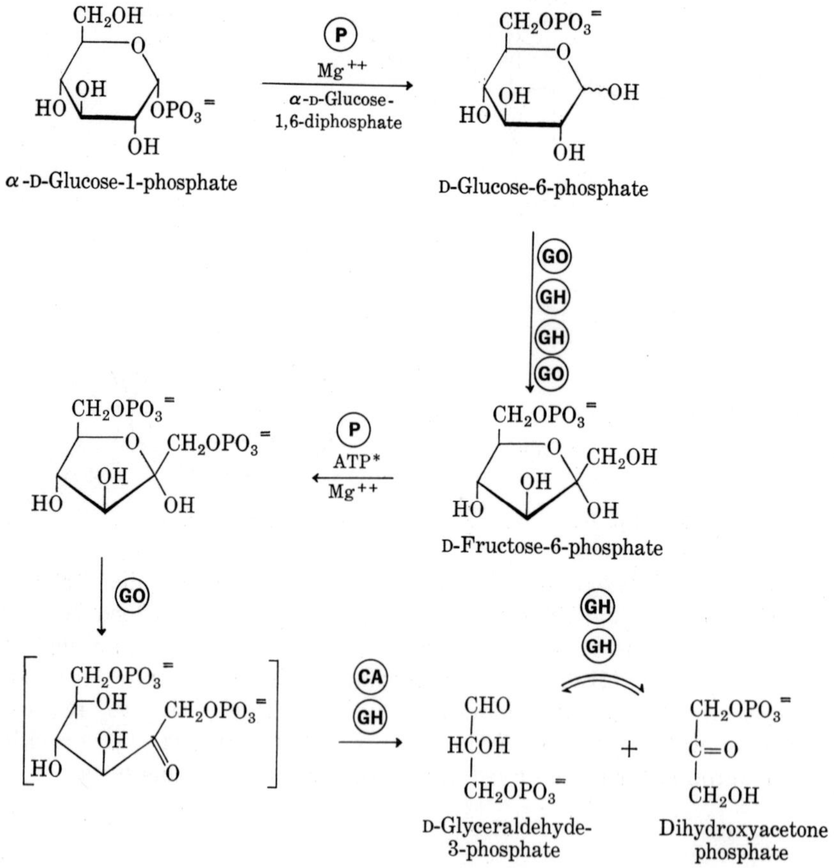

*Adenosine triphosphate

FIG. 1.1. Transformation of α-D-glucose-1-phosphate into triose phosphates.

without implying a mechanism for the process. The classification along these lines aided in the selection of reactions for scrutiny in Part 2 (cf. Sec. 1.9) and should be of some help in focusing attention on the mechanistic problems to be solved in molecular biochemistry.

The degradation of sugar stored within a biological system as a polymer such as glycogen (a derivative of poly-α-1,4-glucose) probably takes place by two major pathways and one minor route. The most important sequence involves the transformation of α-D-glucose-1-phosphate into the triose phosphates (Fig. 1.1) and then into pyruvic acid (Fig. 1.2). The initial step for each route is the conversion of glycogen into α-D-glucose-1-phosphate.

The discussion of reaction sequences will not include, for the most part, identification of the enzymes which catalyze the reactions. The names and other pertinent information may be found in standard works.[2,3]

1.1-1. α-D-Glucose-1-phosphate is converted into glucose-6-phosphate by a reaction in which the 1-phosphate group is transferred to the enzyme and a phosphate group from the enzyme moves to the 6-hydroxyl group. The coenzyme for the reaction, glucose-1,6-diphosphate, apparently serves to produce phosphoenzyme, that is, a phosphate derivative of the enzyme. (The enzyme is phosphoglucomutase in this case.[4])

The formation of D-fructose-6-phosphate from D-glucose-6-phosphate requires opening of the pyranose ring, enolization by loss of a proton, ketonization by gain of a proton, and closing of the furanose ring. It is highly probable that the enzyme catalyzes *both* ring opening and proton

[2] J. B. Neilands and P. K. Stumpf, "Enzyme Chemistry," John Wiley & Sons, Inc., 2d ed., New York, 1958.

[3] "The Enzymes," vols. 1–7, ed. by P. D. Boyer, H. A. Lardy, and K. Myrbäck, Academic Press, Inc., New York, 1959–1962.

[4] It is a matter of some interest that the phosphate of the phosphoenzyme has been found bonded to a serine hydroxyl group[5] (cf. Sec. 3.1C). It was suggested that the identity of the hexapeptide sequence which included the serine phosphate with a hexapeptide derived by degradation of phosphorylated chymotrypsin implied that enzymes with similar functions have similar sequences at the "active site."[5] However, sequences from other hydrolytic enzymes which include a serine phosphate and are also derived by degradation of a phosphorylated enzyme (e.g., pseudocholinesterase and aliesterase[6]) permit only the statement that "the common sequence" is aspartic (or glutamic) acid–serine–glycine. In addition, some doubt has been cast upon the sequence in the hexapeptide derived from phosphoglucomutase.[7] Although the suggestion is interesting, there seems no compelling reason for its correctness on theoretical grounds, and no further discussion of this point appears in Sec. 3.1, except for an allusion to the presence of aspartic (or glutamic) acid in Table 3.1-1.

[5] D. E. Koshland, Jr., and M. J. Erwin, *J. Am. Chem. Soc.*, **79**, 2657 (1957).

[6] H. S. Jansz, D. Brons, and M. A. P. J. Warringa, *Biochim. et Biophys. Acta*, **34**, 575 (1959).

[7] F. Sanger, *J. Polymer Sci.*, **49**, 10 (1961).

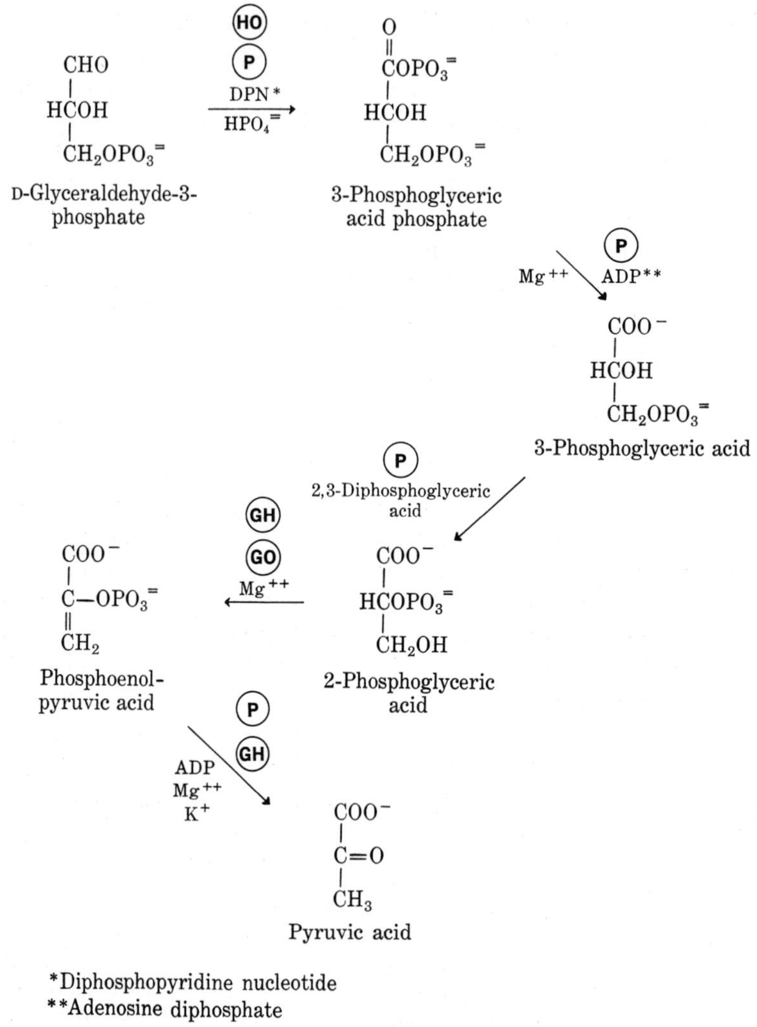

$$CHO$$
$$|$$
$$HCOH$$
$$|$$
$$CH_2OPO_3^=$$

D-Glyceraldehyde-3-
phosphate

(HO) (P) $\xrightarrow[\text{HPO}_4^=]{\text{DPN*}}$

$$\overset{O}{\overset{||}{C}}OPO_3^=$$
$$|$$
$$HCOH$$
$$|$$
$$CH_2OPO_3^=$$

3-Phosphoglyceric
acid phosphate

Mg^{++} (P) ADP**

$$COO^-$$
$$|$$
$$HCOH$$
$$|$$
$$CH_2OPO_3^=$$

3-Phosphoglyceric acid

(P) 2,3-Diphosphoglyceric
acid

$$COO^-$$
$$|$$
$$HCOPO_3^=$$
$$|$$
$$CH_2OH$$

2-Phosphoglyceric
acid

(GH) (GO) Mg^{++}

$$COO^-$$
$$|$$
$$C-OPO_3^=$$
$$||$$
$$CH_2$$

Phosphoenol-
pyruvic acid

ADP
Mg^{++}
K^+
(P) (GH)

$$COO^-$$
$$|$$
$$C=O$$
$$|$$
$$CH_3$$

Pyruvic acid

*Diphosphopyridine nucleotide
**Adenosine diphosphate

FIG. 1.2. Conversion of D-glyceraldehyde-3-phosphate into pyruvic acid.

transfer since the reported rate of ring opening of D-glucose to the aldehyde (less than 10^{-2} sec^{-1}, cf. Table 2.3-5) is considerably less than the over-all rate of isomerization reported for human erythrocyte phosphoglucose isomerase[8] (perhaps 600 to 1000 sec^{-1}), given the assumption that the enzyme has a molecular weight between 100,000 and 150,000. The four steps are illustrated in Fig. 1.3. It is known that the proton transfers are highly stereospecific.[8]

[8] Y. J. Topper, in "The Enzymes," vol. 5, chap. 26, Academic Press, Inc., New York, 1961.

D-Fructose-6-phosphate is converted to D-fructose-1,6-diphosphate by adenosine triphosphate (ATP). The diphosphate is rearranged to the acyclic ketose form, which undergoes dealdolization to an equal mixture of dihydroxyacetone phosphate and glyceraldehyde-3-phosphate. The latter two (the "triose phosphates") are interconvertible by proton loss to the enol, followed by gain of a proton.

D-Glyceraldehyde-3-phosphate is oxidized by diphosphopyridine nucleotide (DPN) and triose phosphate dehydrogenase (TPD) to

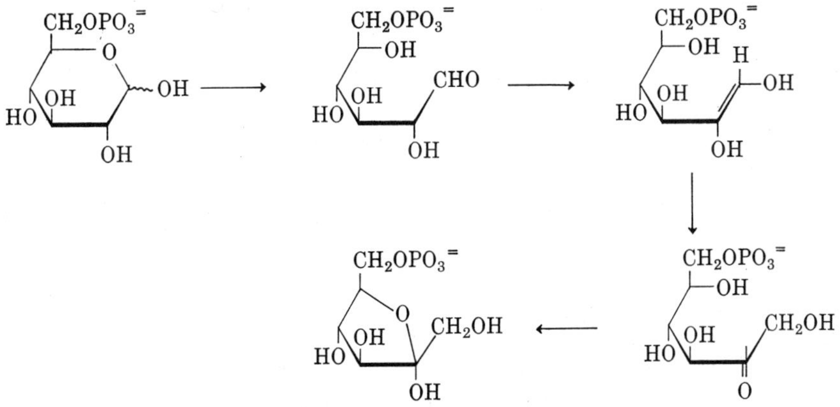

FIG. 1.3. Isomerization of D-glucose-6-phosphate to D-fructose-6-phosphate.

3-phosphoglyceryl-TPD (an acyl enzyme), and the latter reacts with phosphate ion to yield 3-phosphoglyceric acid phosphate and the enzyme (Fig. 1.2). The acyl phosphate reacts with adenosine diphosphate (ADP) to form 3-phosphoglyceric acid and ATP. An isomerization involving 2,3-diphosphoglyceric acid as a coenzyme produces 2-phosphoglyceric acid from the 3-phosphoglyceric acid. A dehydration of 2-phosphoglyceric acid leads to phosphoenolpyruvic acid, and the latter reacts with ADP to give pyruvic acid and ATP (Fig. 1.2).

The interconversion of dihydroxyacetone phosphate and L-glycerol-1-phosphate catalyzed by DPN is of importance in connection with the biosynthesis of fats and lecithin [Eq. (1.0)].

(1.0)

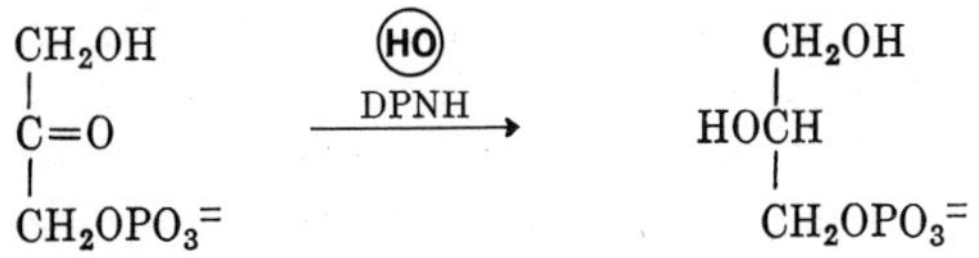

An apparent Walden inversion occurs in the transformation of uridine diphosphate galactose to uridine diphosphate glucose [Eq. (1.1)]. The reaction is, however, catalyzed by an oxidation-reduction coenzyme, DPN, in addition to the enzyme galactowaldenase.

(1.1)

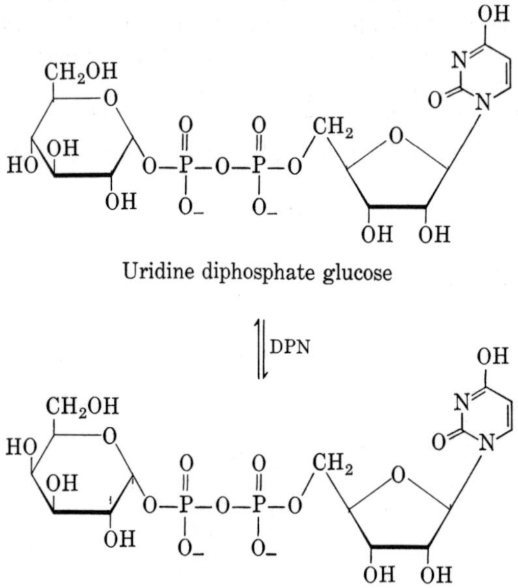

Uridine diphosphate glucose

Uridine diphosphate galactose

1.1-2.   The occurrence of pentose phosphates in metabolizing systems, the results of experiments concerned with the way in which C^{14} is distributed in degradation products from an initial location in glucose, and a requirement in certain systems for triphosphopyridine nucleotide (TPN) rather than DPN has led to the construction of a second scheme of glucose degradation called the pentose phosphate pathway. It is conveniently considered in two sections, the first being the TPN-dependent oxidation of glucose-6-phosphate to ribulose-5-phosphate, the second a moderately complicated set of interconversions between pentoses, trioses, tetroses, hexoses, and heptoses.

D-Glucose-6-phosphate is oxidized by TPN to 6-phospho-δ-glucono-lactone which is hydrolyzed to 6-phosphogluconic acid.   Although it is possible that the acid reacts with TPN in a concerted decarboxylation-oxidation, it is more likely that oxidation with TPN forms a 3-keto acid, which subsequently decarboxylates to an enolate ion, the latter acquiring a proton to yield ribulose-5-phosphate (Fig. 1.4).

D-Ribulose-5-phosphate is converted by enolization and ketonization into two isomeric pentose phosphates, D-ribose-5-phosphate and D-xylulose-5-phosphate.   A two-carbon fragment is removed from the xylulose phosphate by addition of thiamin to the carbonyl group followed by dealdolization, then transferred to the ribose phosphate in an aldol condensation, forming a seven-carbon sugar, D-sedoheptulose-7-phosphate. The three-carbon compound left by the removal of two carbons from D-xylulose-5-phosphate is D-glyceraldehyde-3-phosphate, which can participate in the reaction sequence outlined in Fig. 1.2 or can accept in an aldol condensation a three-carbon fragment removed from the seven-carbon compound to yield D-fructose-6-phosphate. The four-carbon

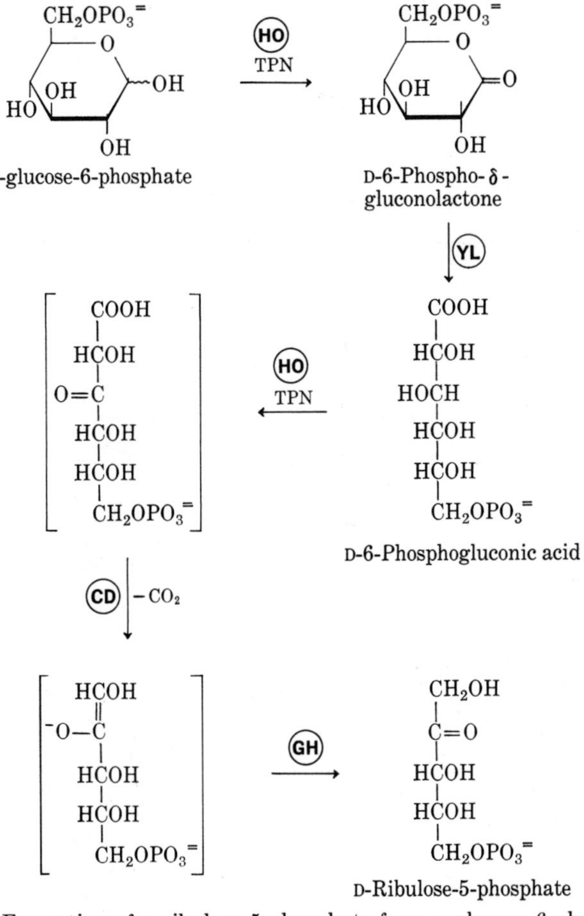

FIG. 1.4. Formation of D-ribulose-5-phosphate from D-glucose-6-phosphate.

remainder of the seven-carbon material accepts another two-carbon fragment from D-xylulose-5-phosphate in a reaction which involves thiamin again to form D-fructose-6-phosphate and D-glyceraldehyde-3-phosphate. The over-all scheme is presented in a simple form in Fig. 1.5, the dealdolization catalyzed by thiamin in Fig. 1.6,[9] and the detailed scheme in Fig. 1.7.

[9] E. Racker, in "The Enzymes," vol. 5, chap. 24A, Academic Press, Inc., New York, 1961.

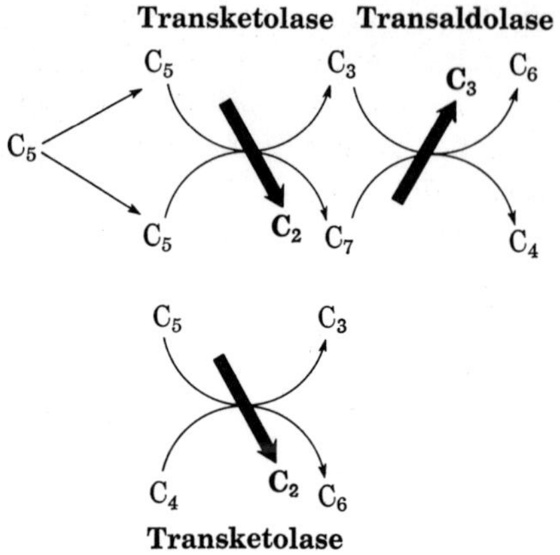

FIG. 1.5. Schematic for pentose phosphate interconversions.

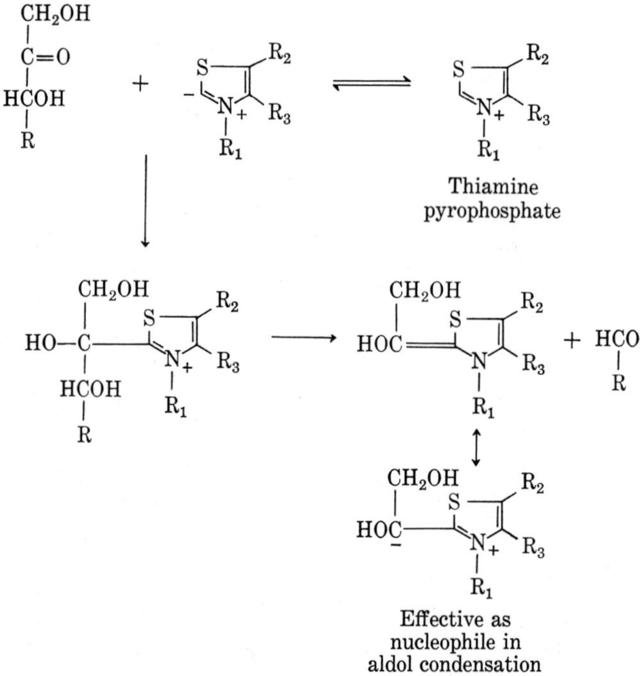

FIG. 1.6. Thiamin-catalyzed dealdolization (for transketolase).

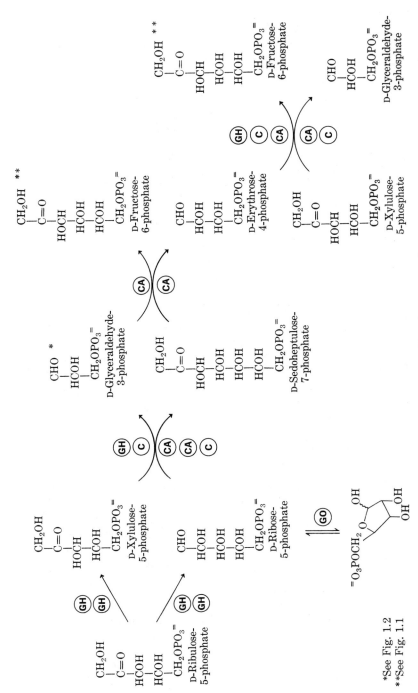

Fig. 1.7. Pentose phosphate interconversions.

*See Fig. 1.2
**See Fig. 1.1

11

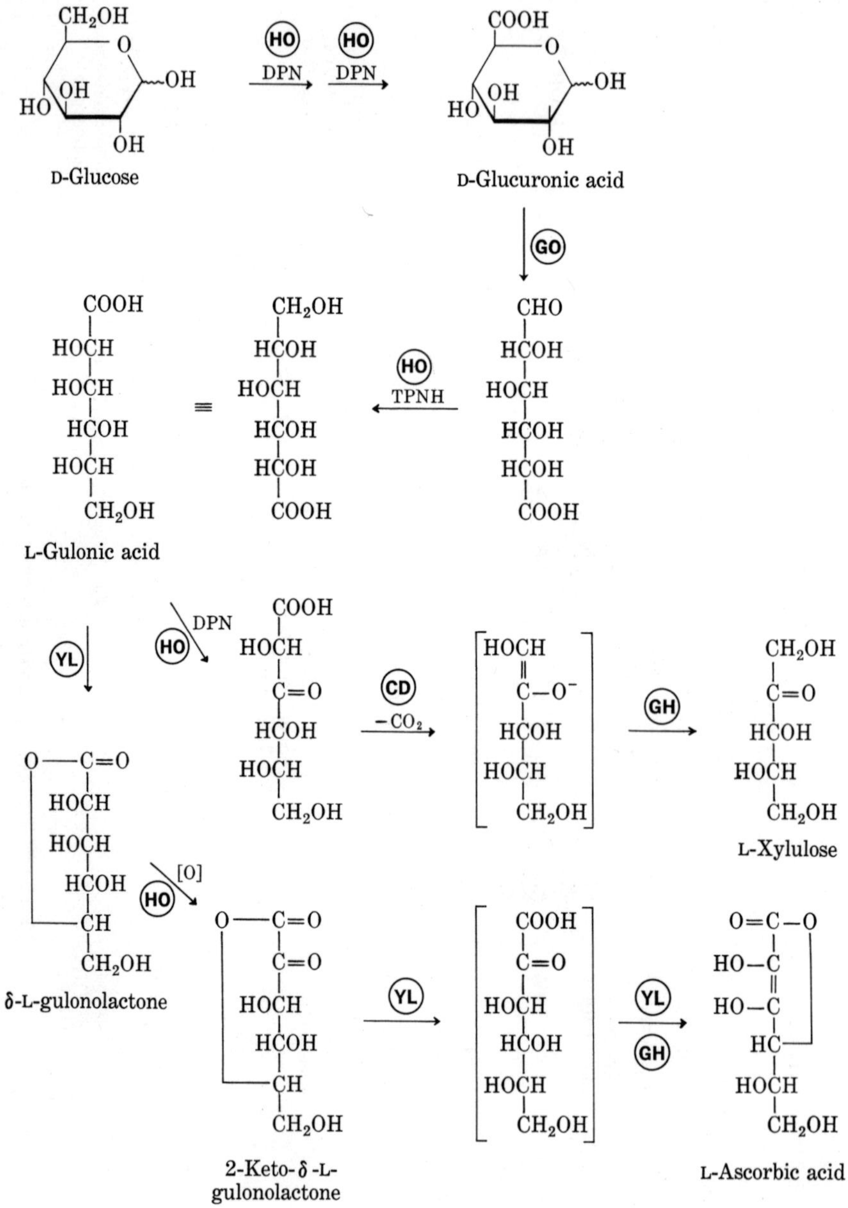

FIG. 1.8. Transformation of D-glucose into L-xylulose and L-ascorbic acid.

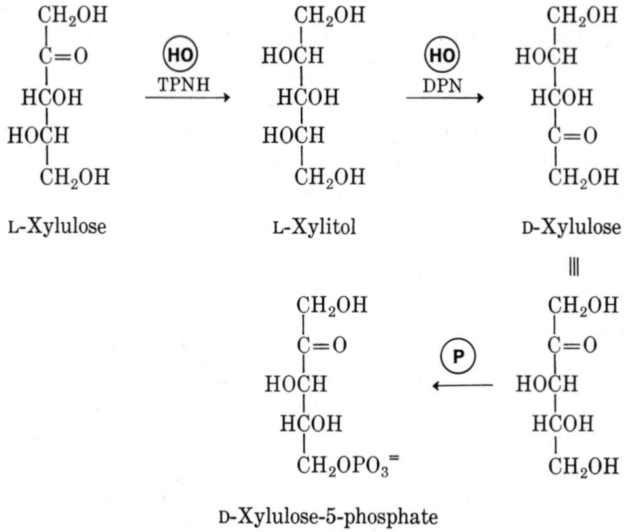

CH₂OH diagram — chemical structures:

L-Xylulose

$$\begin{array}{c} CH_2OH \\ | \\ C=O \\ | \\ HCOH \\ | \\ HOCH \\ | \\ CH_2OH \end{array}$$

(HO) TPNH →

L-Xylitol

$$\begin{array}{c} CH_2OH \\ | \\ HOCH \\ | \\ HCOH \\ | \\ HOCH \\ | \\ CH_2OH \end{array}$$

(HO) DPN →

D-Xylulose

$$\begin{array}{c} CH_2OH \\ | \\ HOCH \\ | \\ HCOH \\ | \\ C=O \\ | \\ CH_2OH \end{array}$$

‖‖

D-Xylulose-5-phosphate

$$\begin{array}{c} CH_2OH \\ | \\ C=O \\ | \\ HOCH \\ | \\ HCOH \\ | \\ CH_2OPO_3^= \end{array}$$

← (P)

$$\begin{array}{c} CH_2OH \\ | \\ C=O \\ | \\ HOCH \\ | \\ HCOH \\ | \\ CH_2OH \end{array}$$

FIG. 1.9. Conversion of L-xylulose into D-xylulose-5-phosphate.

1.1-3. A third mode of glucose degradation occurs to a minor extent, but seems to differ in certain details depending on whether bacteria, mammals, or plants are examined. The biosynthesis of L-ascorbic acid in mammals and bacteria is connected with this pathway,[10,11] but the biosynthesis in plants does not conform to the same pattern.[12,13]

D-Glucose (cf. ref. 10) is oxidized to D-glucuronic acid, possibly with DPN (cf. ref. 10), which is reduced after ring opening with TPNH to L-gulonic acid.[11] L-Gulonic acid is converted to 3-keto-L-gulonic acid with DPN, followed by decarboxylation and protonation to L-xylulose. The lactone, L-gulonolactone, is oxidized by pyridine nucleotide–independent pathway, probably to 2-keto-L-gulonolactone, which can hydrolyze and relactonize with concurrent enolization of the keto group to L-ascorbic acid[14] (Fig. 1.8).

L-Xylulose is reduced by TPNH to L-xylitol, which is oxidized by DPN to D-xylulose. The latter is transformed into D-xylulose-5-phosphate, for which the biochemical transformations have been outlined in Sec. 1.1-2 (Fig. 1.9).

---

[10] M. F. Utter, *Ann. Rev. Biochem.*, **27**, 252–257 (1958).

[11] J. J. Burns and G. Ashwell, in "The Enzymes," vol. 3, chap. 20, Academic Press, Inc., New York, 1960.

[12] F. A. Loewus, R. Jang, and C. G. Seegmiller, *J. Biol. Chem.*, **222**, 649 (1956).

[13] F. A. Loewus and R. Jang, *Biochim. et Biophys. Acta*, **23**, 205 (1957).

[14] J. Kanfer, J. J. Burns, and G. Ashwell, *Biochim. et Biophys. Acta*, **31**, 556 (1959).

1.2. TRICARBOXYLIC ACID CYCLE

Je ne suis point, mon frère, un docteur révéré
Et le savoir chez moi n'est pas tout retiré;
Mais, en un mot, je sais, pour toute ma science,
Du faux avec le vrai faire la différence. . . .

Molière

The pyruvic acid derived from glycolysis (Fig. 1.2) is converted into acetyl coenzyme A in a series of reactions which begins with the addition of thiamin anion to the carbonyl group of the acid.   Decarboxylation of the thiamin addition product yields the intermediate called "active acetaldehyde,"[15] which reacts with lipoic acid to form acetyl lipoic acid. Coenzyme A (written usually as a thiol, coASH) acquires the acetyl group through a transesterification, forming acetyl coA and dihydrolipoic acid.   The latter is reoxidized to lipoic acid by DPN or flavin (Fig. 1.10).

1.2-1.   Acetyl coA and oxaloacetic acid condense to form citric acid,[16] which is dehydrated to *cis*-aconitic acid[17] with subsequent rehydra-

[15] L. O. Krampitz, G. Greull, D. B. S. Millar, J. B. Bicking, H. R. Skeggs, and J. M. Sprague, *J. Am. Chem. Soc.*, **80,** 5893 (1958).

[16] J. Bové, R. O. Martin, L. L. Ingraham, and P. K. Stumpf, *J. Biol. Chem.*, **234,** 999 (1959), have shown that the condensing enzyme does not catalyze exchange of the α-hydrogen of acetyl coA with the medium in contrast to what might have been predicted on the basis of previous generalizations about thioesters.[16a]

[16a] The finding that the maximal rate (measured as initial rates with high substrate concentrations) for the reaction of acetyl coA is 1.4 times that of deuteroacetyl coA is an example of the small magnitude of isotope rate effects in many enzymatic reactions.   The authors are properly cautious in interpreting the result.[16b]

[16b] G. W. Kosicki and P. A. Srere, *J. Biol. Chem.*, **236,** 2566 (1961).

[17] The fact that citric acid formed by hydration of *cis*-aconitic acid with aconitase in D_2O contains considerably more deuterium than citric acid formed from isocitric acid with aconitase in D_2O has been taken as proof that *cis*-aconitic acid is not an "obligatory" intermediate in the tricarboxylic acid cycle.[18,19]   The conclusion justified by such evidence is that the movement of hydrogen from C_1 to C_2 is largely, *but not completely*, intramolecular.   The mechanism suggested to avoid formation of *cis*-aconitic acid postulates a "hydrogen-bridged" carbonium ion as a "common" intermediate between citric, isocitric, and *cis*-aconitic acids.[18,19]   Such intermediates have few, if any, counterparts, although they are popular as descriptions of transition states for carbonium-ion reactions in which hydrogen moves from one carbon to another.   The fact that hydrogen removed from a molecule as a proton does not exchange with the solvent is completely explicable on the basis of inaccessibility, and Sec. 3.1B-2 should be consulted for a more extensive discussion of this point.   The description in this section therefore includes *cis*-aconitic acid as an intermediate in the tricarboxylic acid cycle although it may well be true that it is bound strongly to the enzyme aconitase.

[18] J. F. Speyer and S. R. Dickman, *J. Biol. Chem.*, **220,** 193 (1956).

[19] S. R. Dickman, in "The Enzymes," vol. 5, chap. 30, Academic Press, Inc., New York, 1961.

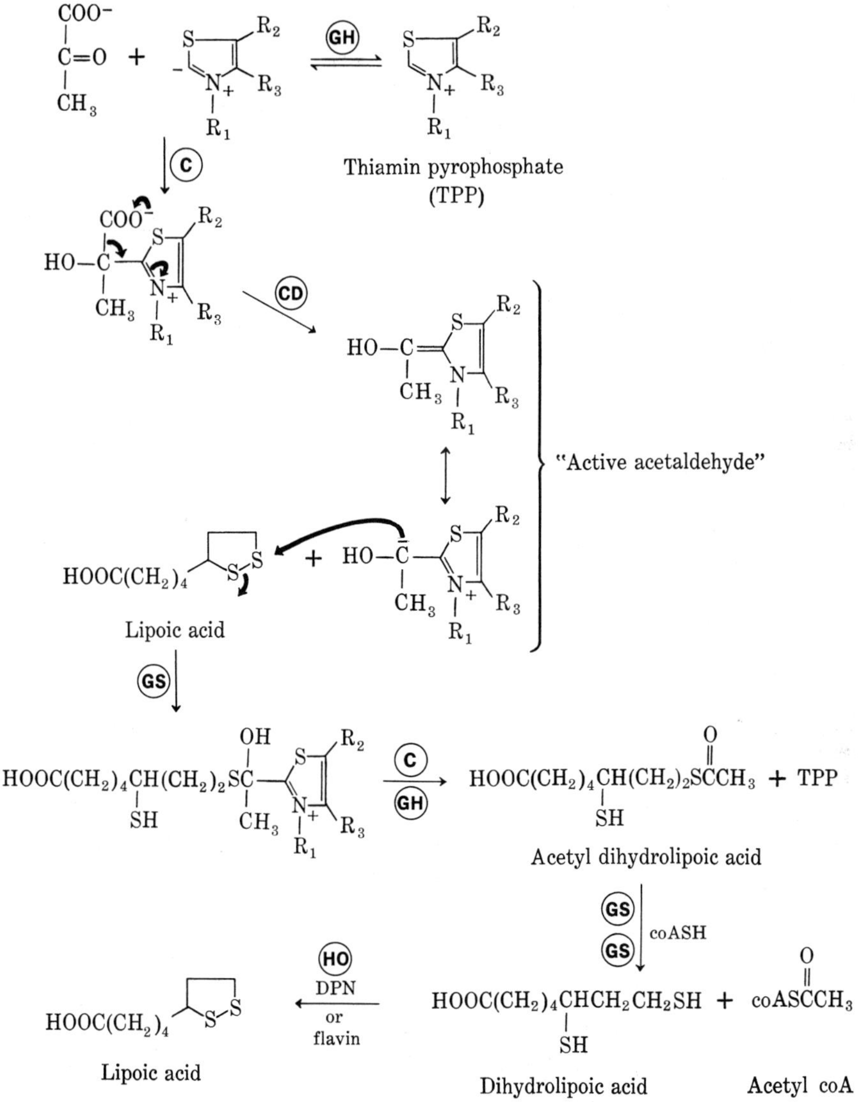

FIG. 1.10. Conversion of pyruvic acid to acetyl coenzyme A.

tion to d-isocitric acid. The stereochemical nature of many of the reactions of the tricarboxylic acid cycle is illustrated in Fig. 3.1, Sec. 3.1B-3. Isocitric acid is oxidized to oxalosuccinic acid, which is decarboxylated to α-ketoglutaric acid. A series of reactions analogous to those described for pyruvic acid in Fig. 1.10 transform the keto acid into succinoyl coA, which reacts with ADP and phosphate ion to form ATP and succinic acid. Succinic acid is oxidized by a flavin to fumaric acid which is hydrated to D(−)-malic acid. Finally, oxaloacetic acid is

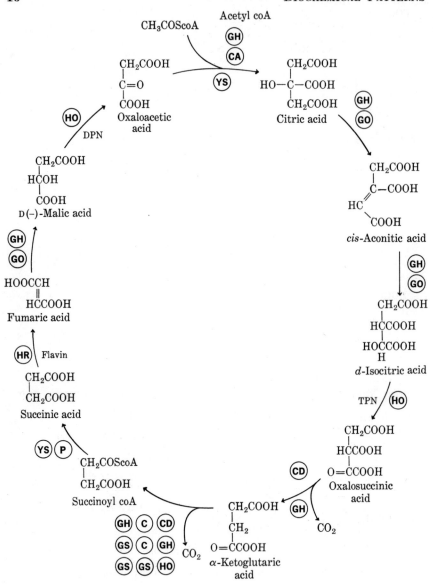

FIG. 1.11. The tricarboxylic acid cycle.

formed by oxidation of malic acid with DPN, and the cycle is complete (Fig. 1.11).

The primary function of the tricarboxylic acid cycle is the transformation of acetyl coA into reduced pyridine nucleotides, reduced flavin, and carbon dioxide. Many of the individual molecules of the cycle are important in biosyntheses of amino acids, porphyrins, purines, and many other substances.

1.3. TERMINAL OXIDATION AND OXIDATIVE PHOSPHORYLATION

Ich glaube, die Wellen verschlingen
Am Ende Schiffer und Kahn;
Und das hat mit ihrem Singen
Die Lorelei getan.

Heinrich Heine

The chemical activities of cells are not distributed uniformly, but are often localized in special subcellular structures. Gross separation by differential centrifugation yields at least three kinds of subcellular units in addition to a liquid containing soluble enzymes. These units are the nucleus, the ribosome (or microsome), and the mitochondrion. It is found that many substrates are not freely exchangeable between the internal portion of the mitochondrion and the cytoplasmic fluid of the cell.[20,21] The tricarboxylic acid cycle, terminal oxidation, and oxidative phosphorylation take place within the mitochondrion. Both the concentration of mitochondria[20] and the detailed structure of the mitochondrion vary with the physiological function of the tissue in which the cell is located.[22]

1.3-1. The reduced flavin, DPNH, and a few other compounds like succinic acid, β-hydroxybutyric acid, and glycerol-1-phosphate [Eq. (1.0), Sec. 1.1] are oxidized by the terminal oxidation sequence which occurs in the mitochondrion. Conversion of ADP to ATP by phosphate ion accompanies the oxidation, and for this reason is called oxidative phosphorylation. The biochemical activity of the mitochondrion depends upon a highly organized, moderately complicated structure. A number of "fragmenting agents" (cholate, thioglycolate, cetyl dimethyl ethyl ammonium bromide, etc.[22]) produce particles of submitochondrial size (as well as solutions) that retain many, but not all, of the catalytic activities found for the mitochondrion.

Studies of the fragments derived from mitochondria and the use of inhibitors which apparently block certain terminal oxidation reactions allow a speculation as to the possible sequence of reactions.[23] Substrates

[20] T. Bücher and M. Klingenberg, *Angew. Chem.*, **70**, 552 (1958).
[21] W. C. Schneider, *Advances in Enzymol.*, **21**, 1 (1959).
[22] D. E. Green and Y. Hatefi, *Science*, **133**, 13 (1961).
[23] D. E. Green, *Advances in Enzymol.*, **21**, 122 (1959).

are oxidized by one of several flavin enzymes, which transfer electrons through what may be a nonheme iron-protein complex $(Fe-B)$[24,24a] to coenzyme $Q_n (n = 6$ to $10)$ or another coenzyme. (n varies with the biological source.)   There is a possibility that the other coenzyme is cytochrome b.   Electron transfer from the coenzymes to cytochrome c_1

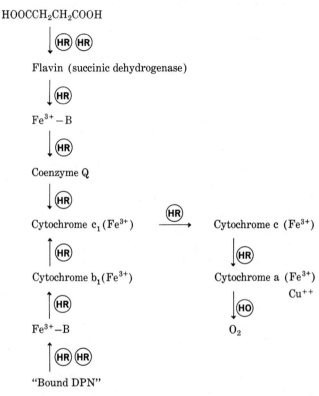

FIG. 1.12. Terminal oxidation sequences.

to cytochrome c to cytochrome a to oxygen then occurs.   The cytochromes are iron-heme-protein-lipid complexes, of which relatively little is known except for cytochrome c.   Cytochrome a contains copper in an amount equivalent to that of the iron-heme, and the copper undergoes oxidation-reduction during terminal oxidation.[25]   The high probability

[24] H. Beinert and W. Lee, *Biochem. Biophys. Research Comm.*, **5**, 40 (1961).

[24a] ESR measurements on particles isolated from *azotobacter vinelandii* containing Fe^{57} show the expected change in the signal assigned to Fe-B for an iron complex containing an iron atom with a nuclear moment in comparison to that observed for particles containing Fe^{56}.   An iron complex is therefore involved intimately in an oxidation-reduction reaction.   (H. Beinert, personal communication.)

[25] R. H. Sands and H. Beinert, *Biochem. Biophys. Research Comm.*, **1**, 175 (1959).

that one-electron transfer occurs between many of the intermediates involved in terminal oxidation requires that a "cross-over point" exist at which a two-electron process is effective in initiating two one-electron transfers. The mechanism of the initial reactions of the terminal oxidation system, that of the flavins with reduced substrates, is still very much in doubt,[26] but the occurrence of what are probably free radicals in many enzymatic flavin reactions[27] permits the tentative labeling of these

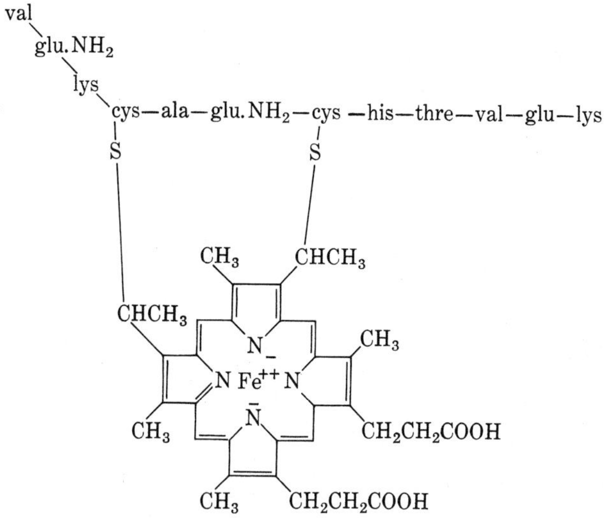

val = valine   cys = cysteine   his = histidine
glu = glutamic acid   ser = serine   thre = threonine
lys = lysine   ala = alanine

Fig. 1.13. Iron protoporphyrin IX in cytochrome c (salmon, beef, horse, pig; in chicken, ser replaces ala).

reactions (in Fig. 1.12) as one-electron (HR) reactions. The heme and a small portion of the protein of cytochrome c are illustrated in Fig. 1.13.

1.3-2. The details of the connection between oxidation and phosphorylation are obscure, but the importance of the subject has occasioned some active speculation about the possibilities. In general, reduction of any species will increase its nucleophilicity and therefore its ability to combine with phosphate ion by displacement of hydroxyl from phosphorus [see Sec. 2.15 and Eq. (1.2)]. The phosphate thus derived

[26] H. Beinert and R. H. Sands, "Free Radicals in Biological Systems," p. 17, Academic Press, Inc., New York, 1961.
[27] H. Beinert, *Biochim. et Biophys. Acta*, **20,** 588 (1956); *J. Biol. Chem.*, **225,** 465 (1957).

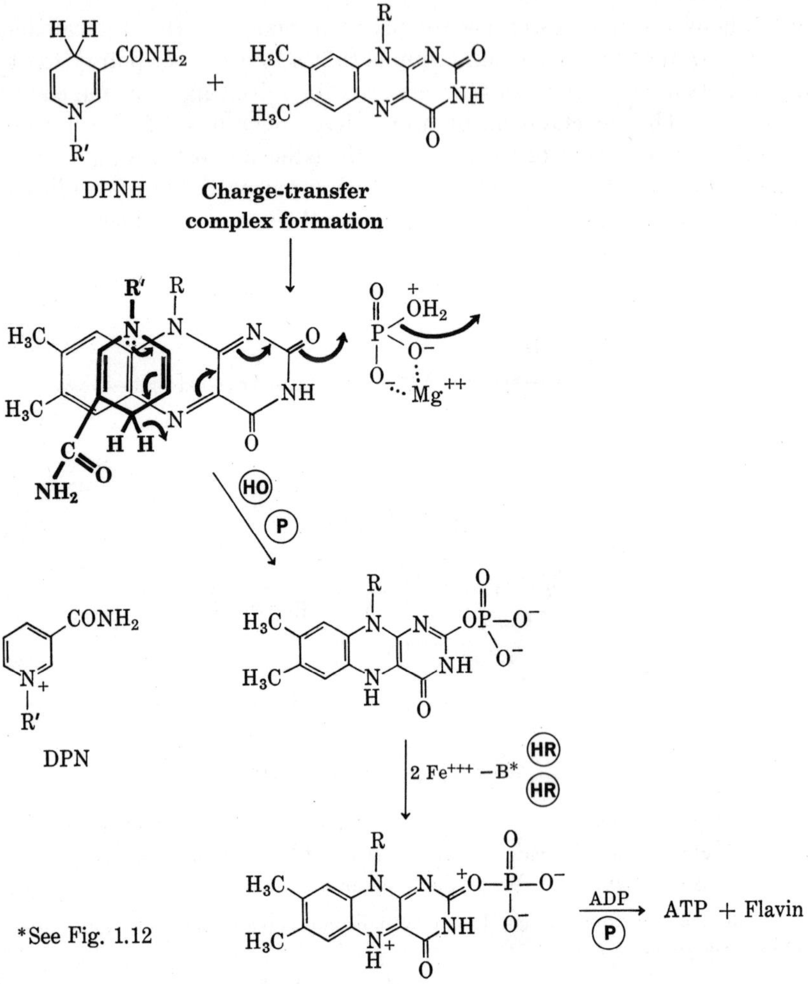

FIG. 1.14. Phosphorylation through DPNH-flavin complex.

can be oxidized, yielding what must be a good phosphate donor or "source" of metaphosphate [see Sec. 2.15 and Eq. (1.3)].

(1.2) $$e^- + x \longrightarrow x^- + \overset{|}{\underset{\diagup}{P}}\text{—OH} \longrightarrow x\text{—P} + \text{"OH}^-\text{"}$$

(1.3) $$x\text{—P} \xrightarrow{\text{oxid.}} x^+\text{—P} \xrightarrow{{}^-\text{O—P}\overset{\parallel}{\diagdown}} x + \underset{\parallel}{\overset{|}{-}}\text{P--O—}\overset{\parallel}{\underset{|}{P}}\text{—}$$

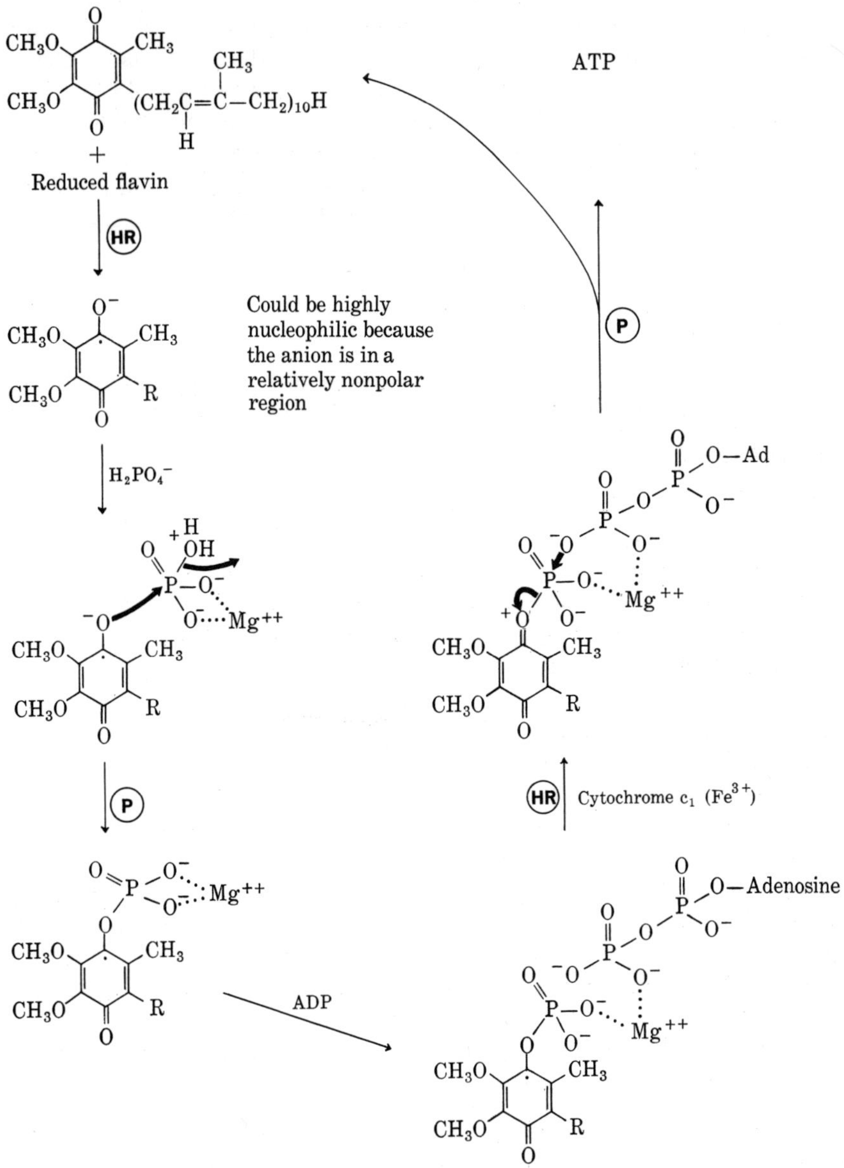

FIG. 1.15. Phosphorylation through coenzyme Q_{10}.

A charge-transfer complex between DPNH and flavin (cf. Sec. 2.13) has been proposed as a possible starting place for the reactions suggested in Eqs. (1.2) and (1.3).[28]   The proposal is outlined in Fig. 1.14.

Another possible locus of phosphorylation is coenzyme Q, which is a p-benzoquinone.   A scheme is given in Fig. 1.15.   A model reaction for the oxidation of the reduced phosphate is known and is shown in Fig. 2.75, Sec. 2.15.

1.4. PHOTOSYNTHESIS

. . . Et je n'ai pas pris peur de ma vision, mais m'assurant avec aisance dans le saisissement, je tiens mon oeil ouvert à la faveur immense, et dans l'adulation.

St. John Perse

The term *photosynthesis* covers a complex set of processes and reactions which lead to the formation of reduced carbon compounds and oxygen from light, carbon dioxide, and water.[29]   At least five areas of importance can be distinguished for study within the context of the problem of photosynthesis, which may be enumerated as follows:

1. Absorption of light by chlorophyll
2. Transfer of energy to appropriate sites
3. Development of reducing power and ATP
4. Development of oxidizing power
5. Utilization of carbon dioxide

Complications exist within each area mentioned, but these will not, in general, be considered in detail.   A list of the important facts or theories which indicate that matters are not so simple as to be divisible into the five areas follows:[30]

1. Other light-absorbing pigments than chlorophyll participate in photosynthesis.

[28] O. Lindberg, B. Grabe, H. Low, P. Siekevitz, and L. Ernster, *Proc. Swedish Biochem. Soc.*, Stockholm, March 8, 1958; B. Grabe, *Biochim. et Biophys. Acta*, **30,** 560 (1958).

[29] A more general description might fit the equation

$$X + Y \xrightarrow{h\nu} X^- + Y^+$$

[30] Cf. "A Symposium on Light and Life," Mar. 28–31, 1960, ed. by W. D. McElroy and B. Glass, The Johns Hopkins Press, Baltimore, 1961.

2. Agreement does not exist on the mechanism of energy transfer.

3. The nature of the electron acceptor is unknown.

4. The route to oxygen is unknown.

5. Carbon dioxide stimulates photosynthesis, a fact which would not be expected in the point of view to be adopted in this section.

The utilization of carbon dioxide is considered first rather than last because it is most closely related to the biochemical patterns described in the preceding sections.

1.4-1. Passage of radioactive carbon dioxide into irradiated growing suspensions of blue-green algae for short periods of time before

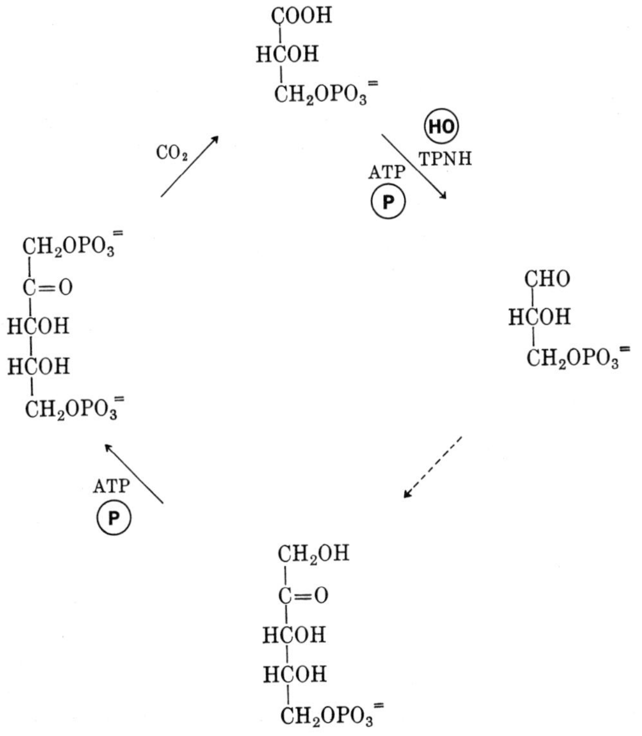

Fig. 1.16. The carbon dioxide–fixation cycle.

the organisms are killed by drowning in hot ethanol permits the identification, by means of paper chromatography, of many of the compounds formed in the early stages of photosynthesis. Four compounds were formed first: 3-phosphoglyceric acid, glyceraldehyde-3-phosphate, ribulose-5-phosphate, and ribulose-1,5-diphosphate. The analytical technique was not sufficiently sensitive to identify the initial acceptor of the carbon dioxide, even with extrapolation to zero time. However, a sudden change in the parameters of the system, such as carbon dioxide concentration or irradiation level, produced transients in the concentrations of the four compounds which occurred in the order of their participation in the carbon dioxide utilization process. Lowered carbon dioxide concentration produced an immediate decrease in the level of radioactive 3-phosphoglyceric acid, followed by successive changes in glyceraldehyde-3-phosphate, ribulose-5-phosphate, and ribulose-1,5-diphosphate.[31] The cycle thus formulated is shown in Fig. 1.16.

Carboxylation is probably catalyzed by an enzyme, carboxydismutase, through a reaction of ribulose-1,5-diphosphate with carbon dioxide. A

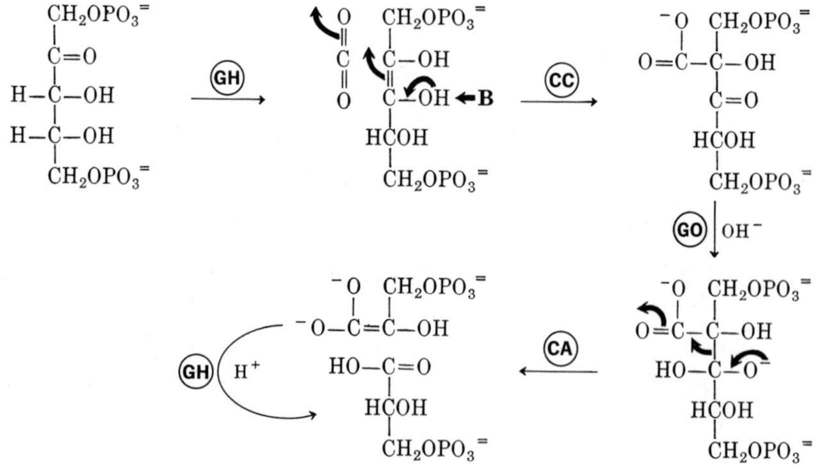

FIG. 1.17. Carboxylation of ribulose-1,5-diphosphate.

possible scheme is shown in Fig. 1.17, in which an enediol acts as nucleophilic agent toward carbon dioxide. Intermediate keto acids have been reported, but the validity of the results has been questioned.[32]

It may be noted that TPNH is the reagent which reduces 3-phosphoglyceric acid to glyceraldehyde-3-phosphate, although in glycolysis DPNH is involved. Glyceraldehyde-3-phosphate can, of course, enter into any of the reactions outlined in Figs. 1.2 and 1.7. Regeneration of ribulose-5-phosphate occurs through the reactions of the pentose phosphates (Fig. 1.7), and ribulose-1,5-diphosphate is formed by reaction of the monophosphate with ATP. Presumably, TPNH constitutes the "reducing power" provided by the photosynthetic apparatus.

[31] M. Calvin, *J. Chem. Soc.*, 1895 (1956).

[32] V. Moses and M. Calvin, *Proc. Natl. Acad. Sci. U.S.*, **44**, 260 (1958); however, cf. **45**, 952 (1959).

1.4-2. The first event in photosynthesis is the absorption of light by the chlorophyll in the plant. Chlorophyll is a dihydroporphin molecule of moderate complexity (the class is called chlorins), shown in Fig. 1.18. A molecule with a conjugated system somewhat like that of

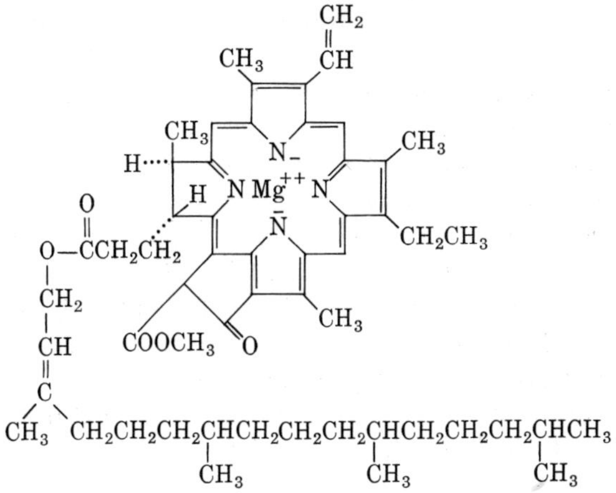

Chlorophyll a

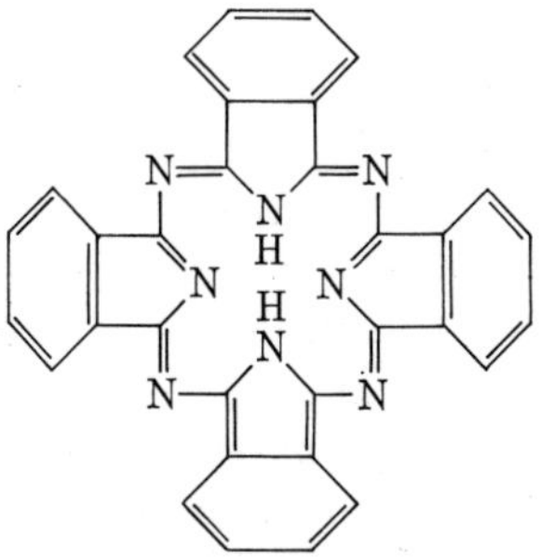

Phthalocyanine

FIG. 1.18. Structure of chlorophyll and phthalocyanine.

the porphins is phthalocyanine, also given in Fig. 1.18. Phthalocyanine is relatively easy to obtain in a pure state, its physical properties are more convenient than those of chlorophyll, and it has been quite useful in a number of model experiments on the properties of such conjugated systems.

The absorption spectrum of chlorophyll is dependent upon its state, especially in the 6000 to 8000 Å region.[33] The maximum in solution[34] is

[33] E. E. Jacobs, A. S. Holt, R. Kromhout, and E. Rabinowich, *Arch. Biochem. Biophys.*, **72**, 495 (1957).

[34] The spectrum was measured for the ethyl chlorophyllide (instead of the phytyl

6600 Å, amorphous chlorophyll has a maximum at ca. 6800 Å, and crystalline chlorophyll has a relatively sharp maximum at ca. 7200 Å. Chlorophyll in living cells has a maximum at 6750 to 6800 Å, and therefore does not appear to exist in a highly ordered state.[35] The most likely arrangement for chlorophyll in the chloroplast, the substructure in the plant cell which contains all of the chlorophyll, is as a somewhat disordered monolayer.[35]

Absorption of light by chlorophyll gives rise to a singlet excited state, but the fluorescence yield (emission of light by the singlet excited state) varies with the environment of the chlorophyll, being at a maximum of 33% in "wet" organic solvents.[36] Flash photolysis of chlorophyll in various media yielded the molecule in a triplet state which could be characterized by its spectrum and instability.[37] The triplet state of the chlorophyll molecule has been detected after flash photolysis of chloroplast preparations.[38] However, there is no evidence concerning the function or nonfunction of the triplet state in photosynthesis.

Light absorption by chlorophyll can be summarized in two equations, (1.4) and (1.5) (C = chlorophyll).

(1.4) $C \xrightarrow{h\nu} C^*$ (singlet) $\rightarrow C + h\nu_f$ (fluorescence)

(1.5) C^* (singlet) $\rightarrow C^*$ (triplet) $\rightarrow C$ (radiationless or phosphorescence)

1.4-3. The fine structure of the basic photosynthesizing unit is of importance to a consideration of the chemistry for two reasons. First, the "reducing power" and the "oxidizing power" should be physically separated so that the converted light energy would not be wasted. Second, it must be possible to utilize the light-absorbing power of a relatively large number of pigment molecules for one chemically active system. Electron microscopy[39,40] has yielded rather fine details of the chloroplast structure, but is unfortunately not now capable of the resolution required; therefore inference based on other information must

---

ester) in acetone solution. Addition of water to this solution resulted in an immediate shift to ca. 6750 Å, presumably from "colloidal amorphous" chlorophyll. As crystallization of the solid occurred, the band at 6750 Å was replaced by a band at 7200 Å.

[35] E. Rabinowich, *Discussions Faraday Soc.*, **27**, 161 (1959).

[36] R. Livingston and A. C. Pugh, *Discussions Faraday Soc.*, **27**, 144 (1959).

[37] R. Livingston and E. Fujimori, *J. Am. Chem. Soc.*, **80**, 5610 (1958).

[38] H. T. Witt and R. Moraw, *Z. physik. Chem. (Frankfurt)*, [N.S.]**20**, 253, 289 (1959).

[39] A. J. Hodge, J. D. McLean, and F. V. Mercer, *J. Biophys. Biochem. Cytol.*, **1**, 605 (1955).

[40] E. Steinmann and F. S. Sjöstrand, *Exptl. Cell Research*, **8**, 15 (1955).

be used. A schematic representation of granular structure in a chloroplast[39] is shown in Fig. 1.19. It is by no means unique, but it serves to
illustrate the problem of separation of oxidizing and reducing powers.

The nature of the "energy carriers" will be discussed in the next few
subsections. Regardless of the nature of the reactions, one set will occur
at the water-chlorophyll interface, and the other at the protein-lipid
interface. The water interface presents no particular difficulty since the
energy carriers are presumably generated in this region, but it is not easy
to see how any readily transmissible energy carriers will move through
some 30 to 35 Å of lipid. Somewhat different arrangements for the
chloroplast[40a] do not solve this problem.

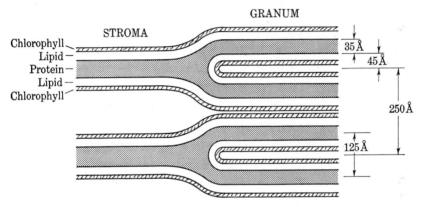

FIG. 1.19. Fine structure of the granular portion of a chloroplast. (*After ref. 39.*)

Even in direct sunlight, each chlorophyll molecule absorbs quanta only
about once every 0.1 sec.[35] Since the enzymes of intermediary metabolism can utilize substrate at least a thousand times faster than this, an
energy-collection mechanism is apparently required to obtain efficient
utilization of the biochemical apparatus attached to photosynthesis.
It has been estimated from flashing light experiments that about 2000
chlorophyll molecules cooperate in the production of one oxygen molecule,
and that 250 chlorophyll molecules constitute one "energy-absorbing
unit."[35] The absorption spectrum of chlorophyll in vivo indicates
relatively little organization in the chlorophyll layer of the chloroplast
(cf. Sec. 1.4-2). It is thus necessary to explain energy transfer in a
somewhat random monolayer collection of chlorophyll molecules.

1.4-4. The nature of the energy-transfer process in the chloroplast is not known. Although the lack of organization in the chlorophyll
monolayer does not favor semiconduction as the mechanism, it cannot be

[40a] J. J. Wolken, *Am. Scientist,* **47,** 202 (1959).

excluded, and the numerous times that semiconduction is invoked in other connections (e.g., ref. 41) as well as its importance to photoconductivity and heterogeneous catalysis make an inquiry into some of its basic principles worthwhile.

Matter can be roughly categorized into three groups by the measurement of the resistance to the passage of an electric current. Insulating substances have conductivities between 10^{-22} and 10^{-10} ohm^{-1} cm^{-1}, semiconducting substances between 10^{-9} and 10^3 ohm^{-1} cm^{-1}, and conducting substances between 10^4 and 10^6 ohm^{-1} cm^{-1}.[42] Two types of conduction are known: ionic conduction, in which charge is carried by the movement of ions; and electronic conduction, in which the movement of electrons occurs.

Ionic conduction results either from the actual transfer of ions in an electric field or, in special cases, such as that of the proton in water, ice, sulfuric acid, and phosphoric acid, from a virtual transfer, in which a proton colliding with an organized group of solvent molecules displaces a proton at the farther end of the group. Ice, in particular, has an extraordinarily high proton conductivity[43] (see also Sec. 3.0).

Electronic conduction can also be divided into two classes, the movement of electrons and the movement of "holes." Although "holes" are filled by transfer of electrons and thus also represent conduction by motion of electrons, conductivity by holes can be differentiated from conductivity by electrons through the Hall effect. A conduction electron would be obtained by the addition of an electron to a perfect lattice, while a conduction hole results from the removal of an electron from the lattice.

Many of the properties of crystals are best considered if we treat them as large molecules, combining the wave functions for the individual molecular orbitals into bands. The filled molecular orbitals result in filled bands, and the empty orbitals become available as conduction bands. The energy required to excite an electron from the filled band into the conduction band (a quantity called the energy gap, ΔE) determines how effective a particular crystal will be as a conductor. Conductors have rather low energy gaps, and semiconductors exhibit values of ΔE too large for thermal energies (for room temperature) to produce conductivity. (The estimation of the number of electrons for a particular energy gap is made by the inclusion of quantum restrictions and other factors in the Boltzmann distribution law.[42]) Resistance in conductors increases with temperature because of scattering of the moving electrons by the atoms or molecules of the conductor; resistance in semiconductors

[41] T. Bücher, *Advances in Enzymol.*, **14**, 1 (1953).

[42] N. B. Hannay, "Semiconductors," p. 1, Reinhold Publishing Corporation, New York, 1959.

[43] M. Eigen, *Z. Elektrochem.*, **60**, 1037 (1956).

normally decreases with temperature increase because the supply of conduction electrons grows faster than the increased resistance to electron motion.

1.4-5. For energy gaps of 2.2 ev (ca. 50.7 kcal/mole) or less, intrinsic semiconductivity is observed. Gaps greater than that value may be narrowed by the introduction of impurities into the crystal lattice. Impurities which are electron-deficient with respect to the lattice (e.g., an atom with one less valence electron than its neighbors) provide the equivalent of a higher filled band, and impurities which have an electron excess lead to a more accessible filled band. Electron-deficient atoms are *acceptors* and produce hole, or *p*-type, conductivity, while atoms with an electron excess are *donors* and give rise to electron,

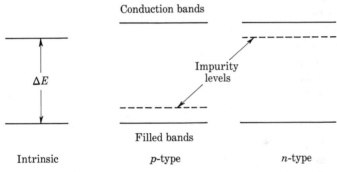

FIG. 1.20. Energy levels in semiconductivity.

or *n*-type, conductivity. Energy-level diagrams for intrinsic, *p*-type, and *n*-type conductivities are illustrated in Fig. 1.20.

Absorption of light leads to the promotion of an electron from the ground state to an excited state. Since the first excited-state orbitals are those which combine to form the conduction bands in the crystal, the position of onset of light absorption is a reasonably good indication of the intrinsic semiconductivity of a crystal. In other words, a low energy gap corresponds to a low energy required for excitation by light. Graphite, which is black (absorbs all visible radiation), has a very low ΔE, in contrast to diamond, a colorless material with a ΔE of at least 5.6 ev. High semiconductivity per se would *not* be expected for protein molecules because the position of light absorption indicates much too high an energy gap (ca. 3 ev).[43a] However, some electron transmission through organized peptide linkages might result from the attachment of two metal atoms to either end (see Sec. 2.12).

Photo- and semiconductivity in the conjugated molecule β-carotene

[43a] M. H. Cardew and D. D. Eley, *Discussions Faraday Soc.*, **27**, 115 (1959).

have been examined and shown to be increased by the presence of oxygen complexed on the surface of the crystals used.[44] A photoconductive process in the polyene *cis*-retinene is postulated to explain the nerve impulse produced when light strikes an appropriate acceptor in the retina of the eye.[45]

The polyene β-carotene has been proposed as an intermediary in the separation of charge within the chloroplast, presumably by transferring an electron from the triplet state of chlorophyll to an appropriate acceptor.[46] However, the postulate of any function for β-carotene must be evaluated in light of irradiation experiments on *Rhodopseudomonas spheroides* (wild) and (mutant) which lead to very similar electron-spin resonance (ESR) signals. The mutant contains no β-carotene.[47] The connection between the ESR signals and photosynthesis has not been established, but some very interesting observations on the model system, phthalocyanine–tetrachloro-*o*-benzoquinone, have been described.[48] The ESR signals in spinach chloroplasts are produced very rapidly by irradiation and disappear only very slowly at $-150°C$.[48]

1.4-6. The basis for the statement that semiconduction is not favored as the energy-transfer mechanism in chloroplasts is the lack of evidence in favor of multimolecular aggregates which could support conduction bands. There are other possibilities for this mechanism.

Absorption of light by a molecule produces an *exciton*, which consists of a "hole" in the ground state from which the electron was excited and an electron in the excited state. If transfer of both hole and electron to another molecule occurs, an intramolecular exciton is said to have been transferred. If the hole or electron is transferred separately, conversion from an intramolecular to an intermolecular exciton has occurred. If, as seems likely, the separation of the hole ("oxidizing or electron-accepting power") from the electron ("reducing or electron-donating power") is a critical one in the photosynthetic sequence, then the intra- to intermolecular exciton conversion could be regarded as the key step in this mechanism for energy transfer.[49]

In summary, some energy-transfer mechanism seems required for light utilization in chloroplasts. Semiconduction seems unlikely, exciton transfer seems possible, but a number of confusing points (the free

---

[44] B. Rosenberg, *J. Chem. Phys.*, **34**, 812 (1961).

[45] B. Rosenberg, report on 139th Am. Chem. Soc. meeting, *Chem. Eng. News*, Apr. 10, 1961, p. 47.

[46] J. R. Platt, *Science*, **129**, 372 (1959).

[47] M. Calvin, in ref. 30, p. 345.

[48] M. Calvin, in ref. 30, pp. 332–340, 340–344.

[49] Transfer mechanisms for electronic excitation are discussed in detail by T. Förster, *Discussions Faraday Soc.*, **27**, 7 (1959).

radicals detected by ESR, the reported triplet state) remain to prevent the adoption of any single explanation at this time.

1.4-7. One of the most exciting developments in the study of photosynthesis was the discovery that chloroplasts could absorb light and form ATP from ADP and phosphate [cf. Eqs. (1.2) and (1.3)] unaccompanied by the formation of TPNH or the evolution of oxygen.[50] The system was oxygen-independent if sufficient quantities of flavin mononucleotide (FMN) or vitamin K_3 (2-methyl-1,4-naphthoquinone)

(a) $\quad$ Chl' $\xrightarrow{\quad h\nu \quad}$ Chl'*

(b) $\quad$ Chl'* $\xrightarrow[\text{transfer}]{\text{Energy}}$ Chl*

(c) $\quad$ Chl* $\xrightarrow{\text{"Separation"}}$ $Chl^+ + e^-$

(d) $\quad$ $e + \text{cofactor}$ $\longrightarrow$ cofactor^-

(e) $\quad$ $\text{Cofactor}^- + P$ $\longrightarrow$ $(\text{cofactorP})^-$

(f) $\quad$ $(\text{CofactorP})^- + \text{CytFe(III)}$ $\longrightarrow$ $(\text{cofactorP}) + \text{CytFe(II)}$

(g) $\quad$ $(\text{CofactorP}) + \text{ADP}$ $\longrightarrow$ $\text{cofactor} + \text{ATP}$

(h) $\quad$ $\text{CytFe(II)} + P$ $\longrightarrow$ CytFe(II)P

(i)** $\quad$ $\text{CytFe(II)P} + Chl^+$ $\longrightarrow$ $\text{CytFe(III)P} + \text{Chl}$

(j) $\quad$ $\text{CytFe(III)P} + \text{ADP}$ $\longrightarrow$ $\text{CytFe(II)} + \text{ATP}$

Net:

$$nP + n\text{ADP} \xrightarrow[\text{CytFe(II)}]{\text{Chl, } h\nu, \text{ cofactor}^*} n\text{ATP}$$

* n is related to the number of intermediate cofactors
**Reaction i involves a pontal oxygen (see text, Sec. 1.4-8)
Chl = chlorophyll;   Cyt = cytochrome;   P = phosphate ion

FIG. 1.21. "Cyclic photophosphorylation."

were present. The process has been called "cyclic photophosphorylation" and is accompanied by the oxidation of cytochromes present in the chloroplast. A scheme which is noncommittal on the question of separation of oxidizing and reducing powers is shown in Fig. 1.21 to illustrate the relationships involved. It has been suggested[50] that "cyclic photophosphorylation" is the most primitive use of photochemical energy by life in the reducing milieu rich in organic compounds which is thought to have existed at the beginning of the evolutionary process.

In the presence of chloride ion and TPN, not only is ATP produced but TPNH and oxygen as well. An enzyme called photosynthetic pyridine

[50] D. I. Arnon, in ref. 30, pp. 489–565.

nucleotide reductase (PPNR), which is specific for TPN, catalyzes the formation of TPNH.[51] The spectrum of PPNR (which should be especially interesting as an enzyme because of its low molecular weight, ca. 15,000) has maxima at 2780, 3270, 4200, and 4600 Å. The latter two are lost if the enzyme is treated with acid or base. The broad nature of the long-wavelength absorption bands as well as their loss on what is presumably denaturation of the enzyme suggests that they might be due

$$(a) \quad \text{Chl}' \quad \xrightarrow{\ h\nu\ } \quad \text{Chl}'^*$$

$$(b) \quad \text{Chl}'^* \quad \xrightarrow[\text{transfer}]{\text{Energy}} \quad \text{Chl}^*$$

$$(c) \quad \text{Chl}^* \quad \xrightarrow{\text{"Separation"}} \quad \text{Chl}^+ + e^-$$

$$(d) \quad \text{H}^+ + 2e^- + \text{TPN} \xrightarrow{\text{PPNR}} \text{TPNH}$$

$$(e)^{**} \text{CytFe(II)} + \text{Chl}^+ \longrightarrow \text{CytFe(III)} + \text{Chl}$$

$$(f) \quad \text{CytFe(III)} + \text{OH}^- \longrightarrow \text{CytFe(II)} + [\text{OH}]^*$$

$$(g) \quad [\text{OH}]^* \longrightarrow \text{O}_2$$

Net:*

$$2\text{TPN} + 2\text{ADP} + 2\text{P} + 2\text{H}_2\text{O} \longrightarrow 2\text{TPNH} + \text{O}_2 + 2\text{ATP}$$

*These are the expressions corresponding to the mechanistically noncommittal scheme in ref. 50, Fig. 19. Phosphorylations are omitted
**Reaction e involves a pontal chlorine (see Fig. 1.23)

Chl = chlorophyll; P = phosphate ion; Cyt = cytochrome

FIG. 1.22. "Noncyclic photophosphorylation."

to a charge-transfer complex.[52] A scheme for "noncyclic photophosphorylation" is given in Fig. 1.22. Some discussion on the formation of oxygen is to be found in the following subsection.

In addition to FMN and vitamin K_3, a number of other compounds have been found or proposed as electron acceptors from the chlorophyll. These include benzoquinone Q-255 ("plastoquinone")[53] as a good possibility and α-lipoic acid[31] and the free radical derived by one-electron oxidation of ascorbic acid ("monodehydroascorbic acid")[54] as speculations. The strain within the disulfide ring of α-lipoic acid (a minimum of

[51] A. San Pietro, in ref. 30, p. 631.
[52] E. M. Kosower, in "The Enzymes," vol. 3, chap. 13, Academic Press, Inc., New York, 1960.
[53] N. I. Bishop, *Proc. Natl. Acad. Sci. U.S.*, **45**, 1696 (1959).
[54] E. Marre and O. Arrigoni, *Biochim. et Biophys. Acta*, **30**, 453 (1958).

16 kcal/mole[55]) makes it an attractive possibility as an electron acceptor, but there is little else to support its direct participation in a reaction with an electron derived from chlorophyll.

Apparently the "reducing power" (the electron) produced by light can be utilized in a number of ways by a small number of electron acceptors, to produce either ATP or TPNH.

1.4-8. The conversion of the "oxidizing power" produced by light (the "hole" in the ground state of the chlorophyll) into oxygen presents a number of puzzling aspects. The requirement for chloride ion in oxygen production,[56] now confirmed,[50] is unusual (chloride may be replaced by bromide). Forming an oxygen molecule in such a way that no free "hot" intermediates, capable of oxidizing organic compounds at random (e.g., OH radical), are generated would appear to be a *sine qua non* for photosynthesis.

It seems possible that the unique role of chloride (or bromide) is as bridging (or pontal, cf. Sec. 2.12) atom in the electron transfer step between a ferrous cytochrome and what we can call Chl^+. In the absence of chloride, water must serve as the pontal group, with oxygen as the pontal atom, and as a consequence, electron transfer between ferrous and Chl^+ *must be much slower than with chloride as the pontal atom.* The dependence of the rate of electron transfer on the nature of the pontal group is shown in Table 2.12-2, and a comparison of chloride with water[57] indicates that a factor of 10^3 to 10^6 in rate might be expected between reactions in which one or the other served as pontal group. Although it is not clear why this should change the course of events in the chloroplast so dramatically, it can be postulated that a reducing cofactor (i.e., FMNH or reduced vitamin K_3) is able to prevent electron transfer from a water oxygen coordinated to the cytochrome iron by supplying an electron at a certain rate, but is unable to do so when the chloride bridge accelerates the rate of electron transfer.

The collection process (energy transfer) for the "hole" produced photochemically permits an oxygen molecule to be generated at one cytochrome iron in a reasonable sequence of reactions. The last intermediate before the release of oxygen, $Fe(II)O_2$, could be regarded as an $Fe(IV)$ derivative $(Fe(IV)O_2^=)$, an oxidation state which has been proposed for a number of reactions of iron.[58,59] A detailed sequence for the production of oxygen is shown in Fig. 1.23.

[55] G. Bergson and L. Schotte, *Arkiv Kemi*, **13**, 43 (1958).

[56] O. Warburg, in "Heavy Metal Prosthetic Groups and Enzyme Action," pp. 213–214, Clarendon Press, Oxford, 1949.

[57] J. Halpern and L. E. Orgel, *Discussions Faraday Soc.*, **29**, 8 (1960).

[58] P. George, *J. Chem. Soc.*, 4349 (1954).

[59] A. E. Cahill and H. Taube, *J. Am. Chem. Soc.*, **74**, 2312 (1952).

(a) Chl' $\xrightarrow{h\nu}$ Chl'^*

(b) Chl'^* $\xrightarrow[\text{transfer}]{\text{Energy}}$ Chl^*

(c) Chl^* $\xrightarrow{\text{"Separation"}}$ $Chl^+ + e^-$

(d) $Chl^+ Cl^- CytFe(II)OH_2$ $\longrightarrow$ $Chl\ Cl^- CytFe(III)OH_2$

(e) $Chl\ Cl^- CytFe(III)OH_2$ $\longrightarrow$ $Chl\ Cl^- CytFe(III)\bar{O}H$

(f) $Chl\ Cl^- CytFe(III)\bar{O}H$ $\xrightarrow{(a)-(c)}$ $Chl^+ Cl^- CytFe(III)\bar{O}H$

(g) $Chl^+ Cl^- CytFe(III)\bar{O}H$ $\longrightarrow$ $Chl\ Cl^- CytFe(IV)\bar{O}H$

(h) $Chl\ Cl^- CytFe(IV)\bar{O}H$ $\longrightarrow$ $Chl\ Cl^- CytFe(II)\overset{+}{\bar{O}}H$

(i) $Chl\ Cl^- CytFe(II)\overset{+}{\bar{O}}H$ $\xrightarrow{OH^-}$ $Chl\ Cl^- CytFe(II)\underset{H}{OOH}$

(j) $Chl\ Cl^- CytFe(II)\underset{H}{OOH}$ $\xrightarrow{(a)-(c)}$ $Chl^+ Cl^- CytFe(II)\underset{H}{OOH}$

(k) $Chl^+ Cl^- CytFe(II)\underset{H}{OOH}$ $\longrightarrow$ $Chl\ Cl^- CytFe(III)\underset{H}{OOH}$

(l) $Chl\ Cl^- CytFe(III)\underset{H}{OOH}$ $\longrightarrow$ $Chl\ Cl^- CytFe(III)\bar{O}OH$

(m) $Chl\ Cl^- CytFe(III)\bar{O}OH$ $\xrightarrow{(a)-(c)}$ $Chl^+ Cl^- CytFe(III)\bar{O}OH$

(n) $Chl^+ Cl^- CytFe(III)OOH$ $\longrightarrow$ $Chl\ Cl^- CytFe(IV)\bar{O}OH$

(o) $Chl\ Cl^- CytFe(IV)\bar{O}OH$ $\longrightarrow$ $Chl\ Cl^- CytFe(II)\overset{+}{O_2}H$

(p) $Chl\ Cl^- CytFe(II)\overset{+}{O_2}H$ $\longrightarrow$ $Chl\ Cl^- CytFe(II)O_2$

(q) $Chl\ Cl^- CytFe(II)O_2$ $\xrightarrow{H_2O}$ $Chl\ Cl^- CytFe(II)OH_2 + O_2$

FIG. 1.23. Formation of oxygen in the chloroplast.

1.5. UREA CYCLE

April is the cruellest month, breeding
Lilacs out of the dead land, mixing
Memory and desire, stirring
Dull roots with spring rain. . . .
                              T. S. Eliot

In humans, nitrogen balance between intake and usage is maintained by mechanisms which eliminate the excess in the form of urea or uric acid. The formation of urea depends on a sequence of reactions known as the "urea cycle." A description of the cycle can be divided into two

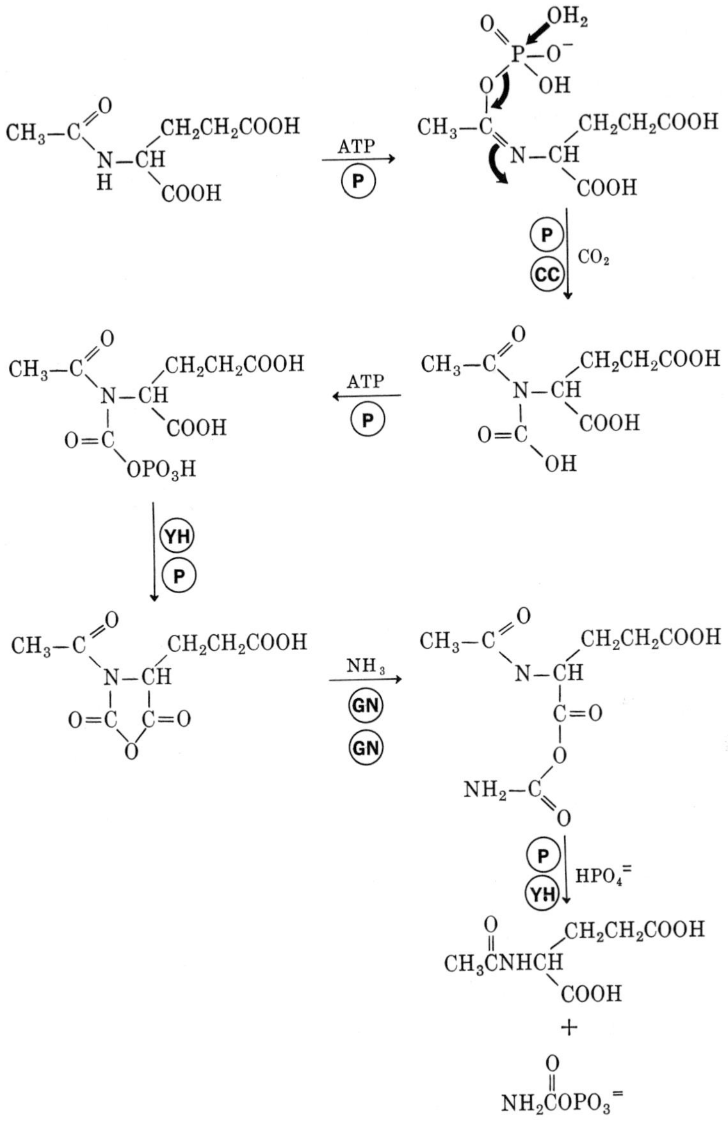

$$O = \overset{OH_2}{\underset{O}{\overset{|}{P}} - O^-}$$

$$CH_3 - C\overset{O}{\diagup}\ \ \underset{\underset{H}{N} - \underset{COOH}{CH}}{}\ \ CH_2CH_2COOH \xrightarrow[\;\;(P)\;\;]{ATP} CH_3 - \underset{N - CH}{C}\ \ CH_2CH_2COOH \underset{COOH}{}$$

$$\xrightarrow[(CC)]{(P)\ CO_2}$$

$$CH_3 - C\overset{O}{\diagup}\ \ \underset{O=C}{\overset{N-CH}{}}\ \ \underset{OPO_3H}{\overset{CH_2CH_2COOH}{COOH}} \xleftarrow[\;\;(P)\;\;]{ATP} CH_3 - C\overset{O}{\diagup}\ \ \underset{O=C}{\overset{N-CH}{}}\ \ \underset{OH}{\overset{CH_2CH_2COOH}{COOH}}$$

$$\downarrow \overset{(YH)}{(P)}$$

$$CH_3 - C\overset{O}{\diagup}\ \ \underset{O=C\ \ C=O}{\overset{N-CH}{}}\ \underset{O}{}\ CH_2CH_2COOH \xrightarrow[\;\;(GN)\;\;(GN)\;\;]{NH_3} CH_3 - C\overset{O}{\diagup}\ \ \underset{C=O}{\overset{N-CH}{}}\ \underset{NH_2 - C\diagdown_O}{\overset{O}{|}}\ CH_2CH_2COOH$$

$$\xrightarrow[(YH)]{(P)}\ HPO_4^=$$

$$\underset{CH_3\overset{O}{\overset{||}{C}}NHCH}{}\ \underset{COOH}{\overset{CH_2CH_2COOH}{}}$$

$$+$$

$$NH_2\overset{O}{\overset{||}{C}}OPO_3^=$$

Carbamyl phosphate

FIG. 1.24. Formation of carbamyl phosphate.

parts, the formation of carbamyl phosphate followed by its conversion to urea.

The carbon of carbamyl phosphate is derived from carbon dioxide. The latter is not a particularly reactive molecule, and its "activation" in some manner is probably a prerequisite to many of its biochemical reactions (see Sec. 2.1). It is known that acetylglutamic acid is a cofactor in the enzymatic synthesis of carbamyl phosphate,[60] and it has been proposed that this cofactor, when appropriately activated, serves a role analogous to that of biotin in the "activation" of carbon dioxide.[61]

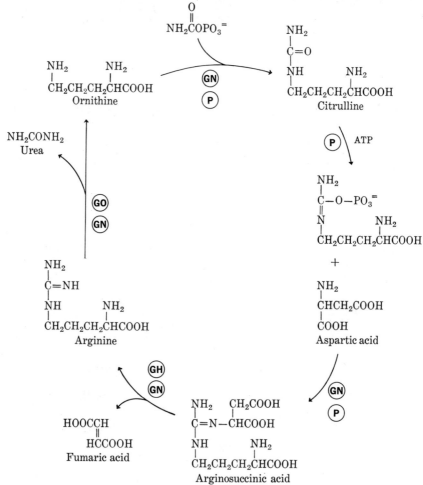

FIG. 1.25 The urea cycle.

A scheme for the formation of carbamyl phosphate from carbon dioxide, ammonia, two molecules of ATP, and acetylglutamic acid is shown in Fig. 1.24. Although speculative, the scheme is consistent with the available information on exchange reactions.[62]

[60] S. Grisolia and P. P. Cohen, *J. Biol. Chem.*, **204**, 753 (1953).

[61] M. E. Jones, *J. Cellular Comp. Physiol.*, **54**, Suppl. 1, 72 (1959).

[62] P. Reichard, *Advances in Enzymol.*, **21**, 268 (1959).

1.5-1. Ornithine reacts with carbamyl phosphate to form citrulline. The latter is "activated" by ATP, possibly with formation of an intermediate phosphate, and reacts with aspartic acid to give arginosuccinic acid. An elimination reaction yields fumaric acid and arginine from arginosuccinic acid. Arginine is hydrolyzed to urea and ornithine, which can begin another cycle by reaction with carbamyl phosphate. These reactions are shown in Fig. 1.25.

1.6. TRANSAMINATION

КТО ЕГО ЗНАЕТ?

Old Russian song

Transamination is a reaction[63] of wide occurrence and of great importance in the biosynthesis of many of the amino acids. The over-all reaction involves the "exchange" of a keto group and an amino group between an α-keto acid and an α-amino acid. The role of the cofactor, pyridoxal phosphate, is moderately well understood, and its participation in the reaction is illustrated in Fig. 1.26.

Transaminations have been implicated in the reactions of L-tyrosine, L-leucine, L-glutamic acid, L-valine, L-serine, and other amino acids. The cofactor, pyridoxal phosphate, exhibits in many cases a relatively tight binding with the enzyme, leading to the supposition that "Schiff base" formation is responsible for the association of the coenzyme with the enzyme.[64] The binding of pyridoxal phosphate to phosphorylase has been proved to result from Schiff base formation by the isolation of ϵ-N-pyridoxyl-lysine after treatment of the enzyme with sodium borohydride and degradation.[65] Thus, it is likely that the presentation in Fig. 1.26 using the aldehyde form of the coenzyme is only an approximation to the reaction catalyzed by the transaminase enzymes. The mechanism of transamination and other aspects of the function of pyridoxal phosphate as coenzyme are considered in Sec. 2.6.

[63] A. E. Braunstein and M. G. Kritzmann, *Enzymologia*, **2**, 129 (1937).

[64] A. E. Braunstein, in "The Enzymes," vol. 2, chap. 6, p. 182, Academic Press, Inc., New York, 1960.

[65] E. H. Fischer, A. B. Kent, E. R. Snyder, and E. G. Krebs, *Abstr. 4th Intern. Congr. Biochem.*, Paper 4-61, p. 45, Vienna, Austria, September, 1958.

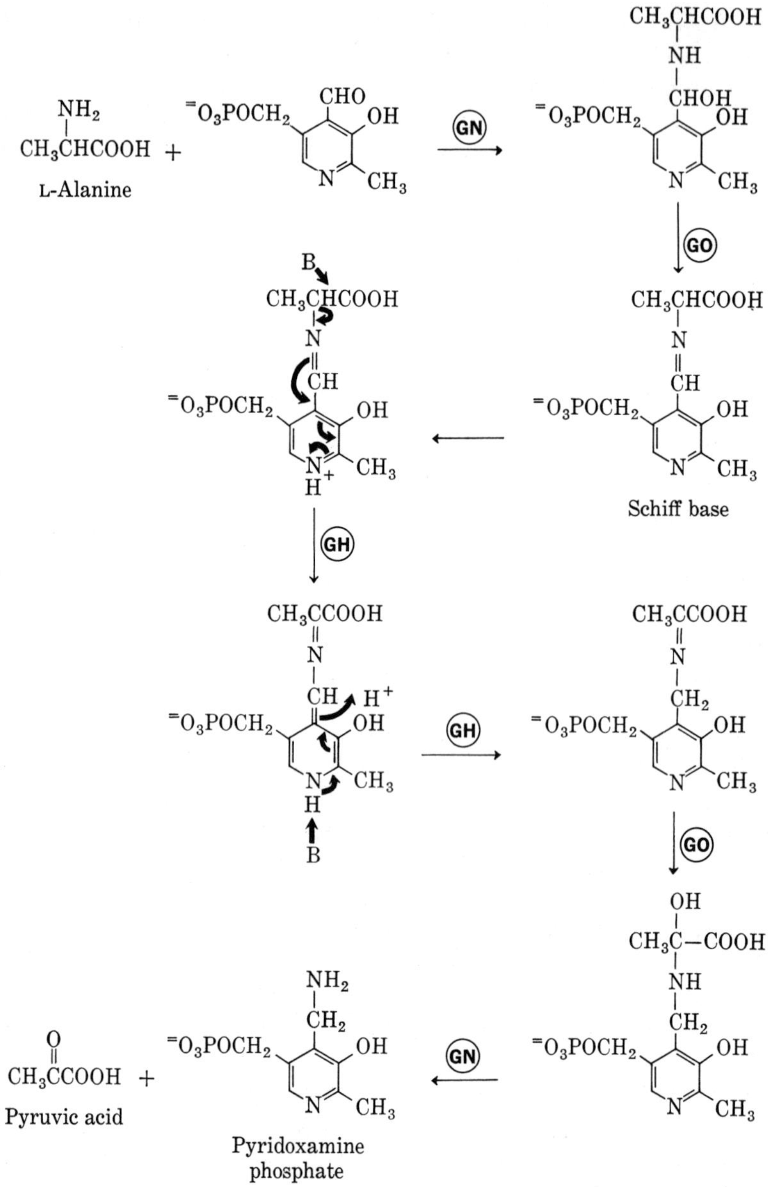

FIG. 1.26. A representative reaction in transamination.

1.7. PURINES AND PYRIMIDINES

Comme, c'est curieux, comme, c'est bizarre, et quelle coincidence!

E. Ionesco

The sequence of pyrimidine and purine rings in deoxyribonucleic acid is probably the source of hereditary information ("the genetic code") in most organisms. The biosyntheses of these heterocyclic ring systems proceed along rather different pathways in spite of their apparent close relationship.

Pyrimidine synthesis begins with the reaction of carbamyl phosphate (Fig. 1.24) and aspartic acid, forming carbamylaspartic acid (ureidosuccinic acid). Exchange experiments provide no support for a carbamylenzyme intermediate,[62] and it seems likely that nucleophilic attack on the carbonyl group of carbamyl phosphate is favored by protonation of the nitrogen.

The carbamylaspartic acid is cyclized to dihydroörotic acid in a reaction which apparently requires no "activating" cofactor. In view of the relatively low nucleophilicity of ureido nitrogen and the low susceptibility of carboxylic acids to nucleophilic attack, facile ring closure might not be expected. Perhaps its occurrence can be explained by concerted removal of a proton from the nucleophilic nitrogen and supply of a proton to the oxygen of the carboxylic acid group undergoing attack.

The oxidation of dihydroörotic acid to orotic acid is not simple, although it is catalyzed by DPN. If DPND (reduced diphosphopyridine nucleotide carrying one deuterium instead of a hydrogen in the 4-position of the dihydropyridine ring, cf. Sec. 2.13) is used to reduce orotic acid to dihydroörotic acid, the deuterium is removed from the DPND, forming DPN, but does not appear in the product, unlike the usual reactions of DPND (see Sec. 2.13). A flavin is thus implicated as an intermediary in the oxidation or reduction reaction, since a reduced flavin would exchange with water before transferring hydrogen to substrate.[66,67]

The route to orotic acid is outlined in Fig. 1.27.

1.7-1. The nucleotide orotidine-5'-phosphate is formed from orotic acid and 5-phospho-α-1-ribosyl pyrophosphate (5-PRPP), a compound with a structure confirmed by synthesis and chemical reactions.[68] Displacement reactions on a five-membered ring are not especially fast and should not be favored by the steric hindrance to

[66] J. L. Graves and B. Vennesland, *J. Biol. Chem.*, **226,** 307 (1957).

[67] H. C. Friedman and B. Vennesland, *Federation Proc.*, **17,** 224 (1958).

[68] G. M. Tener and H. G. Khorana, *J. Am. Chem. Soc.*, **80,** 1999 (1958).

rearward approach (required in bimolecular displacement, S_N2, reactions) provided by the 5 carbon of the ribose. It is suggested that 5-PRPP undergoes enzyme-catalyzed ionization in Sec. 2.15 (p. 261) and this point of view is adopted here.

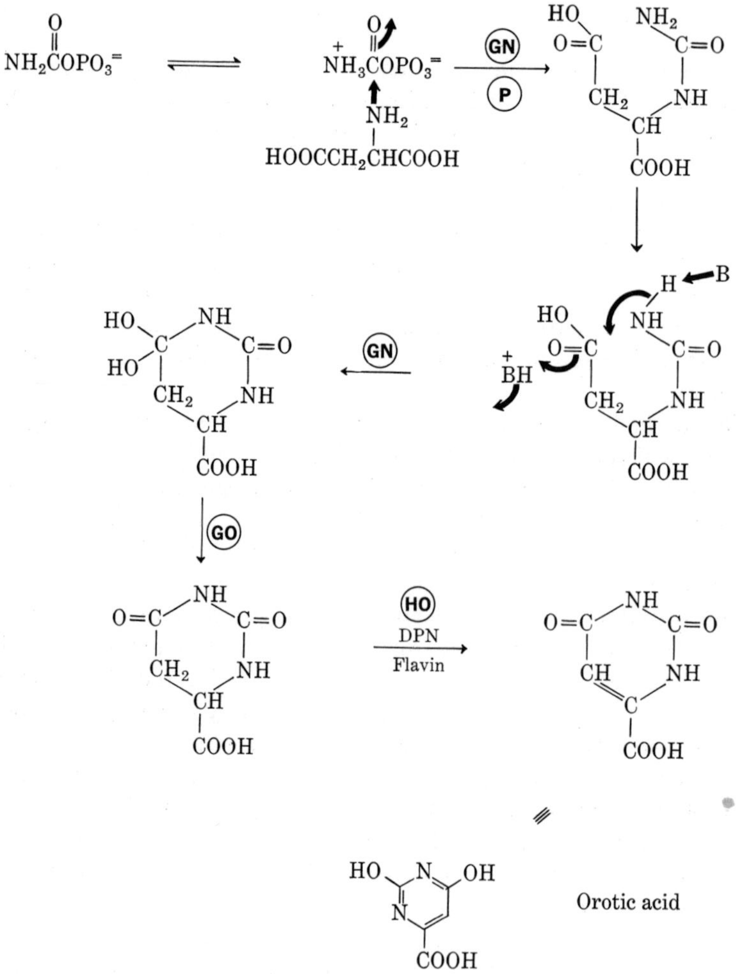

FIG. 1.27. Formation of orotic acid.

Decarboxylation of orotidine-5'-phosphate yields uridine monophosphate (UMP), and the latter can be converted into cytidine triphosphate via UTP (Fig. 1.28).

1.7-2. Purine biosynthesis commences with the reaction of 5-PRPP and the amide of glutamic acid (glutamine) with the formation

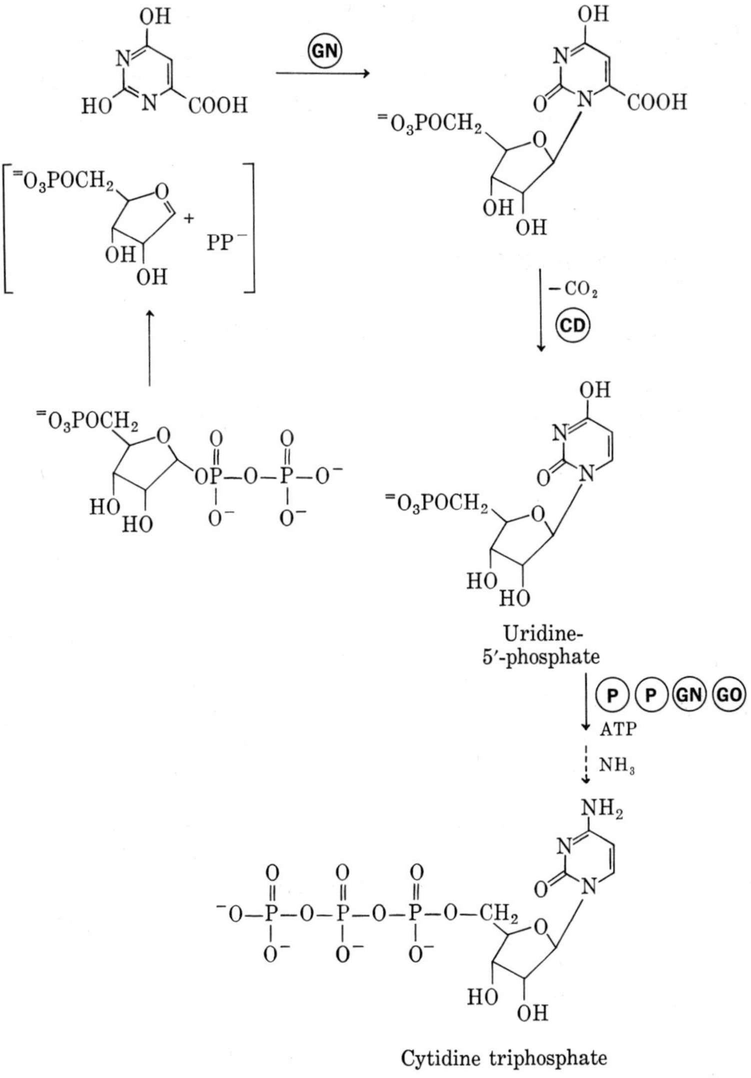

FIG. 1.28. Synthesis of UMP and CTP.

of 5-phosphoribosylamine, an unstable molecule which has not yet been isolated in pure form.[69]   The low nucleophilicity expected for the amide nitrogen of glutamine as well as the stereochemical difficulty cited previously for displacements on 5-PRPP again suggests formation of an enzyme-bound 5-PR+PP− ion pair as an intermediate step.   If the

[69] J. M. Buchanan and S. C. Hartman, *Advances in Enzymol.*, **21**, 236–238, 245–246 (1959).

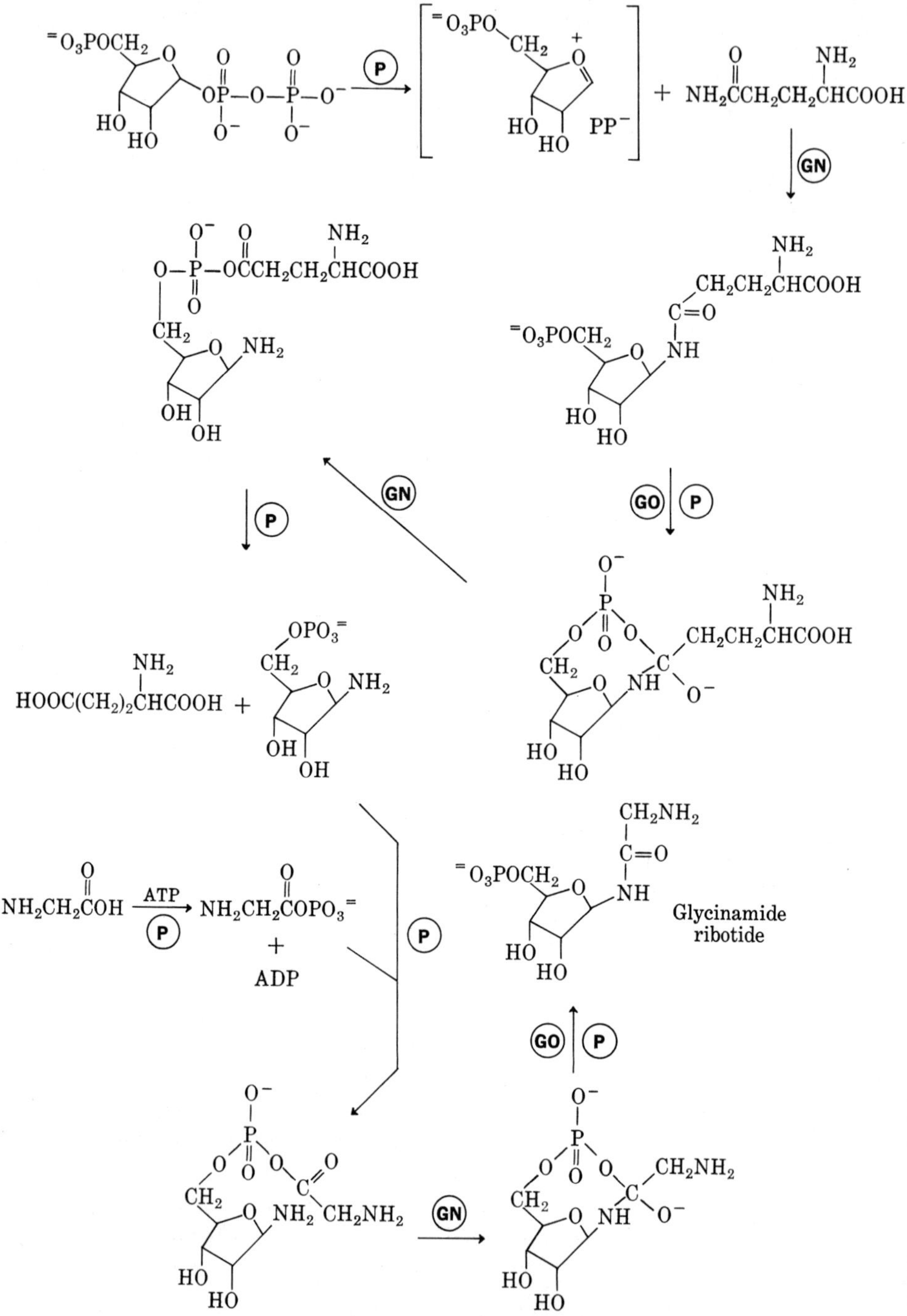

FIG. 1.29. Glycinamide ribotide.

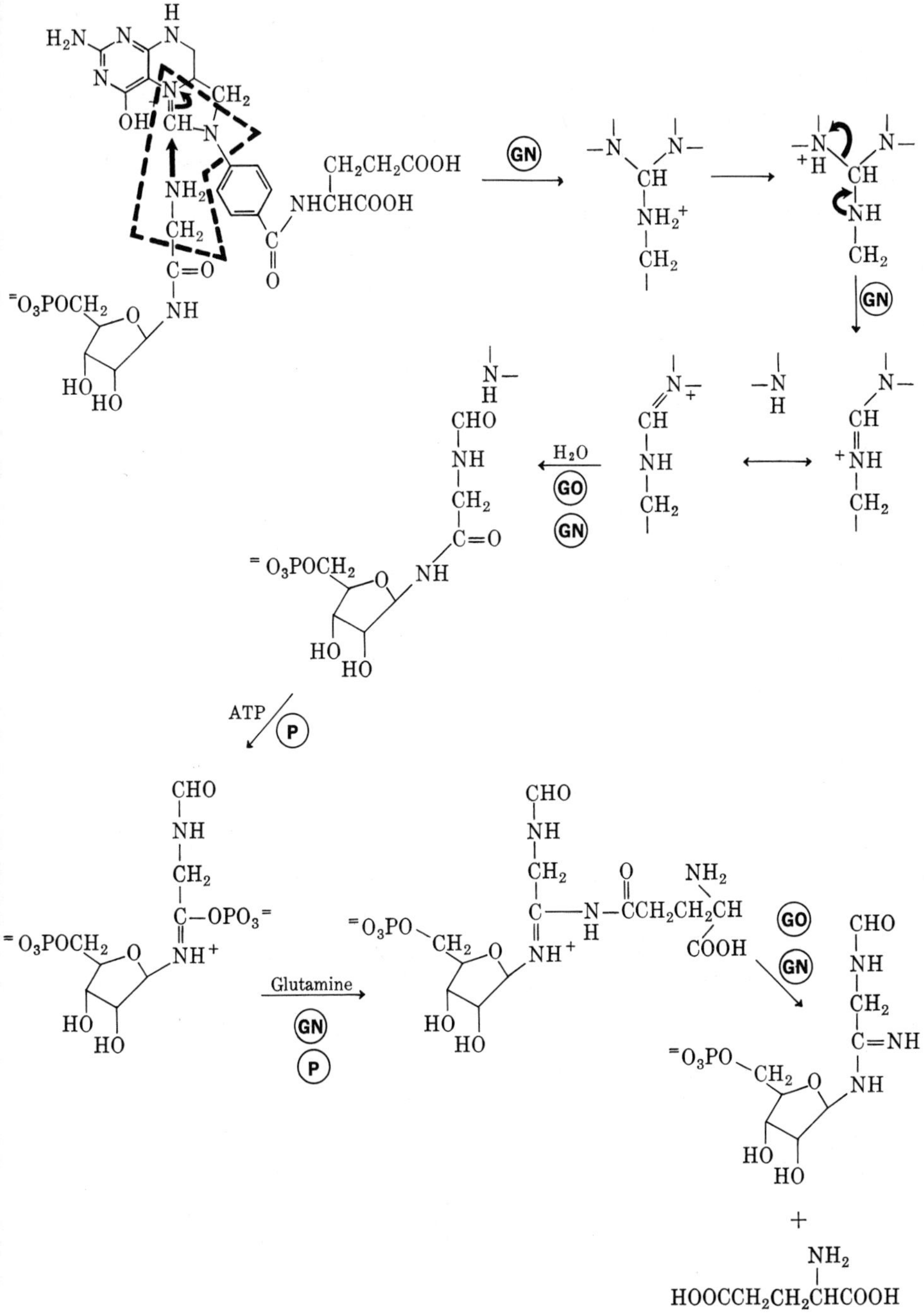

FIG. 1.30. Formation of formylglycinamidine ribotide.

supposition to be cited below for glycinamide ribotide is correct, it would be expected that glutamide ribotide would be readily hydrolyzed by the enzyme, forming 5-phosphoribosylamine. Glycinyl phosphate, derived from glycine and ATP, reacts with 5-PR-amine to give glycinamide ribotide in a reaction which is readily reversible. The simplest way to account for the reactivity of the amide is to postulate an enzyme-promoted "neighboring group" reaction with the 5-phosphate, suggesting an acyl ribosyl phosphate as an intermediate in amide formation and decomposition. The route to glycinamide ribotide as well as these points of interpretation are illustrated in Fig. 1.29.

1.7-3. Glycinamide ribotide acquires an *N*-formyl group through reaction with N^5,N^{10}-anhydroformyl tetrahydrofolic acid. The transformation can be represented by a series of simple steps. The product, formylglycinamide ribotide, is converted to formylglycin*amidine* ribotide by reaction with ATP, probably to form a reactive intermediate, followed by nucleophilic attack of the amide nitrogen of glutamine on that reactive intermediate. It would be expected that the acyl amidine which results from the latter step is readily hydrolyzed to the observed products (Fig. 1.30).

1.7-4. The nitrogen attached to the ribose ring of formylglycinamidine ribotide is situated in the proper geometric relation to the carbonyl of the formyl group for addition. Rapid addition of nitrogen nucleophiles, even to conjugated carbonyl groups, is expected on the basis of investigations of oxime formation (see Sec. 2.6). Thus, the requirement for ATP in the ring-closure reaction is probably connected with the cleavage of the carbon-oxygen bond. A subsequent proton migration leads to 5-aminoimidazole ribotide (5-AIR).

The nucleophilicity of the 4-carbon of the 5-AIR toward carbon dioxide is easily rationalized in terms of analogy with the known nucleophilicity of the β carbon of enamines. The resulting carboxylic acid is converted to an acyl phosphate with ATP, and reaction with aspartic acid forms an amide which yields 5-amino-4-carboxamidoimidazole ribotide and fumaric acid in an elimination reaction similar to one noted in Sec. 1.5.

These reactions are summarized in Fig. 1.31.

1.7-5. Formylation of the amino group in 5-amino-4-carboxamidoimidazole ribotide is accomplished with N^{10}-formyltetrahydrofolic acid. The formyl compound cyclizes, possibly in an "unactivated" reaction (i.e., one requiring no special cofactor), to a carbinolamine which is transformed into inosinic acid by dehydration.

Inosinic acid gives rise to adenylic acid (adenosine-5'-phosphate, AMP) and guanylic acid (guanosine-5'-phosphate, GMP), two other important nucleotides, in multistep reactions.

The final stages of purine nucleotide biosynthesis are outlined in Fig. 1.32.

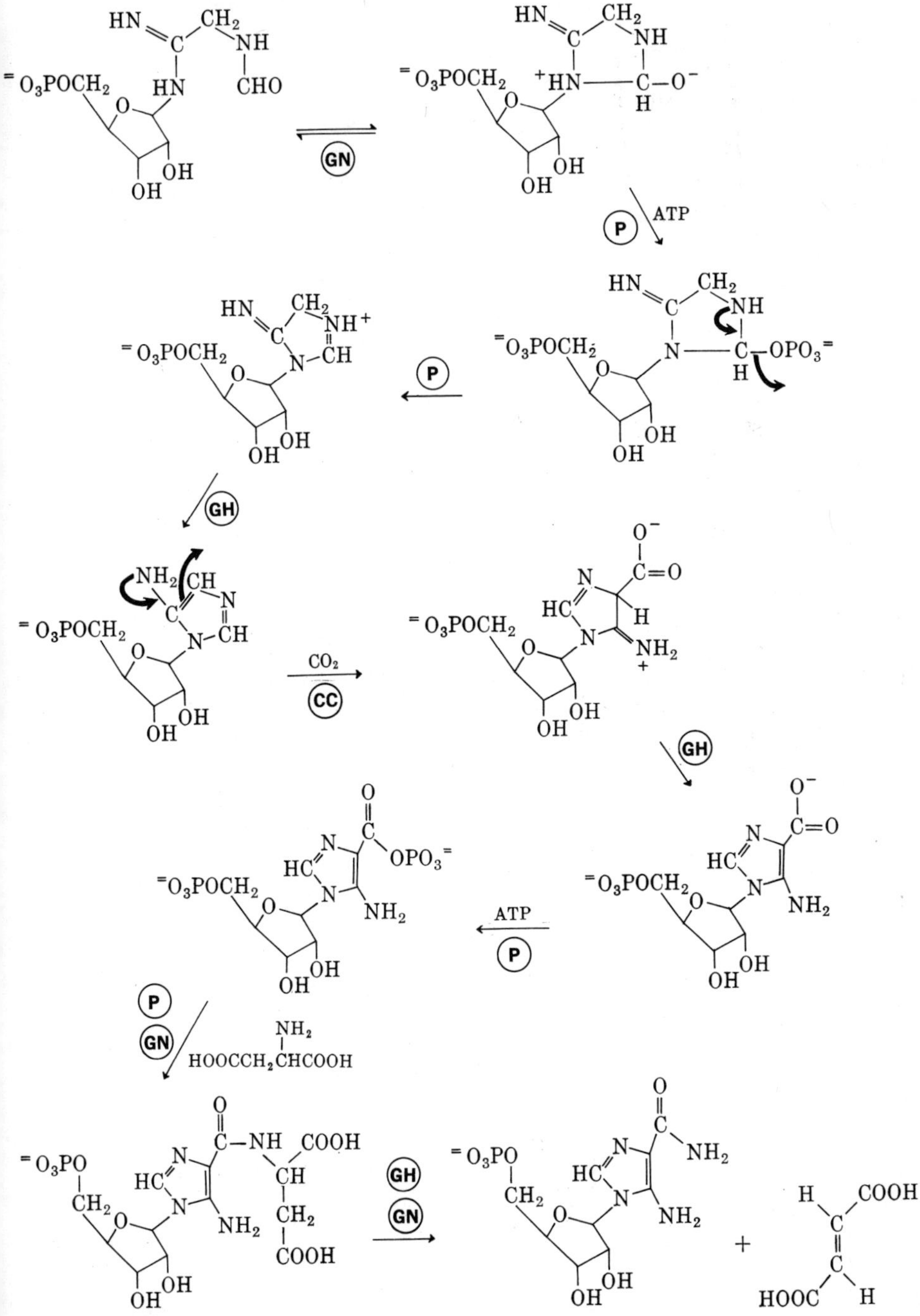

FIG. 1.31. Formation of 5-amino-4-carboxamidoimidazole ribotide.

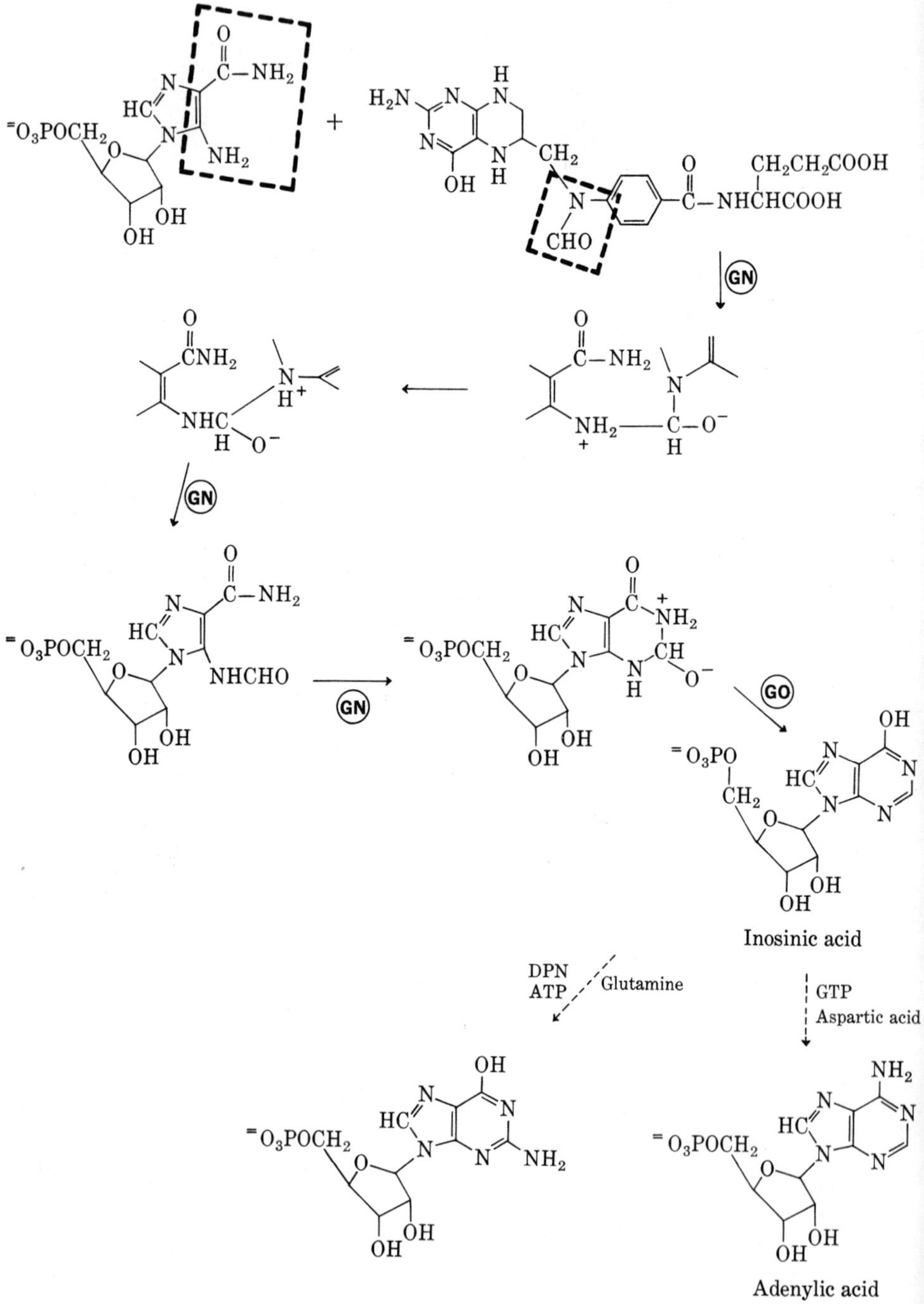

FIG. 1.32. Final steps of purine nucleotide biosynthesis.

1.8. SELECTED BIOSYNTHESES

The organic chemist approaches biogenesis from a purely theoretical point of view by way of generalization derived from comparisons of structures. He is quite unable to arrive at any particular view of the stages of progress of reactions in living cells. This intuitive method has a certain value because the comparison of structures provides evidence in itself, but it must be very carefully used and can never attain the status of actual experiments on the processes *in vitro.*

Sir Robert Robinson[70]

The correlation of the structures of many classes of natural products by "biogenetic" schemes has long been a successful intellectual pastime in organic chemistry. Prominent examples of these efforts are the "isoprene rule,"[71] the "β-arylethylamine hypothesis,"[72] and "acetate (propionate) condensation."[73,74] Useful as these ideas are, especially when the general patterns proposed are consistent with the results of isotopic tracer studies, their intuitive and speculative content should not be confused with experimentally derived facts about *actual* intermediates, *actual* pathways, and *actual* enzyme-catalyzed transformations. With respect to the biosynthesis of cholesterol, for example, no intermediate except squalene[75] was predicted a priori by the "isoprene rule."

1.8-1. The biosyntheses of fatty acids and terpenes start with acetyl coA. Both pathways involve the formation of an acetoacetyl moiety, but there are indications that an "enzyme-bound" acetoacetyl group participates in fatty acid synthesis,[76,77] and free acetoacetyl coA in terpene formation. The over-all pattern of these biosyntheses is illustrated in Fig. 1.33.

Acetate ion is converted into acetyl coA by consecutive reactions with ATP and coASH, the intermediate being "enzyme-bound" acetyl adenylate[78,79] (Fig. 1.34). Descriptive terms for the sequences are given in Fig. 1.33 for portions of the pathways to the observed natural products.

[70] R. Robinson, Chairman's opening remarks, "Ciba Foundation Symposium on the Biosynthesis of Terpenes and Sterols," J. and A. Churchill, Ltd., London, 1959.

[71] L. Ruzicka, *Proc. Chem. Soc.,* 341 (1959).

[72] R. B. Woodward, *Angew. Chemie,* **68,** 13 (1956).

[73] J. N. Collie, *J. Chem. Soc.,* **91,** 1980 (1907).

[74] A. J. Birch, *Fortschr. Chem. org. Naturstoffe,* **14,** 186 (1957).

[75] R. Robinson, *Chem. & Ind. (London),* **53,** 1062 (1934).

[76] F. Lynen, *Bayerische Akad. der Wiss., Mathem.-Naturwiss. Kl.,* Mar. 4, 1960.

[77] A. W. Alberts, P. R. Vagelos, *Federation Proc.,* **20,** 273 (1961).

[78] L. L. Ingraham and D. E. Green, *Science,* **128,** 310 (1958).

[79] P. Berg, *Science,* **129,** 895 (1959).

Many of these will be elucidated in greater detail in subsequent subsections.

1.8-2. The "activation" of acetyl coA in the synthesis of fatty acids seems to differ from that involved in a number of other condensation

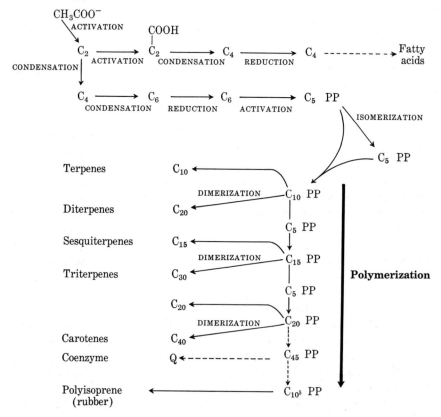

FIG. 1.33. Biosynthetic pathways to terpenes and fatty acids.

reactions. In fatty acid synthesis, malonyl coA is generated by the reaction of carbon dioxide, ATP, and acetyl coA, probably in a sequence which includes a biotin-carboxylic acid as an intermediate.[80,81,81a] It seems highly probable that malonyl coA reacts with an enzyme thiol

[80] S. J. Wakil, *J. Am. Chem. Soc.*, **80**, 6465 (1958).

[81] J. V. Formica and R. O. Brady, *J. Am. Chem. Soc.*, **81**, 752 (1959).

[81a] The carbon dioxide–dependent fatty acid synthetic pathway is much more important than the mitochondrial pathway which is the reverse of "β-oxidation" through acyl coA, condensation to acyloacetyl coA, reduction to β-hydroxyacyl coA, dehydration to α,β-enoyl coA, and reduction to acyl coA. Cf. ref. 81*b*.

[81b] S. J. Wakil, *J. Lipid Research*, **2**, 1 (1961).

group (ESH) to yield malonyl SE and coASH, followed by decarboxylation to give an enzyme-stabilized enol of acetyl coA.   The latter reacts
with acetyl coA to form acetoacetyl SE,[76] which can undergo condensation

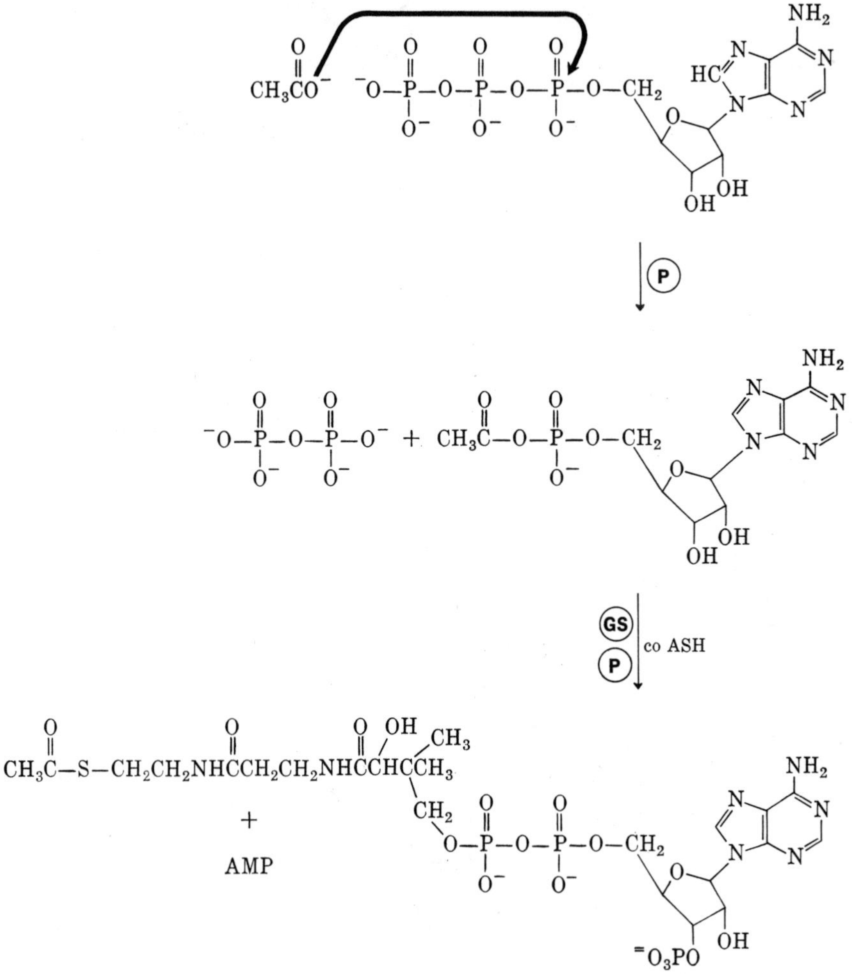

FIG. 1.34. Formation of acetyl coA from acetate ion.

to palmitic acid in the presence of TPNH and additional malonyl coA.
The critical evidence in support of this pathway is the fact, originally
found for deuterium[82] and confirmed quantitatively for tritium,[83] that one
hydrogen of each original malonyl coA appears in the fatty acid product.

[82] R. Sonderhoff and H. Thomas, *Ann.*, **530**, 195 (1937).
[83] S. J. Wakil and R. Bressler, *J. Biol. Chem.*, **236**, 1643 (1961).

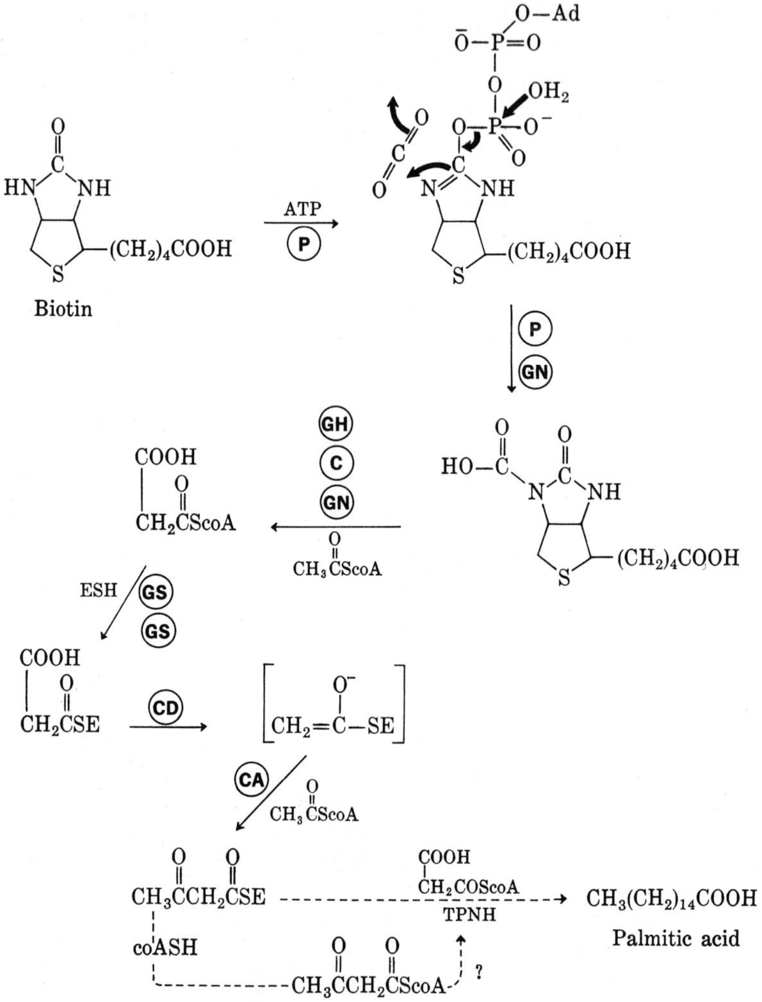

FIG. 1.35. Acetyl coA to fatty acids.

In the case of palmitic acid ($C_{15}COOH$), from 5 to 6.8 "original" hydrogens are found in comparison with a theoretical number of 7 (ref. 83) (Fig. 1.35).

The synthetic pathway utilized by the usual enzyme preparations[83,83a] is not able to operate with many of the intermediates known for fatty

[83a] However, cf. the probable mechanism for the formation of unsaturated fatty acids in anaerobic bacteria.[83b]

[83b] G. Scheuerbrandt, H. Goldfine, P. E. Baronowsky, and K. Bloch, *J. Biol. Chem.*, **236**, PC70 (1961).

acid degradation, such as α,β-unsaturated acyl coA, β-hydroxyacyl coA, or even hexanoyl coA.[84] Detailed mechanisms for the steps of fatty acid synthesis cannot be written with the information available.

1.8-3. In condensation reactions of acetyl coA other than those described in the foregoing subsection, removal of the proton on the α position is catalyzed by the enzyme. In the case of citric acid, the carbonyl acceptor for the $CH_2COScoA$ moiety must be present to effect the reaction. The enzyme does not catalyze exchange of α-hydrogen of acetyl coA with water, measured with tritium[16] or deuterium.[85] For both citric acid and hydroxymethylglutaryl coA formation, the acetyl coA group which is added suffers hydrolysis of the thioester linkage. Formation of acetoacetyl coA apparently occurs without affecting the thioester group. The simplest notion to explain this result is that hydrolysis of the thioester group shifts the condensation equilibrium in the direction of products, and that the hydrolysis is catalyzed by the enzyme which catalyzes the condensation.[86]

The formation of 3-hydroxy-3-methylglutaryl coA is shown in the first portion of Fig. 1.36.

1.8-4. A key advance in the development of the study of terpene biosynthesis is the discovery of mevalonic acid.[88] Mevalonic acid is formed by reduction of hydroxymethylglutaryl coA by TPNH,[89] and the reaction proceeds through mevaldic acid as an intermediate.[90] The latter is tightly bound to the enzyme, but it seems possible that the formation of an enzyme–mevaldic acid–TPNH complex results in a shift of an equilibrium to the side of free aldehyde group which is then reduced by the TPNH to mevalonic acid.

The biosynthesis of mevalonic acid is summarized in Fig. 1.36.

1.8-5. Mevalonic acid reacts with ATP in three successive steps catalyzed by different enzymes. The third phosphorylation leads to a decarboxylation, forming isopentenyl pyrophosphate.[91] Proof for the

---

[84] S. J. Wakil, personal communication.

[85] A. Marcus and B. Vennesland, *J. Biol. Chem.*, **233**, 727 (1958).

[86] A β-lactone has been proposed as an intermediate in the citric acid condensation to explain the hydrolysis, but this explanation would make reversal of the reaction difficult to explain. However, formation of acetoacetyl coA from 3-hydroxy-3-methylglutaryl coA has not been demonstrated. (A. Eschenmoser and D. Arigoni, personal communication to F. Lynen.[87])

[87] L. Jaenicke and F. Lynen, in "The Enzymes," vol. 3, chap. 11, Academic Press, Inc., New York, 1960.

[88] A fascinating description of the serendipitous finding of mevalonic acid is given by K. Folkers, C. H. Shunk, B. O. Linn, F. M. Robinson, P. E. Wittreich, J. W. Huff, J. L. Gilfillan, and H. R. Skeggs, in ref. 70, p. 20.

[89] J. J. Ferguson, I. F. Durr, and H. Rudney, *Federation Proc.*, **17**, 219 (1958).

[90] J Brodie and J. W. Porter, *Biochem. Biophys. Research Comm.*, **3**, 173 (1960).

[91] G. Popják and J. W. Cornforth, *Advances in Enzymol.*, **22**, 295–309 (1960).

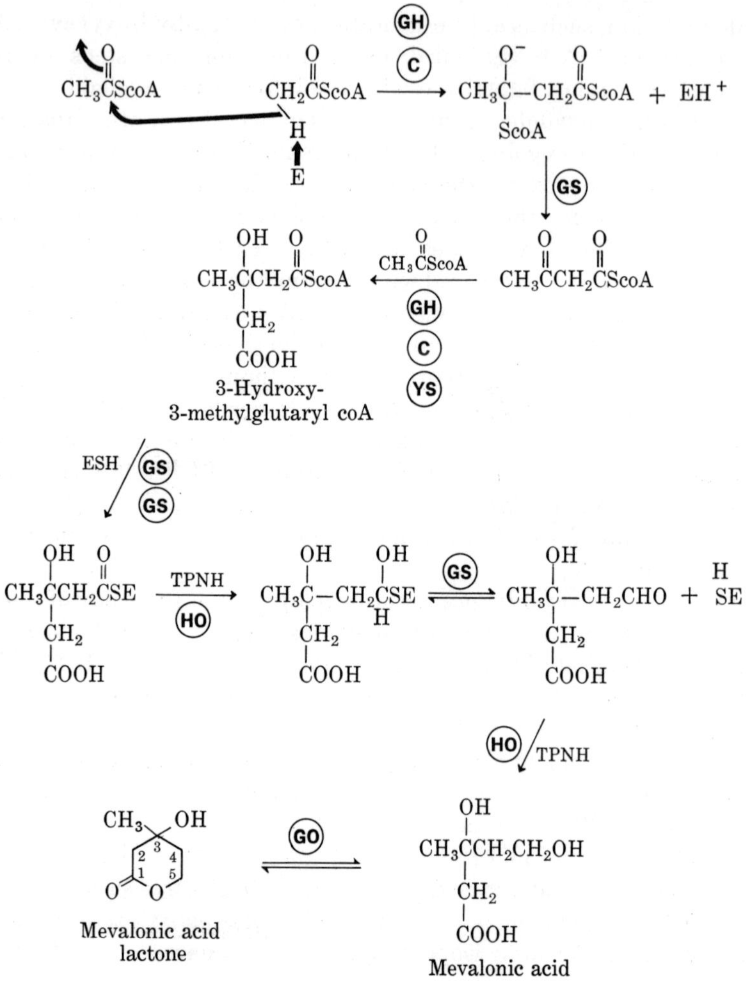

FIG. 1.36. Biosynthesis of mevalonic acid.

location of the third phosphate group on the tertiary hydroxyl of mevalonic acid has been obtained by labeling that hydroxyl with oxygen-18,
and finding that the phosphate produced in the decarboxylation contained one atom of oxygen-18.[92,92a] Isopentenyl pyrophosphate is isom-
erized to 3,3-dimethylallyl pyrophosphate, and both compounds have
been prepared synthetically.[93] The isomerase is inhibited by "SH

[92] M. Lindberg, C. Yuan, and K. Bloch, *Federation Proc.*, **20**, 230 (1961).

[92a] M. Lindberg, C. Yuan, A. de Waard, and K. Bloch, *Biochem.*, **1**, in press (1962).

[93] F. Lynen, B. W. Agranoff, H. Eggerer, U. Henning, and E. M. Moslein, *Angew. Chem.*, **71**, 657 (1959).

reagents" (e.g., *p*-chloromercuribenzoic acid), leading to the proposal that the isomerization was accomplished through addition, then elimination of an enzyme thiol group [Eq. (1.6)]. Support for the mechanism

$$
(1.6) \quad \overset{\overset{\text{C}}{|}}{\text{C}}{=}\text{C}{-}\text{C}{-}\text{C}{-}\text{X} \xrightarrow{\text{ESH}} \overset{\overset{\text{C}}{|}}{\underset{\underset{\text{SE}}{|}}{\text{C}{-}\text{C}}}{-}\text{C}{-}\text{C}{-}\text{X} \xrightarrow{-\text{ESH}} \overset{\overset{\text{C}}{|}}{\text{C}}{-}\text{C}{=}\text{C}{-}\text{C}{-}\text{X}
$$

was based on the formation of felinine from cysteine and mevalonic acid.[94] However, the radiochemical results[94] indicate that leucine is considerably more efficient as a precursor of felinine [Eq. (1.7)] than mevalonic acid, suggesting that β-methylcrotonyl coA is the acceptor for

$$
(1.7) \quad \overset{\overset{\text{NH}_2}{|}}{\text{HOOCCHCH}_2\text{SH}} + \text{CH}_3\overset{\overset{\text{CH}_3}{|}}{\text{C}}{=}\text{CHCOScOA}
$$

$$
\downarrow
$$

$$
\overset{\overset{\text{NH}_2}{|}}{\text{HOOCCHCH}_2\text{S}}\overset{\overset{\text{CH}_3}{|}}{\underset{\underset{\text{CH}_3}{|}}{\text{C}}}\text{CH}_2\text{CH}_2\text{OH}
$$

Felinine

thiol addition. Since good precedents are lacking for the mechanism of Eq. (1.6), the isomerization is best regarded at this time as resulting from a concerted addition and removal of a proton [Eq. (1.8)]. There is

$$
(1.8) \quad \overset{\overset{\text{C}}{|}}{\text{C}}{=}\text{C}\overset{\overset{\text{H}}{|}}{-}\text{C}{-}\text{C}{-}\text{X} \underset{\text{H}^+}{} \longrightarrow \overset{\overset{\text{C}}{|}}{\text{C}}{-}\overset{}{\underset{\underset{\text{H}}{|}}{\text{C}}}{=}\text{C}{-}\text{C}{-}\text{X}
$$

little reason to believe that the isomerization reaction [Eq. (1.8)] leads to indiscriminate exchange of protons with the solvent;[95] if protons are involved in the mechanism, they must be shielded from exchange with the solvent (see Sec. 3.1).

The formation of the pentenyl pyrophosphates from mevalonic acid is shown in Fig. 1.37.

[94] P. V. Avizonic and J. C. Wriston, Jr., *Biochim. et Biophys. Acta*, **34**, 279 (1959).

[95] G. Popják, D. S. Goodman, J. W. Cornforth, R. H. Cornforth, and R. Ryhage, *Biochem. Biophys. Research Comm.*, **4**, 138 (1961).

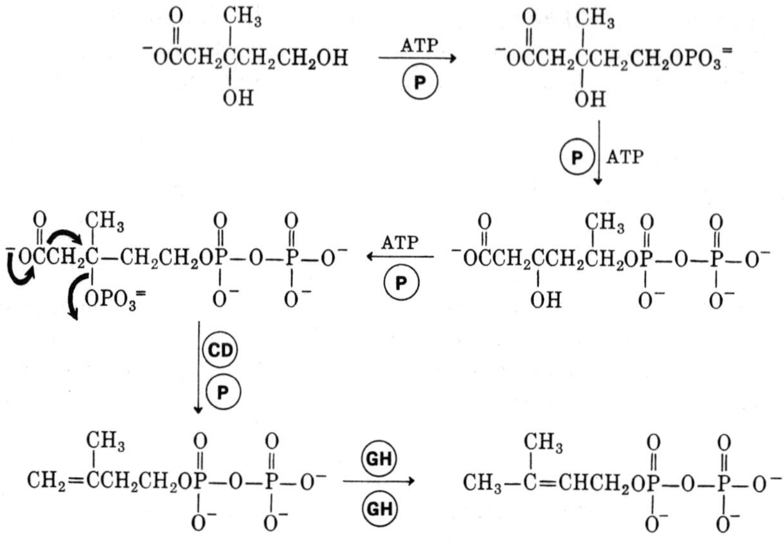

$$^-OCCH_2\overset{\overset{\displaystyle CH_3}{|}}{C}CH_2CH_2OH \xrightarrow[\enclose{circle}{P}]{ATP} {}^-OCCH_2\overset{\overset{\displaystyle CH_3}{|}}{C}CH_2CH_2OPO_3^=$$

FIG. 1.37. Formation of pentenyl pyrophosphates.

1.8-6. The "propagation" step in the biopolymerization to terpenes is the nucleophilic attack of isopentenyl pyrophosphate on an allylic pyrophosphate to form the homologous allylic pyrophosphate containing five additional carbon atoms. Dimethylallylpyrophosphate yields geranyl pyrophosphate, and the latter, in turn, gives rise to farnesyl pyrophosphate.

It is of great interest to evaluate the reactivities of pyrophosphates in replacement reactions with a nucleophile, N [Eq. (1.9)]. Using 3,3-dimethylallyl chloride as an appropriate reference compound, we can

(1.9) $$N + CH_3\overset{\overset{\displaystyle CH_3}{|}}{C}=CHCH_2OPOPO^- \longrightarrow CH_3\overset{\overset{\displaystyle CH_3}{|}}{C}=CHCH_2-N + HOP-O-P-O^-$$

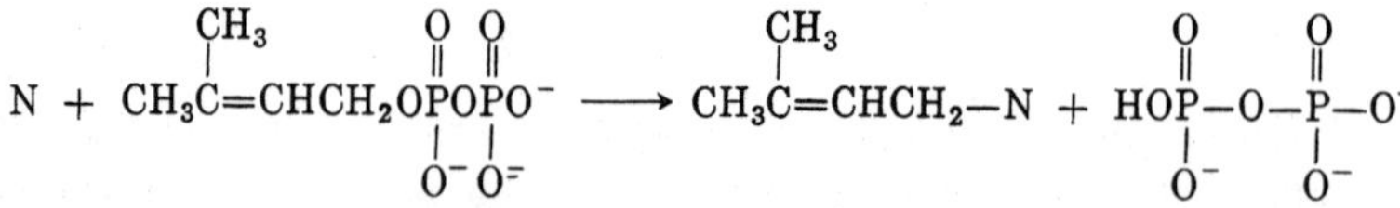

estimate a rate of solvolysis in water, according to Eq. (1.10), from the reported rate in ethanol and the fact that the sensitivity of the solvolysis rate to solvent change is 0.974 that of t-butyl chloride.[96,97] The rate

[96] R. H. DeWolfe and W. G. Young, *Chem. Revs.*, **56**, 790 (1956).

[97] The correlation of solvolysis rates with those of t-butyl chloride is known as the mY treatment.[98]

[98] A. H. Fainberg and S. Winstein, *J. Am. Chem. Soc.*, **78**, 2770 (1956).

constant for solvolysis of 3,3-dimethylallyl chloride in water at 25°C is ca. 5 sec^{-1}. Geranyl pyrophosphate has been reported to hydrolyze in 0.1 N hydrochloric acid at 25°C with rate constant of ca. 7 × 10^{-3} sec^{-1} (ref. 93). Any reasonable estimate of the acid dissociation constants of monoalkyl pyrophosphates (compare the monoalkyl phosphate dissociation constants with those for phosphoric acid in Table 2.15-2) suggests that a substantial portion of the geranyl pyrophosphate will be present as the monoanion, and that the solvolysis is described by Eq. (1.11). Thus, chloride ion as a leaving group is at least 10^3 times better than

$$(1.10) \quad \underset{\overset{|}{CH_3}}{CH_3-C=CHCH_2Cl} \quad \xrightarrow[-Cl^-]{H_2O} \quad \left[\underset{\overset{|}{CH_3}}{CH_3C\text{···}CH\text{···}CH_2} \right]^+$$

$$\underset{\overset{|}{OH}}{CH_3\overset{CH_3}{\underset{|}{C}}-CH=CH_2} \quad + \quad \underset{\overset{|}{CH_3}}{CH_3C=CHCH_2OH}$$

$$(1.11) \quad \underset{\overset{|}{CH_3}}{CH_3C}=CHCH_2CH_2\underset{\overset{|}{CH_3}}{C}=CHCH_2O\overset{\overset{O}{\|}}{\underset{\overset{|}{OH}}{P}}-O-\overset{\overset{O}{\|}}{\underset{\overset{|}{O^-}}{P}}-OH$$

$$-H_2P_2O_7^= \Big| H_2O$$

$$\left[\underset{\overset{|}{CH_3}}{CH_3C}=CHCH_2CH_2\underset{\overset{|}{CH_3}}{C}\text{···}CH\text{···}CH_2 \right]^+$$

Geraniol + nerolidol

the dianion of pyrophosphoric acid. (The difference in ionizing powers of 0.1 N hydrochloric acid and water is ignored.)

Under highly ionizing conditions, the solvolysis products are derived entirely from the carbonium ion. Direct demonstration of this conclusion is found in the fact that the same product ratios are obtained under highly ionizing conditions from 3,3-dimethylallyl chloride and from the isomeric dimethylvinylcarbinyl chloride.[96] However, as the polarity of the solvent is decreased, the product mixtures derived from the isomers diverge in composition, i.e., in the ratio of tertiary product to primary product. With sodium methoxide in methanol, 3,3-dimethylallyl chloride yields exclusively 3,3-dimethylallyl methyl ether, and dimethylvinylcarbinyl chloride gives a mixture containing 67% dimethylvinylcarbinyl methyl ether and 33% 3,3-dimethylallyl methyl ether.[96] The primary halide reacts exclusively by bimolecular nucleophilic displacement, and the tertiary halide possibly through a combination of displacement and ionization processes.[99]

The large rate advantage conferred by the dialkyl substituents on the allylic system is most evident in highly polar solvents. The 3,3-dimethyl-allyl chloride is more than 10^5 times as reactive as allyl chloride in 50% ethanol-water, but only 17 to 28 times as fast in bimolecular displacement reactions like displacement of chloride ion by iodide ion, etc.[100] In other words, as the ionizing power of the solvent falls, the contribution of the bimolecular (S_N2) displacement process becomes more important. Another way of expressing the same idea is to say that the covalent contribution of the bond between the attacking nucleophile (either solvent or other agent) and the allylic system rises with decreasing ionizing power of the solvent or increasing nucleophilicity of the nucleophile.

Since the polarity of the "medium" in which the "propagation" step of terpene biosynthesis takes place is unknown, conclusions about the mechanism of the step must be based on inference. It is likely that two of the allylic pyrophosphate negative charges are neutralized before reaction can occur, and it seems possible that magnesium ion serves this purpose in the biochemical system. Two facts suggest that the biochemical reaction is a bimolecular nucleophilic displacement rather than an ionization reaction through a carbonium ion intermediate.[91] First, the pyrophosphate monoanion is considerably poorer than chloride as a leaving group in ionization reactions, and yet it is easy to observe S_N2 reactions for primary allylic chlorides. Special solvation of the allylic carbonium ion which could overcome the rate disadvantage of the pyrophosphate leaving group might be imagined, but it is very difficult to understand how such special "enzymic solvation" could control the ratio of tertiary to primary product for the compact allylic carbonium ion. Second, the formation of terpenes appears to be highly *position-specific*, with "propagation" occurring only through reaction at the primary carbon atom.

We conclude that the "propagation" step is an unusual bimolecular displacement reaction, and that the "medium" in which it occurs is of moderate (or low) polarity, possibly a lipid-water interface. The mechanism is indicated in Fig. 1.38.[101]

1.8-7. A more detailed examination of a plausible transition state for the mechanism depicted in Fig. 1.38 reveals a rather special situation (Fig. 1.39). The removal of the proton from the isopentenyl

---

[99] The tertiary halide can isomerize to the primary halide in media of intermediate or low polarity through "internal return," i.e., formation of an "intimate ion pair" which does not dissociate to the carbonium ion, and can also undergo "abnormal" bimolecular displacement (S_N2') to form primary product (cf. ref. 96).

[100] A. Streitwieser, Jr., *Chem. Revs.*, **56**, 593 (1956).

[101] The belief that ionization of the allylic pyrophosphate is unnecessary for the "propagation" step has been expressed without supporting arguments by A. R. Todd, *J. Cellular Comp. Physiol.*, **54**, Suppl. 1, 70 (1959).

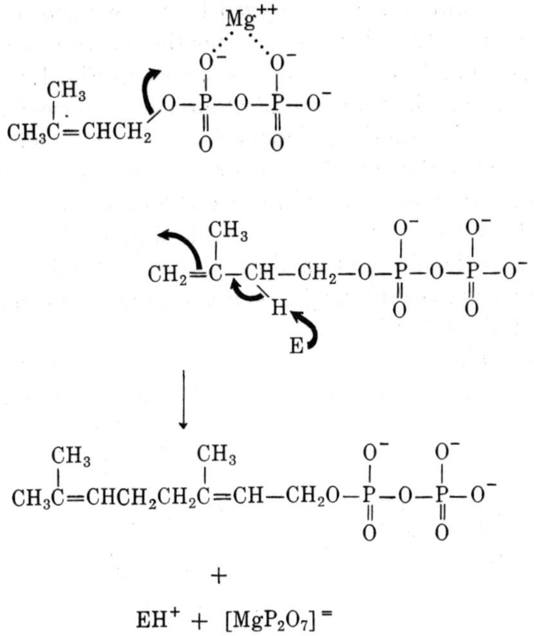

$$Mg^{++}$$

$$CH_3C=CHCH_2 \quad O-P-O-P-O^-$$

$$CH_2=C-CH-CH_2-O-P-O-P-O^-$$

$$\begin{array}{c} CH_3 \qquad\qquad CH_3 \\ CH_3C=CHCH_2CH_2C=CH-CH_2O-P-O-P-O^- \end{array}$$

$$+$$

$$EH^+ + [MgP_2O_7]^=$$

FIG. 1.38. The "propagation" step in terpene biosynthesis.

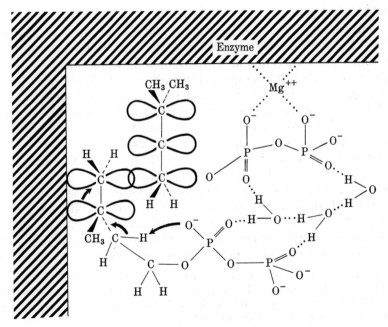

FIG. 1.39. A transition state for the "propagation" step.

pyrophosphate might well be catalyzed by the oxygen of the pyrophosphate group, and "extra" driving force for the reaction might be ascribed to the hydrogen bonding by water, as shown in Fig. 1.38. Although it might seem reasonable that an allyl-enzyme intermediate should be formed, and thus obviate the necessity for a crowded transition state, no enzyme group with the appropriate properties readily comes to mind. The transition state shown does indicate the need for study of reactions at interfaces between relatively immiscible liquids of different polarity, either at the gross level exemplified by "interfacial polymerization"[102] or at the micellar level (which might be a good model for enzymatic situations represented by Fig. 1.38).

1.8-8. The most careful and extensive study of the formation of squalene was carried out with doubly labeled mevalonic acid-2-C^{14}-5,5-d_2.

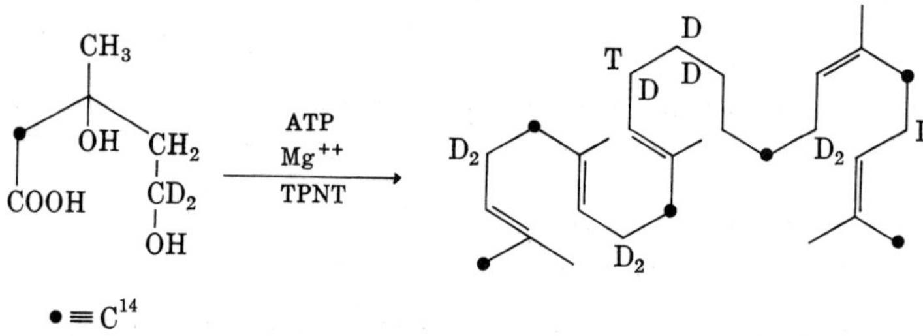

FIG. 1.40. Labeled squalene from mevalonic acid.

It is known[91] that TPNH is required for the condensation of farnesyl pyrophosphate (C_{15}) to squalene (C_{30}). The reducing agent was supplied as TPNT (tritium labeled TPNH) or as TPNH in THO (water containing tritium). The deuterium–carbon-14 ratio in the squalene proved that 11 of the 12 deuterium atoms expected from the mevalonic acid were present in the squalene. One hydrogen was derived from TPNH, since the use of TPNT led to the presence of one tritium atom in the squalene. However, TPNH in THO did *not* introduce any tritium into the squalene. (The microsomal preparations used to catalyze the reactions were free of activities that cause exchange between TPNH and THO.) The labeled squalene thus produced is shown in Fig. 1.40.

The isotope results pose severe limitations to the writing of even hypothetical mechanisms for the formation of squalene. Previous proposals[91,103] fail by this criterion. A mechanism is outlined in Fig. 1.41, using thiamin anion, which leads to the correct isotope results but includes a last reduction step that lacks good precedent.[104] The chief

[102] P. W. Morgan and S. L. Kwolek, *J. Chem. Educ.*, **36**, 182 (1959).

[103] F. Lynen, H. Eggerer, U. Henning, and I. Kessel, *Angew. Chem.*, **70**, 739 (1958).

[104] Helpful discussion with Prof. David M. Lemal, Chemistry Department, University of Wisconsin, is gratefully acknowledged.

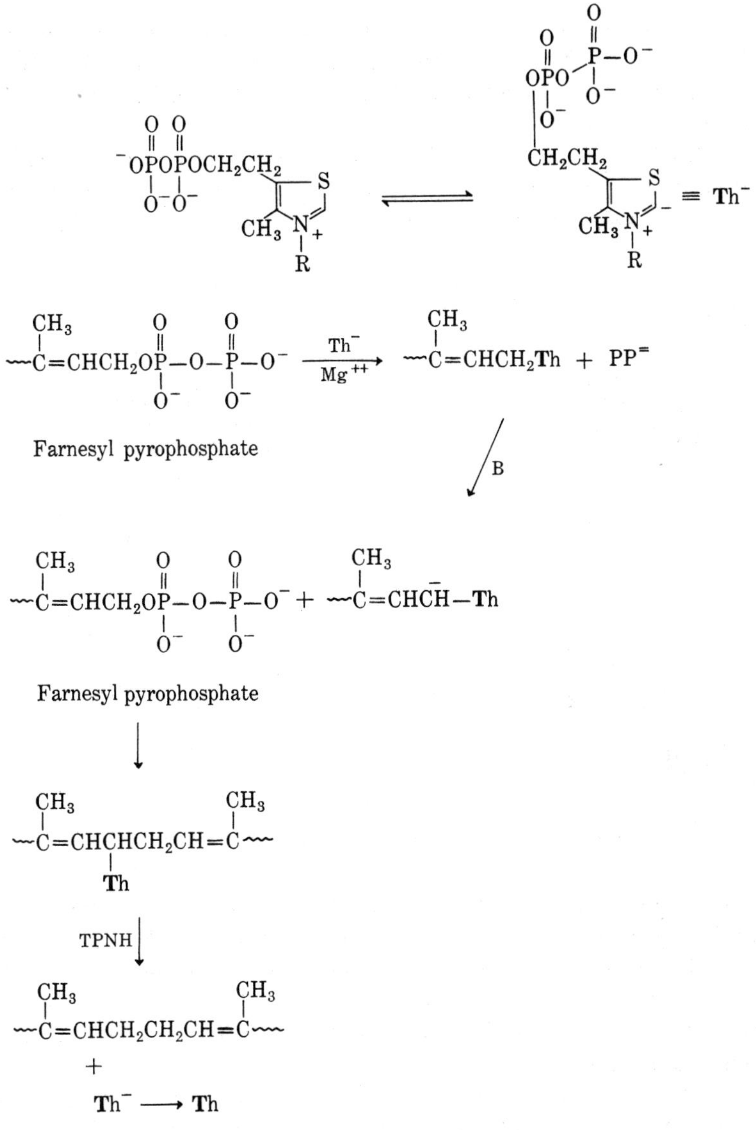

Fig. 1.41. The dimerization of farnesyl pyrophosphate to squalene.

problem is that thiamin anion is probably not a very good leaving group, and its displacement by a hydride ion donated by TPNH must be favored by special factors. One possible source of driving force for the reaction is the tendency for highly polar regions (like the thiamin) to "squeeze out" nonpolar molecules (like squalene). If as many as three additional strong hydrogen bonds could be formed in the transition state for displacement of thiamin anion, the transition free energy might be lowered as much as 12 to 15 kcal/mole. Better leaving groups have been suggested for the reduction step,[95] but do not present attractive possibilities for the linking of the two C_{15} groups.

1.8-9. Squalene is cyclized to lanosterol in a concerted reaction involving the acquisition of an oxygen atom from oxygen gas rather than water at the carbon atom which becomes C-3 in the triterpenoid.[105]   An

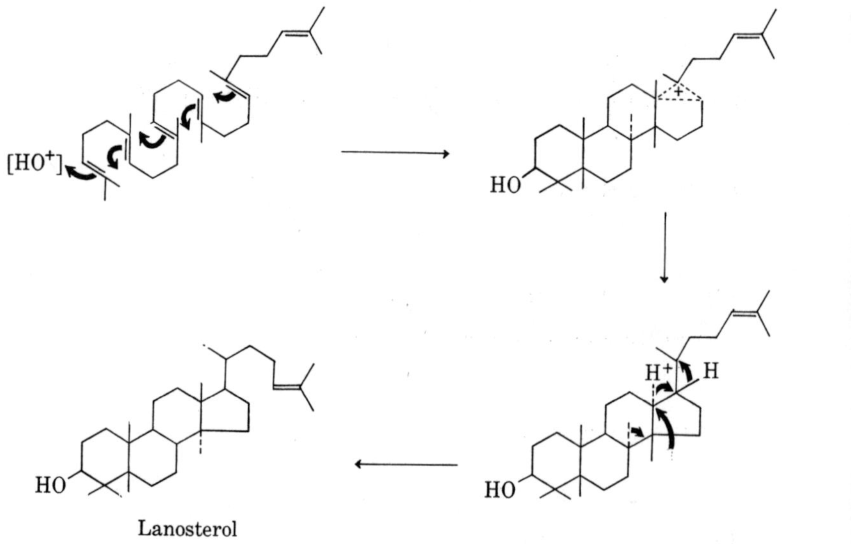

Lanosterol

FIG. 1.42. Conversion of squalene to lanosterol.

elegant set of experiments utilizing mevalonic acid labeled with C^{13} in the 3'- and 4-positions in the biosynthesis of cholesterol together with isotopically normal mevalonic acid led to the formation of doubly labeled acid on degradation ($C^{13}H_3C^{13}OOH$) and the conclusion that two concerted 1,2-methyl group shifts had occurred in the transformation of squalene to lanosterol (Fig. 1.42).[106]

The remaining steps in the biosynthesis of cholesterol are chemically obscure, although many of the intermediates have been identified.[91]

If the structural relationships suggested by the "isoprene rule" are correct, an enormous number of naturally occurring organic compounds must arise by means of the pathways described in this section. We can look forward with anticipation to the elucidation of the details of the

[105] T. T. Tchen and K. Bloch, *J. Biol. Chem.*, **226**, 921, 931 (1957).

[106] J. W. Cornforth, R. H. Cornforth, M. G. Horning, A. Pelter, and G. Popják, in ref. 70, p. 119.

biochemical conversions, especially in those areas where the relationships between molecules are only dimly seen.

1.9. SUMMARY

J'ai beau m'dir' que rien n'est eternel
J'peux pas trouver ca tout naturel
Et jamais je ne parviens
A prendr' la mort comme ell' vient
J'suis un pauvre fossoyeur.
G. Brassens

This first part, entitled Biochemical Patterns, has been a survey of intermediary metabolism and other topics, peppered with mechanistic discussion and spiced by the inclusion of intermediates where this seemed reasonable and proper.   Many reactions were labeled according to a list of "types" to be found in Table 1.9-1.   The "types" were chosen from possibilities in three categories: (*a*) bond cleavage or formation, (*b*) group

TABLE 1.9-1. REACTION "TYPES"[a]

	H oxidation-reduction
HO	Hydride transfer, two-electron transfer (GH, GH)
HR	Hydrogen atom transfer, one-electron transfer (GH, e^-)

	C carbon-carbon bond formation
C	Carbon-carbon bond formation
CA	Aldol condensation
CC	Carboxylation
CD	Decarboxylation
CR	Rearrangement

	G carbon–other atom bond formation
GH	Carbon-hydrogen bond formation
GN	Carbon-nitrogen bond formation
GO	Carbon-oxygen bond formation
GS	Carbon-sulfur bond formation

	Y hydrolysis reactions (GO, GX)
YL	Lactone hydrolysis (GO, GO)
YS	Thioester hydrolysis (GS, GO)
YH	Anhydride hydrolysis (GO, GO)

	P phosphate ester reactions
P	Phosphate ester reactions (GO or PO)[b]

[a] Either formation or cleavage where applicable.
[b] Types of phosphate ester reactions are discussed in Sec. 2.15.

reactions, and (c) oxidation-reduction.   Except for electron transfer, categories (b) and (c) could have been broken down into bond cleavages or formation and in that way fitted into category (a), but such "types" were retained to emphasize the occurrence of particular combinations or because the choices were not well enough defined.   Possible further classification is indicated in the table.

It seems useful to have the kind of classification given in Table 1.9-1 to underscore the possible parallelisms between apparently different reactions catalyzed by enzymes, and to point out the specific processes which should be understood in detail.   To a great extent, the selection of topics in Part 2 (Chemical Patterns) was guided by the census of reaction "types" shown in Table 1.9-2.   The organization of Part 2, however, was designed partly on the basis of reaction "types" and partly for convenience in treating certain topics.

TABLE 1.9-2. CENSUS OF REACTION "TYPES"

P	46
GH	38
GN	28
HO	22
GO	21
HR	16
GS	13
C	11
CA	10
CD	8
CC	3
YL	4
YS	3
YH	2
Total	225

A number of the subjects covered in Part 1 suggest the need for some new areas of physical-organic research or for expansion of efforts where there has been relatively little to date.   Reactions at phase boundaries present special features not found in homogeneous-solution reactions, and yet clearly of importance in many physical and biological phenomena. Investigations into the semiconductor theory of catalysis involve reactions at phase boundaries.   Photoactivation of reactions at phase boundaries is another area of great interest in connection with photosynthesis, and one potentially as broad as solution or gas-phase photochemistry.   Energy-transfer processes in one or both of the phases are responsible for the difference from single-phase photochemistry.

Although some topics have been slighted in Part 1 (e.g., C_1 transformations involving folic acid, porphin biosynthesis, aromatic ring degradations and transformations, etc.), only a few additional reaction "types" would be required for their discussion. These topics are therefore suggested to the reader as an exercise in "type" analysis.

Considering the vast number of enzyme-catalyzed reactions, it is a challenge to know that no well-defined mechanism has yet been elucidated for such a reaction. It is in hope of achieving this goal that the discussion of Part 2 is written, but it must be remarked that the considerations advanced in Part 3 concerning the "active site" imply that much more effort along both theoretical and experimental lines will be necessary before clear ideas about enzyme-catalyzed reaction mechanisms can emerge.

PART 2
CHEMICAL PATTERNS

2.0. REACTION MECHANISMS

> We cannot truly account for our acceptance of such theories [those of modern physics] without endorsing our acknowledgement of a beauty that exhilarates and a profundity that entrances us.
>
> *M. Polanyi*

The mechanism of a chemical reaction is a description of the behavior of all the constituent parts of the reactants over the time period required for the transformation of the reactants in their initial states into the products in their final states. At least one configuration of greatest energy will exist for the chemical reaction; this arrangement is called the *transition state*. Multiple transition states often occur in chemical reactions; the configurations which are more stable than the transition states represent *intermediates*. The stability of intermediates can vary from those which survive one vibrational period (ca. 10^{-13} sec) to those which can readily be isolated. A reaction is conveniently represented by a plot of energy content against the "reaction coordinate" (a parameter which reflects the extent of reaction). A reaction in which one stable and two unstable intermediates are formed is represented by such a plot in Fig. 2.0.

A description of the transition state (or states) is a reasonable goal in efforts to explain the mechanism of a reaction, although it is not always possible to decide why one transition state is favored over another. In many cases, the composition of the transition state can be defined by an

65

investigation of the *kinetics* of the reaction, i.e., a study of how the reaction rate varies with the composition of the reaction mixture. The *stoichiometry* of the reaction (i.e., a balanced equation for the reaction) indicates the pathway to which the transition state leads.

The techniques for the separation and analysis of products of a reaction have reached a level of sophistication suitable for a determination of the complete stoichiometry of any simple reaction. Chromatographic separations, isotope tracers, and ultraviolet, visible, infrared, and nuclear magnetic resonance (NMR) spectroscopic identifications and analyses are all, among other techniques, available to the chemist.

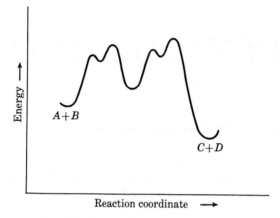

FIG. 2.0. Energy diagram for a reaction.

The time scale of those reactions of interest in molecular biochemistry is enormous, ranging from the 10^{-15} sec required for the transformation of a ground state into an electronic excited state by absorption of a photon to the ca. 10^{+15} sec half-life for a hypothetical very slow reaction. The latter limit is set by accessible temperatures and methods for following reactions which occur only to a small extent. However, very slow reactions are of interest in the consideration of the chemical evolution which presumably preceded biological evolution on the primeval earth.

Very fast reactions (half-lives down to 10^{-9} or 10^{-10} sec) can be studied by relaxation spectrometry [sudden change of a solution parameter (like pressure, etc.) and analysis of the kinetics of the recovery of the initial state ("relaxation")] or NMR. Examples of fast reactions of great biological importance are proton-hydroxide ion, ion-pair formation, and enzyme-substrate combination.

The kinetics of enzyme-catalyzed reactions can be studied but are not easily explained in terms of chemical mechanisms or transition states. As the discussion on the "active site" of enzymes will show (Sec. 3.1), the enzyme is a reagent that is poorly defined in a chemical sense, that is, as a particular arrangement of atoms and groups from which one can expect certain kinds of behavior.

The approach of molecular biochemistry is to try to understand the mechanism of reactions which have a stoichiometry like that of an enzyme-catalyzed reaction (or other process) in the hope that this mechanism (or these mechanisms) will provide insight into the *possible* mechanisms for the enzymatic reaction.

2.1. CARBOXYLATION

Non sono mai stato
tanto
attacato alla vita.
G. Ungaretti

An enormous reservoir of carbon dioxide exists in the atmosphere (2.3×10^{12} tons) and the oceans (130×10^{12} tons) of the earth.[1] Virtually all transfer of carbon dioxide from the geosphere to the biosphere occurs by means of carboxylation reactions, of which the most important is the reaction of ribulose-1,5-diphosphate with carbon dioxide in plants.

2.1-1. Carbon dioxide in aqueous solution exists in equilibrium with carbonic acid, bicarbonate ion, and carbonate ion. Carbonic acid has been prepared by the reaction of hydrogen chloride with a suspension of sodium bicarbonate in ether, and an etherate can be crystallized at low temperatures and analyzed.[2] In aqueous solution, a large proportion of dissolved carbon dioxide is present as carbon dioxide and only very little as carbonic acid. ($[H_2CO_3]/[CO_2] = 0.0037$ at 25°C.) Carbonic acid is actually about as strong as formic acid, with $K = 1.3 \times 10^{-4}$.[3] Equilibration between carbon dioxide and carbonic acid or bicarbonate is relatively slow (see Sec. 2.1-3), and biological systems contain an enzyme, carbonic anhydrase, which catalyzes the reaction.[4]

Carbon dioxide is a stable and relatively unreactive molecule. Two types of "activation" exist for reactions of carbon dioxide. The first, electrophilic, is uncommon in extreme form and involves the interaction of a strong Lewis acid (electron acceptor) with the oxygen electrons, thus

[1] G. N. Plass, *Sci. American*, **201**, 41 (1959).

[2] A. G. Galinos and A. A. Carotti, *J. Am. Chem. Soc.*, **83**, 752 (1961).

[3] Cf. discussion by R. P. Bell, "The Proton in Chemistry," p. 30, Cornell University Press, Ithaca, N.Y., 1959.

[4] R. P. Davis, in "The Enzymes," vol. 5, chap. 33, Academic Press, Inc., New York, 1961.

creating a positive center at the carbon atom.   Benzene, chlorobenzene, and toluene can be carboxylated to benzoic acid, *p*-chlorobenzoic acid, and *p*-toluic acid, respectively, by reaction with carbon dioxide and aluminum chloride under pressure.[5]   The second type of "activation" involves the use of a nucleophile strong enough to add to the carbon-oxygen double bond.   Reaction of carbon dioxide with a Grignard reagent to form the magnesium carboxylate can be cited in this regard. However, distinguishing such cases from those cited in the next subsection may be a matter of taste.

   2.1-2.   Attack on the carbon of carbon dioxide by a reasonably strong nucleophile with simultaneous electrophilic "activation" by a cation at the oxygen is probably the best description of most reactions of carbon dioxide.   The specific nature of the cation influences the course of the reaction.   Dry sodium phenolate reacts with carbon dioxide ($125°C$, 4–7 atm) to produce sodium salicylate, although the reaction with potassium phenolate at a higher temperature[6] leads to potassium *p*-hydroxybenzoate.[7]

   Chelation is probably an important factor in stabilizing the product of nucleophilic addition "activated" by a divalent cation.   An example of the phenomenon is the formation of magnesium nitroacetate by the reaction of nitromethane with magnesium methyl carbonate[9] (Fig. 2.1).

   The apparent instability of carboxylate free radicals, $RCO_2\cdot$, implies that they need not be considered in biochemical reactions of carbon dioxide.   However, the one-electron reduction product of carbon dioxide has been reported as an intermediate in electroreduction of carbon dioxide[10] and as present in sodium formate crystals after damage by γ rays.[11]

   2.1-3.   The rate constant for hydration of carbon dioxide in water at pH 7.0 and $0°$ C is 2.0×10^{-3} sec^{-1}, and that for dehydration of

[5] C. A. Thomas, "Anhydrous Aluminum Chloride in Organic Chemistry," p. 508, Reinhold Publishing Corp., New York, 1941.

[6] Cf. discussion in A. S. Lindsey and H. Jeskey, *Chem. Revs.*, **57**, 583, 589 (1957).

[7] The addition of radioactive sodium phenyl carbonate, $Na^+ \ \overset{O}{\overset{\|}{O}}COC_6H_5$, does not introduce carbon-14 into sodium salicylate as rapidly as free carbon dioxide.   Oxygen attack on carbon of carbon dioxide in the reaction of phenolate therefore represents a parasitic equilibrium.[8]

[8] E. A. Shilov, I. V. Smirnow-Zamkov and K. I. Matkovskii, *Ukrain. Khim. Zhur.*, **21**, 484 (1955); *Chem. Abstr.*, **50**, 10692 (1956).

[9] M. Stiles and H. L. Finkbeiner, *J. Am. Chem. Soc.*, **81**, 505 (1959).   Cf. also M. Stiles, *Ann. N.Y. Acad. Sci.*, **88**, 332 (1960), for further discussion and application of this idea.

[10] J. Jordan and P. T. Smith, *Proc. Chem. Soc.*, 246 (1960).

[11] D. W. Ovenall and D. H. Whiffen, *Proc. Chem. Soc.*, 420 (1960).

carbonic acid 2.0 sec^{-1} [ref. 4 and Eq. (2.0)].   Hydroxide ion is approximately 6×10^6 times as reactive toward carbon dioxide as water[4] [Eq. (2.1)].

(2.0) $H_2O + O{=}C{=}O \rightarrow H_2CO_3$
(2.1) $HO^- + O{=}C{=}O \rightarrow HCO_3^-$

Both the enzymatic hydration and dehydration reactions have been followed at 0.5°C using a "stopped flow" apparatus and an indicator.[12]

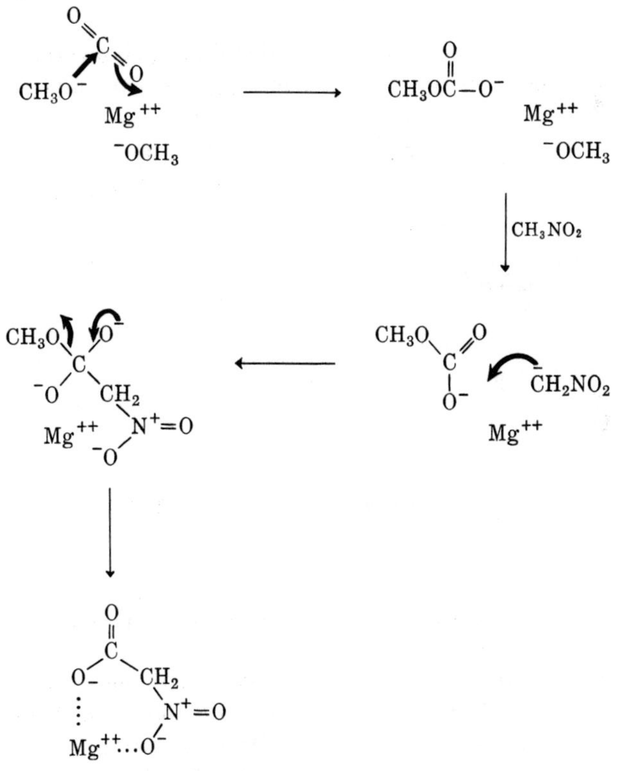

Fig. 2.1. Formation of magnesium nitroacetate.

It was concluded from the pH dependence of the kinetic parameters that the mechanism must involve at least a hydroxide ion and a carbon dioxide molecule bound at adjacent sites on the enzyme.   A simpler mechanism predicated on the interconversion of enzyme-bound carbon dioxide and carbonic acid was excluded on the grounds that a minimum value for one

[12] H. DeVoe and G. B. Kistiakowsky, *J. Am. Chem. Soc.*, **83**, 274 (1961).

of the rate constants[13] would have to exceed the value estimated for the combination of carbonic acid and the enzyme on the basis of diffusion control[14] by an order of magnitude. It is of interest that the *minimum* value of the rate constant estimated for the conversion of OH^-—E—CO_2 into E—HCO_3^- is 8×10^4 sec^{-1}, some 4×10^7 greater than that for non-enzymatic hydration by water but comparable to what may be expected for a high local concentration of hydroxide ion. If the zinc ion which the enzyme contains functions as an electrophilic catalyst, the actual rate of addition of hydroxide ion to carbon dioxide on the enzyme may be considerably greater than the minimum estimated from the kinetic parameters.

2.1-4. A classification of biochemical carboxylation reactions on the basis of their "energy requirements" has been attempted,[15] without

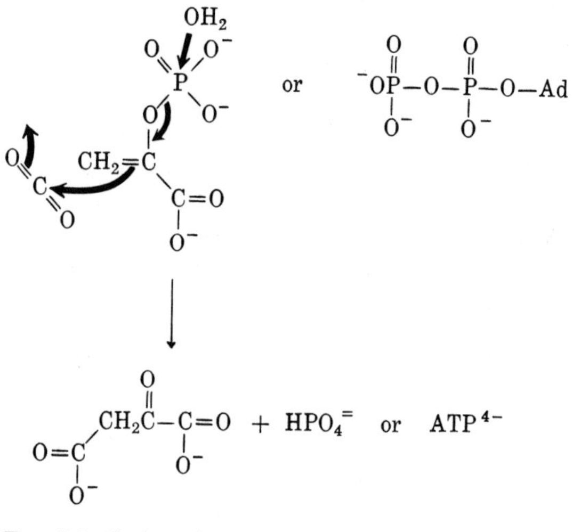

FIG. 2.2. Carboxylation of phosphoenolpyruvic acid.

revealing very much about the mechanism. Although one can make a rough division of carboxylation reactions into those which involve preliminary reaction of the carbon dioxide with a cofactor and those in which the substrate acquires the carboxyl group by direct reaction with carbon dioxide, all carboxylation reactions can be understood as a nucleophilic attack of an anionic substrate atom on a carbonyl group. Cofactors include biotin, possibly acetylglutamic acid (see Sec. 1.5), and other unknown compounds.[16,17]

[13] L. Peller and R. A. Alberty, *J. Am. Chem. Soc.*, **81**, 5907 (1959).

[14] R. A. Alberty and G. G. Hammes, *J. Phys. Chem.*, **62**, 154 (1958).

[15] M. Calvin and N. G. Pon, *J. Cellular Comp. Physiol.*, **54**, Suppl. 1, 51 (1959).

[16] E. R. Stadtman and P. R. Vagelos, *J. Cellular Comp. Physiol.*, **54**, Suppl. 1, 71 (1959).

[17] R. W. Swick and H. G. Wood, *Proc. Natl. Acad. Sci. U.S.*, **46**, 28 (1960).

Carboxylation of phosphoenolpyruvic acid is illustrated in Fig. 2.2 as a nucleophilic attack on phosphorus by either water or ADP,[18] generating a nucleophilic carbon which can add to the carbonyl group of carbon dioxide.

"Activation" of carbon dioxide by cofactors like biotin may be related to the requirement for a more reactive carbonyl group than that offered by bicarbonate ion. An investigation of how much of the oxygen originally present in the carbon dioxide is retained in the carboxylic acid product would be of interest.

2.2. DECARBOXYLATION

Et sur elle courbé, l'ardent Imperator
Vit dans ses larges yeux étoilés de points d'or
Toute une mer immense où fuyaient des galères.
J.-M. de Hérédia

The most important process through which carbon dioxide is returned from the biosphere to the geosphere is decarboxylation of a carboxylic acid [Eq. (2.2)]. Most decarboxylations involve the anion [Eq. (2.3)] of

$$(2.2) \qquad\qquad RCOOH \rightarrow RH + O{=}C{=}O$$

the acid; a discussion of the mechanisms of such reactions revolves

$$(2.3) \qquad\qquad RCOO^- \rightarrow R^- + O{=}C{=}O$$

around the means used to avoid accumulation of the negative charge on an atom which is not particularly electronegative.

2.2-1. Three general mechanisms can be distinguished for decarboxylation, one of which is further divisible into four subcategories. These are listed in Table 2.2-1.

TABLE 2.2-1. MECHANISMS OF DECARBOXYLATION

Mechanism	Description
CD-1	Electrophilic attack of positive species on developing anion
CD-2	Dispersal of charge within molecule on:
-a	Neutral atom
-b	Positively charged atom
-c	Atom with orbital which is electronegative due to high proportion of s character
-d	Atom polarized by metal ion
CD-3	Expulsion of negative species

[18] J. L. Graves, B. Vennesland, M. F. Utter, and R. J. Pennington, *J. Biol. Chem.*, **223,** 551 (1956).

2.2-2. The only example of mechanism CD-1 which comes readily to mind is the thermal decomposition of a mixture of sodium acetate and soda lime into methane and calcium carbonate. Presumably a methide ion would be unlikely at moderate temperatures, and it seems probable that a bicarbonate ion acts as a proton donor to the methyl group as carbon dioxide is formed [Eq. (2.4)]. The stereo-

$$(2.4)$$

chemistry and mechanism of many electrophilic substitutions at saturated carbon have been investigated.[19]

2.2-3. Decarboxylation of β-keto acids is much faster than that of the corresponding anions (Table 2.2-2). The rate is insensitive to solvent polarity in the case of acetoacetic acid.[20] Both facts are in agreement with a cyclic transition state for the decarboxylation of the acid [Eq. (2.5)]. The enol is the initial product of decarboxylation and can be trapped by a reagent like bromine. A specific enol can be gen-

$$(2.5)$$

erated by decarboxylation; the principle is useful in the preparation of 2,2-dibromocyclohexanone[21] [Eq. (2.6)].

$$(2.6)$$

Decarboxylative formation of the enol of an acetyl-S-enzyme was suggested (Sec. 1.8) as an intermediate step in fatty acid synthesis.

Decarboxylation of a vinylogous β-keto acid has been proposed to explain the pH-rate profile for the loss of carbon dioxide from p-hydroxycinnamic acid.[22] The reaction has a minimum rate at pH 3.5, a small

[19] D. J. Cram, L. K. Gaston, and H. Jäger, *J. Am. Chem. Soc.*, **83**, 2183 (1961), and previous references.

[20] F. H. Westheimer and W. A. Jones, *J. Am. Chem. Soc.*, **63**, 3283 (1941).

[21] E. J. Corey, *J. Am. Chem. Soc.*, **75**, 3297 (1953).

[22] L. A. Cohen and W. M. Jones, *J. Am. Chem. Soc.*, **82**, 1907 (1960).

Table 2.2-2. Relative Rates of Decarboxylation

Acid	Acid	Anion
Acetoacetic	53	1
α,α-Dimethylacetoacetic	180	1
Camphor-3-carboxylic	34	1
Dihydroxymaleic	1	40
Malonic	10	1

"maximum" at pH 5, and a maximum rate (for pH > 2) at pH 8.5. Ordinarily, cinnamic acid anions do not decompose at all at alkaline pH. The stability of the dianion is shown by the negligible rate at high pH, but the two maxima in the pH-rate profile suggest that the rate of formation of the appropriate monoanion is a function of dianion concentration and pH [Eq. (2.7].

(2.7)

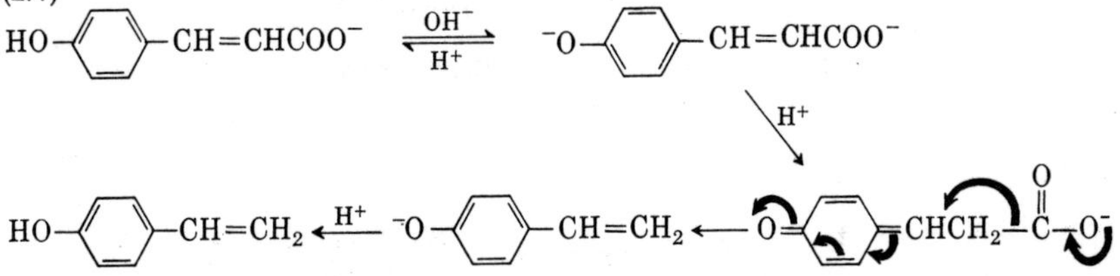

A cyclic transition state involving a carbon-carbon double bond in place of a carbon-oxygen double bond has been suggested for the decarboxylation of 2,2-dimethyl-3-butenoic acid, which forms only 2-methyl-2-butene and carbon dioxide at 260°C, although the isomeric 4,4-dimethyl-2-pentenoic acid is unchanged after 5 hours at 300°C[23] [Eqs. (2.8) and (2.9)].

(2.8)

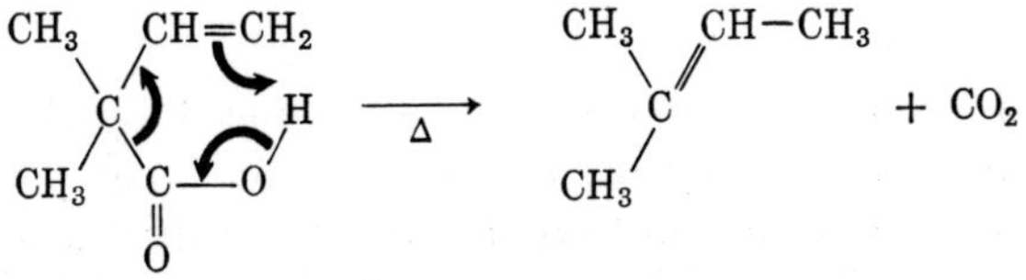

(2.9)

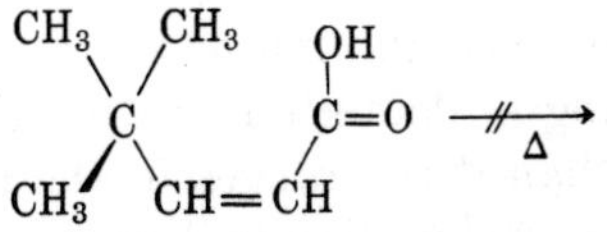

In mechanism CD-2a, the neutral atom acceptor for the negative charge left behind by the departing carbon dioxide must be acidic enough

[23] R. T. Arnold, O. C. Elmer, and R. M. Dodson, *J. Am. Chem. Soc.*, **72,** 4359 (1950).

to exist as the anion or be able to participate in a cyclic transition state in which a hydrogen is acquired as the carbon dioxide is formed.

2.2-4. Decarboxylation of a β-keto acid to an enol does not occur if the formation of the enol is too unfavorable on energetic grounds. Bicyclic β-keto acids like camphenonic and ketopinic acids [Eq. (2.10)] are stable to heat because the enols resulting from decarboxylation would have double bonds at bridgeheads. The energy required to produce the necessary nonplanar double-bond system would be very large; in fact, a reliable empirical organic chemical principle (Bredt's rule) states that double bonds at bridgehead carbons are impossible. The geometric requirements for the rule are illustrated by the results for β-keto acids containing larger rings[24] [Eqs. (2.11) and (2.12)].

(2.10)

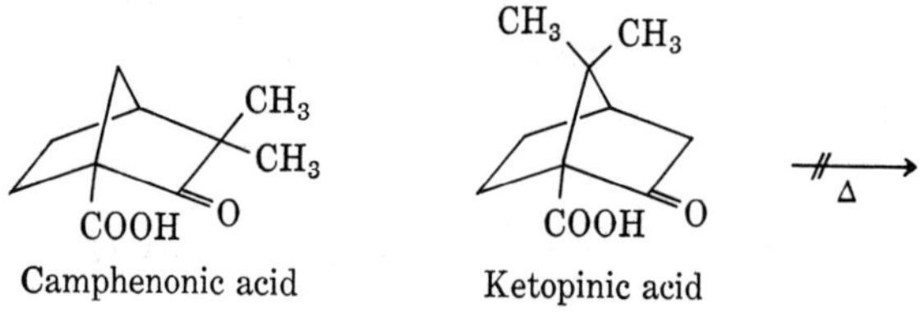

Camphenonic acid   Ketopinic acid

(2.11)

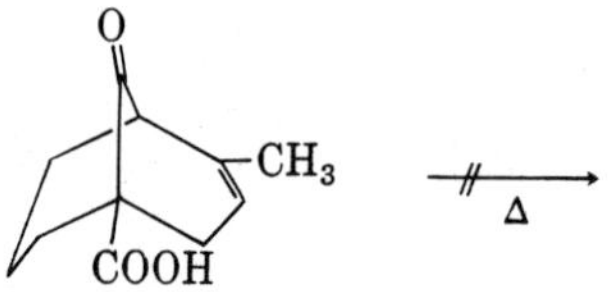

Stable in quinoline
for 30 min at 250°C

(2.12)

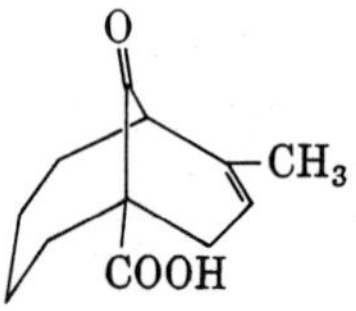

Decarboxylated
readily at 240°C

2.2-5. The enol or enolate ion produced by decarboxylation often may give rise to several possible carbonyl compounds as final products. In general, the most rapidly formed product will be *least stable* thermodynamically[25] (kinetic control), but the *most stable* product will result if the reaction conditions permit equilibration.

Cyclohexenylacetonitrile exchanges deuterium with ethanol-d and ethoxide ion much more rapidly than it rearranges to the isomeric conjugated nitrile[26] [Eq. (2.13)]. Decarboxylation of 4-phenylcyclohexane-

[24] V. Prelog et al., *Helv. Chim. Acta*, **31**, 92 (1948); **32**, 1284 (1949).
[25] G. S. Hammond, *J. Am. Chem. Soc.*, **77**, 334 (1955).
[26] C. K. Ingold, E. de Salas, and C. L. Wilson, *J. Chem. Soc.*, 1328 (1936).

(2.13)

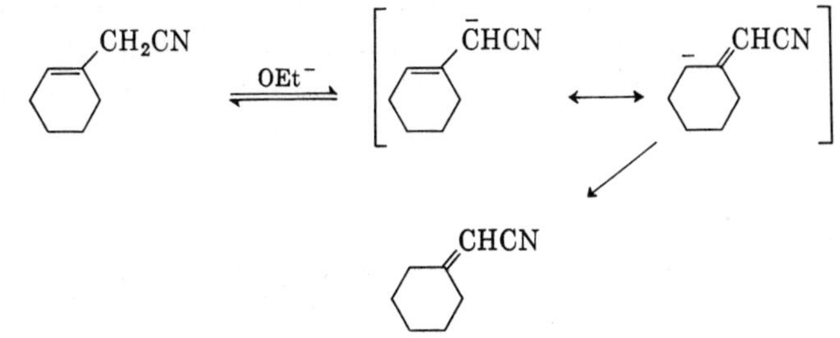

1,1-dicarboxylic acid produces 61% *cis*-4-phenylcyclohexane carboxylic acid compared with the 11% of the *cis* acid present at equilibrium.[27] The intermediate enol reacts more rapidly with an equatorial proton donor (the hindered collidinium ion). The unstable product of kinetic control is favored by an additional steric factor in the transition state to product [Eq. (2.14)]. Another example of the formation of product

(2.14)

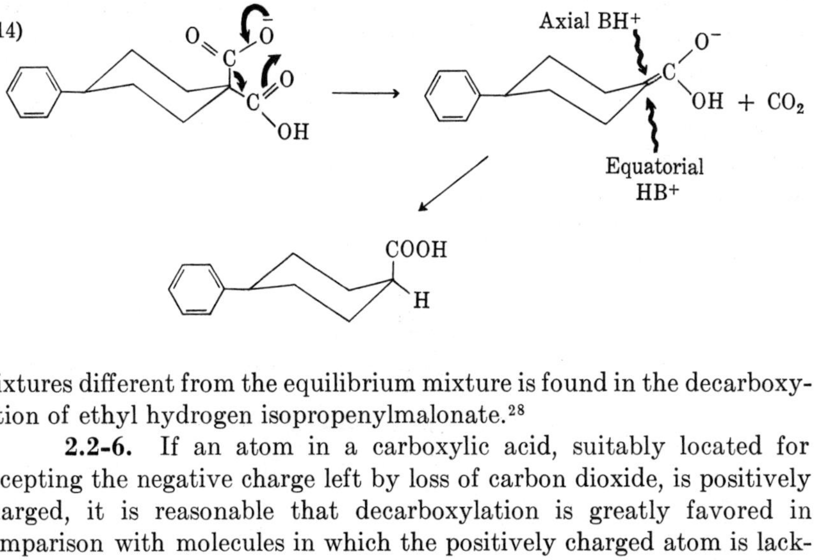

mixtures different from the equilibrium mixture is found in the decarboxylation of ethyl hydrogen isopropenylmalonate.[28]

2.2-6. If an atom in a carboxylic acid, suitably located for accepting the negative charge left by loss of carbon dioxide, is positively charged, it is reasonable that decarboxylation is greatly favored in comparison with molecules in which the positively charged atom is lacking (mechanism CD-2*b*). The positive center may be generated, if it is not already present, by the addition of a positive species like hydrogen ion or bromonium ion to an atom or unsaturated system, or by the ionization of a good leaving group. An interesting case which is an example of the last possibility is 3,3-dimethyl-β-propiolactone. Although the compound can be isolated as a liquid, rapid decomposition ensues when the

[27] H. E. Zimmerman and H. J. Giallombardo, *J. Am. Chem. Soc.*, **78**, 6259 (1956).
[28] E. J. Corey, *J. Am. Chem. Soc.*, **74**, 5897 (1952); **75**, 1163, 3297 (1953).

lactone is dissolved in water.[29]   The pure lactone is a relatively nonpolar liquid, but it might well ionize in a highly polar solvent (water).   The relief of strain on ionization [Eq. (2.15)] is probably the factor which converts the relatively poor leaving group, carboxylate ion, into a good

$$
(2.15) \qquad
\begin{array}{c}
CH_3 \\
| \\
CH_3-C-CH_2 \\
| \quad\quad | \\
O-C=O
\end{array}
\qquad\longrightarrow\qquad
\begin{array}{c}
CH_3 \quad O \\
| \quad\quad \| \\
CH_3\underset{+}{C}-CH_2C-O^-
\end{array}
$$

leaving group.   The betaine which results from ionization then decarboxylates to give the observed products[29a] [Eq. (2.16)].   The high

$$
(2.16) \qquad
\begin{array}{c}
CH_3 \quad O \\
| \quad\quad \| \\
CH_3\underset{+}{C}-CH_2C-O^-
\end{array}
\qquad\longrightarrow\qquad
\begin{array}{c}
CH_3 \\
| \\
CH_3C=CH_2
\end{array}
+ CO_2
$$

apparent sensitivity of the reaction to medium places the decarboxylation in class CD-2b, since the similar concerted reactions classified as CD-3 should be less sensitive to the solvent.

The basic nitrogen atom forms an excellent acceptor for the negative charge when quaternized.   Pyridylacetic acids decarboxylate easily [Eq. (2.17)]; if the carbon bearing the carboxylic acid group is asymmetrically substituted and the compound resolved, the pyridine resulting from decarboxylation is racemic, as would be expected from a planar intermediate.[30]

(2.17)

Positively charged nitrogen is the charge acceptor in thiamin-catalyzed decarboxylations (Fig. 1.10, Sec. 1.2) and in pyridoxal-catalyzed decarboxylations (Fig. 2.3) of α-amino acids.

[29] T. L. Gresham, J. E. Jansen, F. W. Shaver, and W. L. Beears, *J. Am. Chem. Soc.*, **76**, 486 (1954).

[29a] A mechanistic study which supports this formulation has been carried out by H. T. Liang and P. D. Bartlett, *J. Am. Chem. Soc.*, **80**, 3585 (1958).

[30] W. v. E. Doering and V. Z. Pasternak, *J. Am. Chem. Soc.*, **72**, 143 (1950).

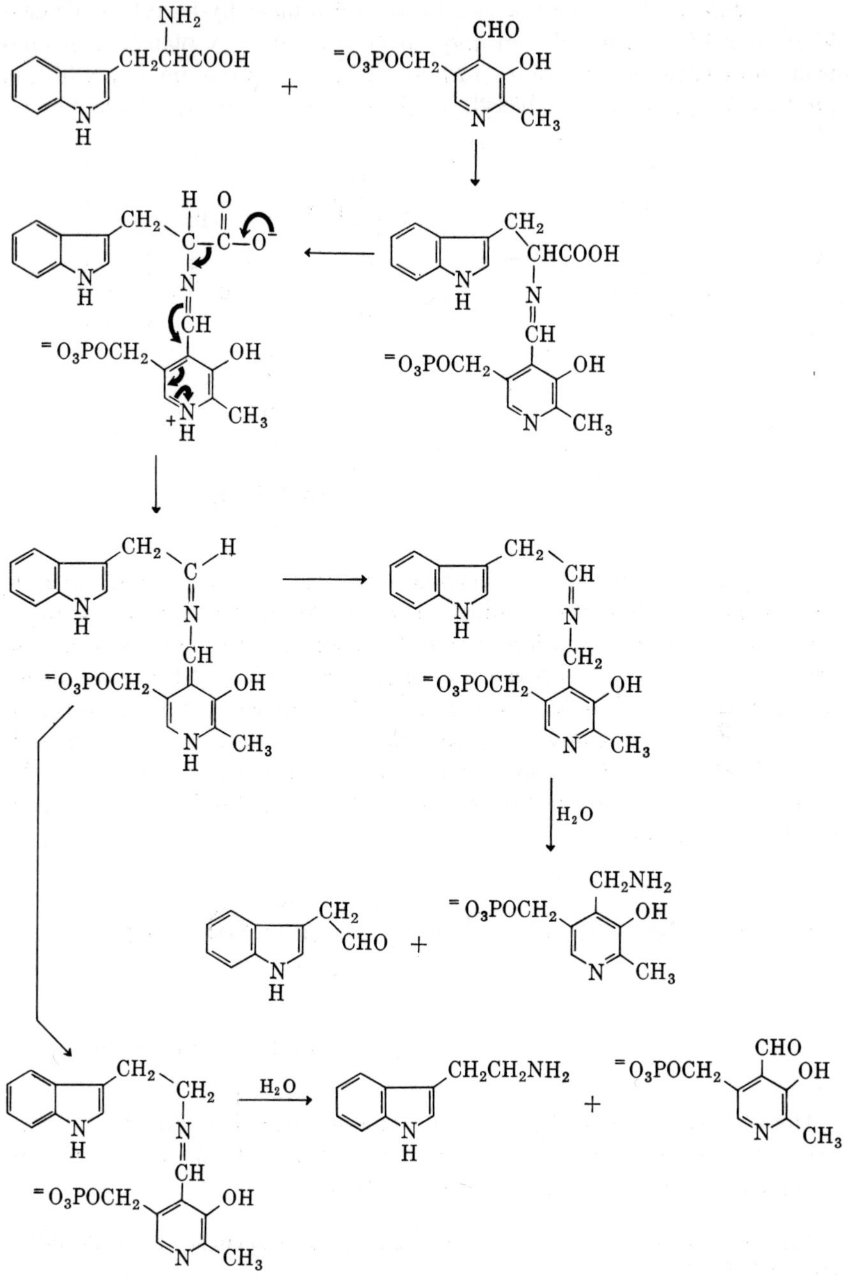

FIG. 2.3. Pyridoxal-catalyzed decarboxylation of tryptophan.

2.2-7. Bromine reacts with 3,5-dibromo-4-hydroxybenzoic acid to form 2,4,6-tribromophenol and carbon dioxide. A plausible mechanism postulates intermediate formation of a bromonium ion addition product followed by decarboxylation of the zwitterion [Eq. (2.18)].[31]

Semiquantitative studies on acid-catalyzed decarboxylation of cinnamic acids suggested that proton addition to the double bond gave rise to an α-phenylalkyl carbonium ion, which decarboxylated by attack of a base (presumably water) and formation of a styrene [Eq. (2.19)]. Evidence for the mechanism was based on the fact that replacement of the β-hydrogen by methyl and phenyl increased the decarboxylation rates by factors of ca. 5000 and 10,000, respectively. These large rate factors would be expected if the only effect of the substituent were to stabilize the α-phenylalkylcarbonium ion.[32]

Detailed study of acid-catalyzed cinnamic acid decarboxylation confirms the mechanism written in Eq. (2.19). Hydrogen-deuterium exchange is faster than decarboxylation.[33]

[31] E. Grovenstein, Jr., et al., *J. Am. Chem. Soc.*, **75**, 2639 (1953); **77**, 3795 (1955); **78**, 569, 2560 (1956).

[32] W. S. Johnson and W. E. Heinz, *J. Am. Chem. Soc.*, **71**, 213 (1949).

[33] D. S. Noyce, Paper presented at the Seventh Reaction Mechanisms Conference, Princeton University, Sept. 7–10, 1960, Princeton, N.J.

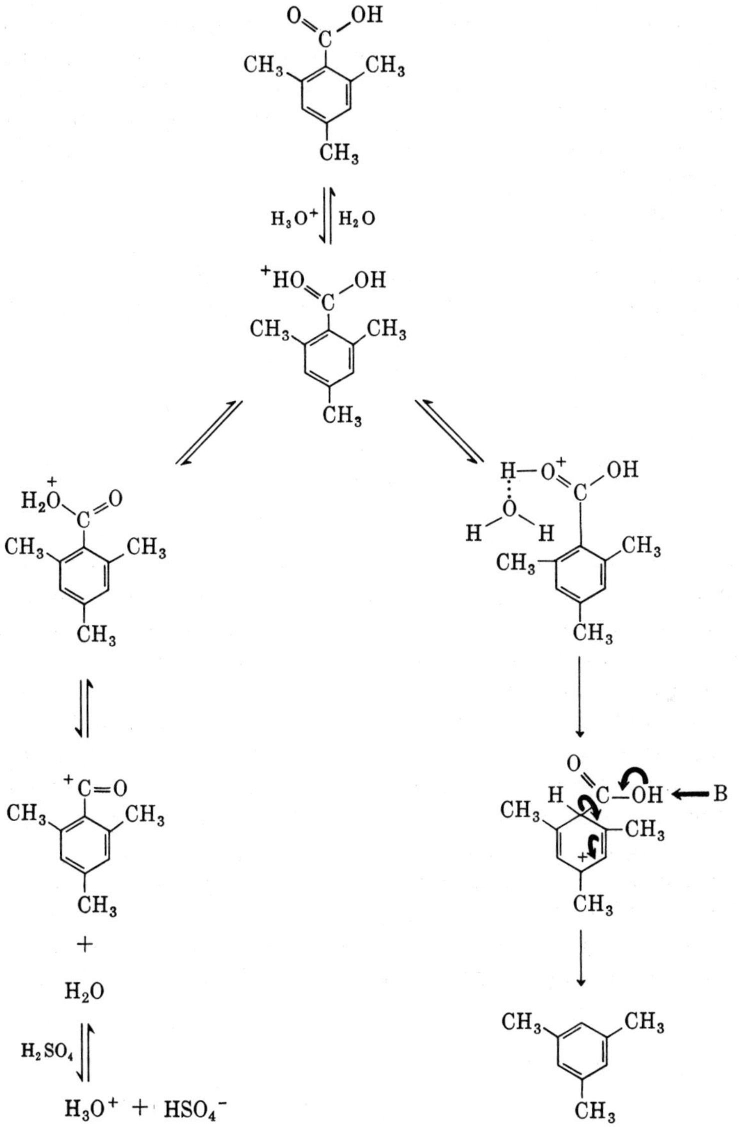

FIG. 2.4. Decarboxylation of 2,4,6-trimethylbenzoic acid.

Certain aromatic acids can be decarboxylated in strongly acid solution. Decarboxylation of 2,4,6-trimethylbenzoic acid (mesitoic acid) occurs most easily in sulfuric acid containing ca. 1 mole of water per liter because more concentrated acid yields the stable acylium ion (Fig. 2.4). The rate of decarboxylation was proportional to the acid concentration.[34]

[34] W. M. Schubert, *J. Am. Chem. Soc.*, **71**, 2639 (1949).

2.2-8. If the carboxylic acid is attached to a carbon with an electronegative bonding orbital, decarboxylation to the simple anion is possible (mechanism CD-2c). Orbital electronegativity is primarily a function of the s character, and ability to accommodate negative charge increases as the orbital changes from sp^3 to sp^2 to sp. Electron-withdrawing substituents on the carbon which carries the orbital in question will also increase the electronegativity of the orbital.

Phenylpropiolic acid decarboxylates on heating with water at 120°C [Eq. (2.20)]. Both o-nitro- and p-nitrophenylpropiolic acids lose carbon dioxide by boiling with water. Although quantitative measurements have not been made, there is qualitatively only a small difference between the unsubstituted and substituted acids. The electronegativity of the

(2.20)

sp-acceptor orbital is thus the most important factor in determining ease of decarboxylation. The three nitro groups of 2,4,6-trinitrobenzoic acid increase the electronegativity of the sp^2-acceptor orbital on the benzene ring to the point where decarboxylation occurs on boiling with water.

A proximate positive charge is effective in raising electronegativity. Pyridine-2,3-dicarboxylic acid loses carbon dioxide readily, forming pyridine-3-carboxylic acid (nicotinic acid), but pyridine-3,4-dicarboxylic acid decarboxylates only at high temperature, forming a mixture of pyridine-3- and -4-carboxylic acids.[35] Although calculation indicates that the positively charged protonated nitrogen would interact with a 2-negative charge much more than with a 3- or 4-negative charge,[36] the relative stabilities of the dicarboxylic acids suggest that some additional factor may be in operation. The 1-methyl betaine of the pyridine-2-carboxylic acid is far less stable than the corresponding 3- and 4-betaines[37]

(2.21)

[Eq. (2.21)]. The intermediate carbanion can be trapped by carbonyl compounds (the Hammick reaction).[38]

[35] T. W. J. Taylor and W. Baker, "Sidgewick's Organic Chemistry of Nitrogen," p. 534, Oxford University Press, London, England, 1942.

[36] E. M. Kosower and J. A. Skorcz, J. Am. Chem. Soc., **82**, 2195 (1960).

[37] E. M. Kosower and J. W. Patton, J. Org. Chem., **26**, 1318 (1961).

[38] Cf., for example, H. Rapoport and E. J. Volcheck, Jr., J. Am. Chem. Soc., **78**, 2451 (1956).

Trihaloacetic acid anions decarboxylate easily, the trichloro anion being more labile than the trifluoro anion. Thus, the effect of the halogens on the electronegativity of the acceptor orbital must be supplemented by the dispersion of charge into the upper orbitals of chlorine, bromine, and iodine, with fluorine being relatively ineffective in this regard [Eq. (2.22)].

$$(2.22) \qquad X_3CCOO^- \longrightarrow X_3C^- \longrightarrow X_3CH$$
$$+$$
$$O=C=O$$

2.2-9. A multiply charged cation can aid in the accommodation of the negative charge left by decarboxylation. One imaginative description of the ability of metallic cations to provide high local concentrations of positive charge is that such cations provide "superacid catalysis in neutral solution"[39] (the decarboxylation mechanism is CD-2d).

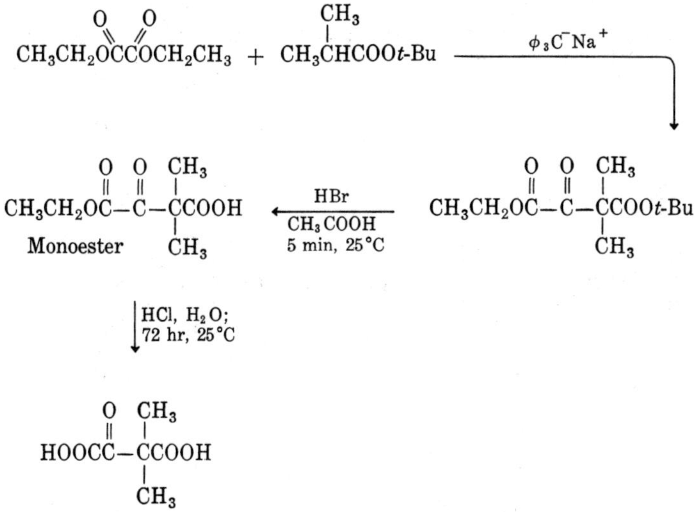

FIG. 2.5. The synthesis of dimethyloxaloacetic acid and a monoethyl ester.

The effect of metal ions on the decarboxylation of dimethyloxaloacetic acid and a monoester derivative has been investigated.[40] The preparation of the compounds is shown in Fig. 2.5. The monoester monoanion loses carbon dioxide about twenty times as fast as the monoanion of the diacid, a ratio consistent with the expected proportions of isomeric anions estimated from the relative acid dissociation constants of pyruvic and

[39] F. H. Westheimer, *Trans. N.Y. Acad. Sci.*, **18**, 55 (1955).
[40] R. Steinberger and F. H. Westheimer, *J. Am. Chem. Soc.*, **73**, 429 (1951).

acetoacetic acids [Eq. (2.23)]. (The increased electronegativity of the carbonyl group because of its attachment to a carboxyl or carbethoxyl group is presumably responsible for the marked rate advantage of the monoanions over the acids, in contrast to most of the comparisons listed in Table 2.2-2 for β-keto acids.) Spectrophotometric examination of the

(2.23)
$$\underset{\underset{CH_3}{|}}{\overset{\overset{O}{\|}}{HOOCCC}}\overset{CH_3}{-}COO^- \rightleftharpoons {}^-OOCC\underset{\underset{CH_3}{|}}{\overset{\overset{O}{\|}}{CC}}COOH$$

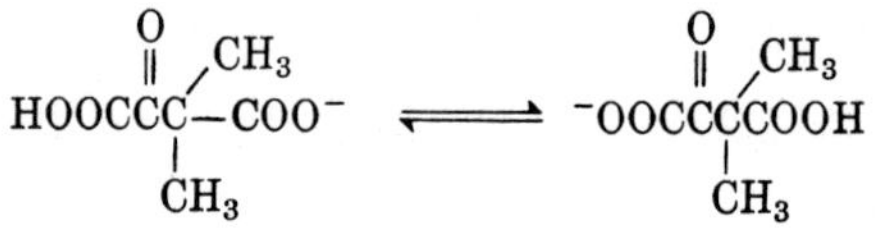

solution of dimethyloxaloacetic acid at the beginning, middle, and end of a rate run showed the transformation of a substance absorbing like a ketone (dimethyloxaloacetic acid, λ_{max} ca. 3300 Å, ϵ_{max} 30) into a strongly absorbing intermediate (the enol of α-ketoisovaleric acid, λ_{max} ca. 2400 Å, ϵ_{max} 7500) and finally to α-ketoisovaleric acid (λ_{max} ca. 3100 Å, ϵ_{max} 30). The intermediate enol could be trapped by reaction with bromine.

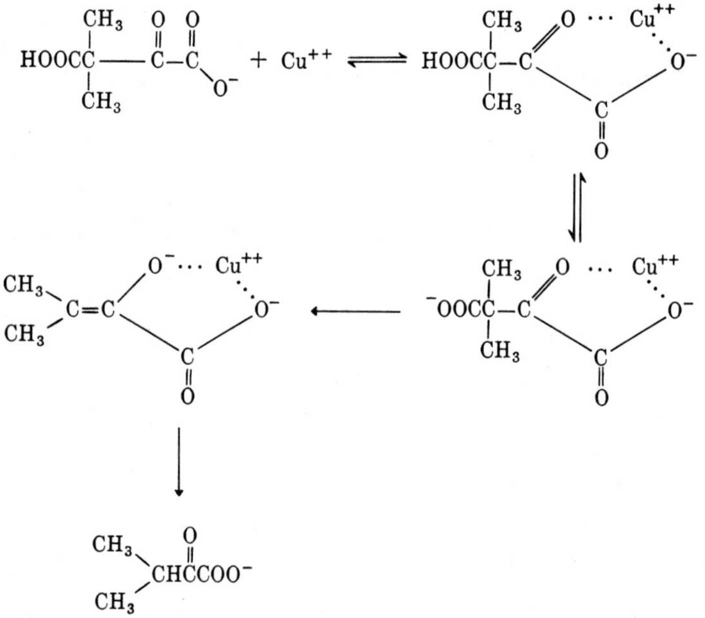

FIG. 2.6. A mechanism for metal ion-catalyzed decarboxylation.

A variety of metal ions were found to accelerate the decarboxylation of dimethyloxaloacetic acid.   Given certain assumptions,[41] ferric ion causes

[41] Initial concentration of acid equal to ferric ion concentration, and dissociation constant for the ferric complex of dimethyloxaloacetic acid equal to 2.5×10^{-6} M.[42]

[42] R. Graham, Dissertation, University of Chicago, 1953, quoted in ref. 43.

[43] F. H. Westheimer, in "The Enzymes," vol. 1, chap, 6, p. 277, Academic Press, Inc., New York, 1959.

a rate increase of a factor of 125. Cupric and aluminum ions are apparently similar to ferric ion in catalytic activity, but do not affect the decarboxylation rate of the monoester monoanion, implying that a free carboxyl group next to the charge-acceptor carbonyl group is necessary for the catalytic effectiveness of the metallic ions. A plausible mechanism for metal ion–catalyzed decarboxylation is shown in Fig. 2.6.

A correlation has been made between the catalytic effectiveness of metal ions in the decarboxylation of acetone dicarboxylic acid and their complexing constants with malonic acid [Eq. (2.24) and (2.25)].[44,45] It

was concluded that the effect on decarboxylation rate reflected the complexing ability of the metal ion with the transition state. However, the decarboxylation rate involves two free-energy changes, that of complexing of the ground state with the metal ion, and the difference between the ground-state complex and the transition-state complex. One free-energy change is involved in the formation of the malonate metal ion complexes. Since stability constants of metal ion complexes are very sensitive to ligand structure, and do not even show the same order with a given series of metal ions and different ligands, it is difficult to interpret the correlation reported.[46]

2.2-10. The expulsion of a negative species in a process concerted with the loss of carbon dioxide is an effective pathway for decarboxylation (mechanism CD-3). Loss of carbon dioxide competes well with intramolecular displacement in β-halo acids[47] [Eq. (2.26)].

[44] J. E. Prue, *J. Chem. Soc.*, 2331 (1952).

[45] J. J. Hoppe and J. E. Prue, *J. Chem. Soc.*, 1775 (1957).

[46] R. J. P. Williams, in "The Enzymes," vol. 1, chap. 9, p. 407, Academic Press, Inc., New York, 1959.

[47] R. Fittig and F. Binder, *Ber.*, **10**, 513 (1877).

(2.26) 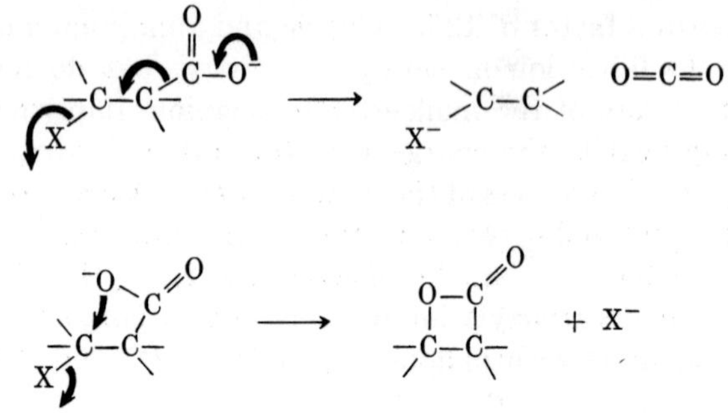

The decarboxylation of *cis*- and *trans*-cinnamic acid dibromides is *trans* in stereochemistry, as are bimolecular (E2) elimination reactions. *Trans*-dibromide yields pure *cis*-β-bromostyrene on treatment with sodium bicarbonate in acetone in the dark (Fig. 2.7). (Light isomerizes the *cis*- to the *trans*-β-bromostyrene.) In polar solvents like water, ionization of the bromine on the carbon alpha to the benzene ring leads

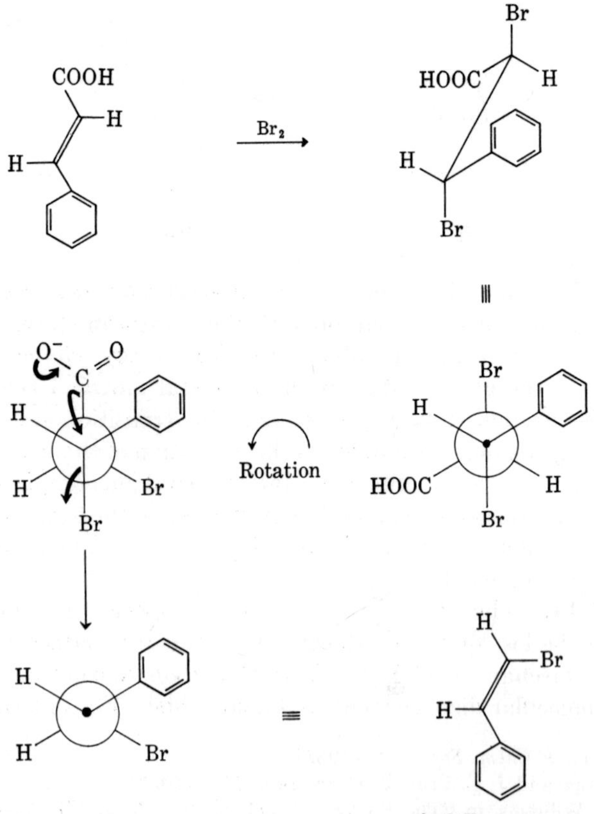

cis-β-Bromostyrene

FIG. 2.7. Concerted decarboxylation of *trans*-cinnamic acid dibromide.

to a mixture of β-bromostyrenes with a high proportion of the more stable *trans* isomer.[31,48] Nonpolar solvents favor the concerted mechanism. The ionization pathway can be repressed by a *p*-nitro substituent on the benzene ring; the *trans-p*-nitrocinnamic acid dibromide yields *cis-p*-nitro-β-bromostyrene over a greater range of solvent polarity than the unsubstituted dibromide. *Cis*-cinnamic acid dibromide decarboxylates to *trans*-β-bromostyrene, possibly by a concerted reaction.

The "bromodecarboxylation" of α-amino acids[49] [Eq. (2.27)] can also

(2.27)

be explained in terms of the concerted mechanism.

2.2-11. Some decarboxylations proceed through mechanisms which are difficult to specify. The ferric tartrate-catalyzed reactions of dimethylglycine oxide are such reactions.[50] A number of other decarboxylations involve electron transfer from the carboxylate ion to a metal ion or an electrode, but the nature of the transition state to products is not yet clear.

Bis-decarboxylation of 1,2-dicarboxylic acids[51] is most conveniently carried out with lead tetraacetate in benzene in the presence of one or two moles of pyridine or triethylamine.[52,53] An example is presented in

(2.28)

(or diacid)

Eq. (2.28). Both a cyclic mechanism [Eq. (2.29)],[51] and a concerted, fragmentation-type[54] mechanism akin to CD-3[53] have been proposed [Eq. (2.30)].

[48] S. J. Cristol and W. P. Norris, *J. Am. Chem. Soc.*, **75**, 632, 2645 (1953).
[49] N. Konigsberg, G. Stevenson, and J. M. Luck, *J. Biol. Chem.*, **235**, 1341 (1960).
[50] C. C. Sweeley and E. C. Horning, *J. Am. Chem. Soc.*, **79**, 2620 (1957).
[51] W. v. E. Doering, M. Farber, and A. Sayigh, *J. Am. Chem. Soc.*, **74**, 4370 (1952).
[52] C. A. Grob, M. Ohta, E. Renk, and A. Weiss, *Helv. Chim. Acta*, **41**, 1191 (1958).
[53] C. A. Grob, M. Ohta, and A. Weiss, *Angew. Chem.*, **70**, 343 (1958).
[54] C. A. Grob, *Experientia*, **13**, 126 (1957); "Theoretical Organic Chemistry," Kekule Symposium, September, 1958, p. 114, Butterworth & Co. (Publishers) Ltd., London, 1959.

(2.29)

(2.30)

A decarboxylative fragmentation occurs during electrolytic oxidation of some γ-hydroxy acids.[55] A possible mechanism, involving simultaneous transfer of two electrons from the organic molecule to the electrode, is shown in Fig. 2.8. The formation of other products[56] indicates an appreciable lifetime for reactive intermediates at the electrode surface.

A particularly interesting decarboxylation of uncertain mechanism is that induced photochemically in benzenediazonium-2-carboxylate, which leads to benzyne.[56a,56b]

2.2-12. A number of biochemical decarboxylations seem to follow some of the chemical mechanisms which have been defined. Quantitatively, the most important decarboxylations are those of pyruvic acid and α-ketoglutaric acid in the tricarboxylic acid cycle, and these are probably decarboxylations with a positively charged nitrogen as the charge acceptor (Fig. 1.10). It is not yet possible to say whether or not the enzyme serves any other function than specificity in the decarboxylation step. Amino acid decarboxylations are catalyzed by pyridoxal (Fig. 2.3), and positively charged nitrogen is therefore again the charge acceptor in decarboxylation. The acetoacetic acid decarboxylase from *Clostridium acetobutylicum* has been crystallized and contains no biotin.[57] The mechanism of the enzymatic decarboxylation is obscure, and it is claimed that metal ions promote neither the enzymatic[58] nor the nonenzymatic reactions.[59,60]

[55] E. J. Corey and R. R. Sauers, *J. Am. Chem. Soc.*, **81**, 1743 (1959).

[56] E. J. Corey, N. L. Bauld, R. T. La Londe, J. Casanova, Jr., and E. T. Kaiser, *J. Am. Chem. Soc.*, **82**, 2645 (1960).

[56a] M. Stiles and R. G. Miller, *J. Am. Chem. Soc.*, **82**, 3802 (1960).

[56b] R. S. Berry, G. N. Spokes, and M. Stiles, *J. Am. Chem. Soc.*, **82**, 5240 (1960).

[57] G. A. Hamilton and F. H. Westheimer, *J. Am. Chem. Soc.*, **81**, 2277 (1959).

[58] R. Davies, *Biochem. J.*, **37**, 230 (1943).

[59] H. Krebs, *Biochem. J.*, **36**, 303 (1942).

[60] A. Kornberg, S. Ochoa, and A. Mehler, *J. Biol. Chem.*, **174**, 159 (1958).

An attempt has been made to define the decarboxylation mechanism of oxaloacetic acid catalyzed by the enzyme from *Micrococcus lysodeikticus*[61] by an examination of the carbon dioxide produced from a mixture of $HOOCCOCH_2COOH$ and $HOOCCOCH_2C^{13}OOH$. In a hypothetical reaction involving only the cleavage of a carbon-carbon bond, a C^{12}—C^{13}

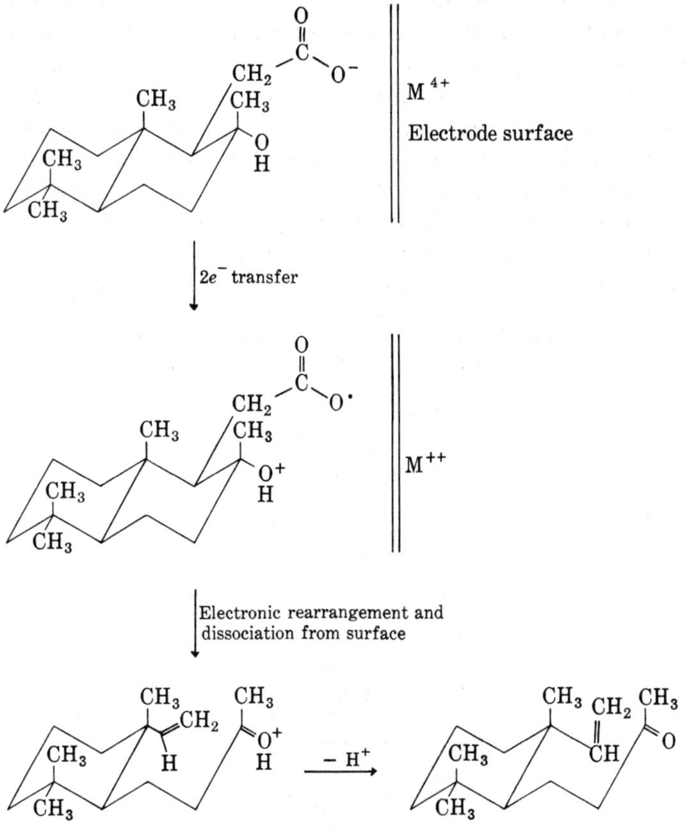

FIG. 2.8. Mechanism of electrolytic oxidation.

bond would cleave more slowly than a C^{12}—C^{12} bond. Thus, if the CH_2—COOH bond breakage were the slowest step in decarboxylation, an "isotope effect" would be observed, and the carbon dioxide produced in the first part of the reaction would have a higher $C^{12}O_2$ content than expected from the isotopic composition of the oxaloacetic acid. In manganese-ion-catalyzed *nonenzymatic* decarboxylation, a fractionation factor (k^{12}/k^{13}) was observed with magnitude 1.06. No fractionation at all was *observed* in the enzyme-catalyzed decarboxylation. On the basis

[61] S. Seltzer, G. A. Hamilton, and F. H. Westheimer, *J. Am. Chem. Soc.*, **81**, 4018 (1959).

of a three-step mechanism, it was concluded that "desorption" of carbon dioxide was the rate-determining step. It was also suggested that a four-step mechanism (given below) was consistent with the data on the same basis.[61]

The simplest mechanism which seems reasonable for the oxaloacetic acid decarboxylase is four-step [Eqs. (2.31) to (2.34)] on the ground that the enzyme must be specific for carbon dioxide, in order for the reaction to be reversible.[62,63] Furthermore, it seems somewhat unusual that a "desorption" step would be much slower than a bond-cleavage step. Derivation of an expression for the ratio of maximum rates expected for the C^{12}—C^{13} and C^{12}—C^{12} cases, using a general formulation for enzymatic reactions with multiple intermediates[13] and the four-step mechanism, is shown in Eqs. (2.35) to (2.38). It can be seen that failure to observe an isotope effect results from particular values of the rate constants without identifying a single step as rate-determining.[64] We can

$$E = \text{enzyme} \qquad S = \text{oxaloacetic acid}$$
$$P = \text{pyruvic acid} \qquad S_1 = \text{pyruvic acid enol}$$

$$(2.31) \qquad E + S \underset{k_{-1}}{\overset{k_1}{\rightleftharpoons}} ES$$

$$(2.32) \qquad ES \underset{k_{-2}}{\overset{k_2}{\rightleftharpoons}} ES_1\text{—}CO_2$$

$$(2.33) \qquad ES_1\text{—}CO_2 \underset{k_{-3}}{\overset{k_3}{\rightleftharpoons}} ES_1 + CO_2$$

$$(2.34) \qquad ES_1 \underset{k_{-4}}{\overset{k_4}{\rightleftharpoons}} E + P$$

$$(2.35) \qquad \frac{V}{(E)_0} = \frac{1}{\displaystyle\sum_{i=1}^{3}\sum_{s=i}^{3}\frac{K_i^s}{k_{(s+1)}}}$$

$$(2.36) \qquad \left[\frac{V}{(E)_0}\right]^{-1} = \frac{1}{k_2} + \frac{k_{-2}}{k_2 k_3} + \frac{1}{k_3} + \frac{1}{k_4}$$

$$(2.37) \qquad \frac{V^*}{V} = \frac{\dfrac{1}{k_2} + \dfrac{k_{-2}}{k_2 k_3} + \dfrac{1}{k_3} + \dfrac{1}{k_4}}{\dfrac{1}{k_2^*} + \dfrac{k_{-2}^*}{k_2^* k_3^*} + \dfrac{1}{k_3^*} + \dfrac{1}{k_4^*}}$$

$$(2.38) \qquad \frac{V^*}{V} = \frac{k_2^*}{k_2} \left[\frac{1 + \dfrac{k_{-2}}{k_3} + \dfrac{k_2}{k_3} + \dfrac{k_2}{k_4}}{1 + \dfrac{k_{-2}^*}{k_3^*} + \dfrac{k_2^*}{k_3^*} + \dfrac{k_2^*}{k_4^*}}\right]$$

* For C^{13}

[62] L. O. Krampitz, H. G. Wood, and C. H. Werkman, *J. Biol. Chem.*, **147**, 243 (1943).
[63] M. F. Utter and H. G. Wood, *J. Biol. Chem.*, **164**, 455 (1946).
[64] Advice of Dr. L. Peller is gratefully acknowledged.

assume that k_2 will exhibit an isotope effect, since this is the step in which the C^{12}—C^{13} bond is broken. From the nonenzymatic results, k_2/k_2^* is at least 1.06. If the experimental error, which is unavoidably large in measurements of the type used,[61] does not permit a differentiation between an isotope effect of 1.01 and 1.00, then no isotope effect would be observed if the ratio of the brackets following k_2/k_2^* in Eq. (2.38) is at least 1.05. If k_2 were indeed much smaller than any of the other rate constants (and therefore, rate-determining) and k_{-2} roughly equal to k_3, then V^*/V would exhibit an isotope effect. However, if most of the rate constants are comparable in magnitude, V^*/V may easily be approximately 1. Writing the relationship of the expressions in brackets explicitly as Eq. (2.39), it is reasonable that the isotope effects on k_{-2} and k_3 are similar so that the ratios k_{-2}/k_3 and k_{-2}^*/k_3^* are the same. The same point can be made for k_2/k_3 and k_2^*/k_3^*, resulting in expression (2.40).

$$(2.39) \qquad \left[1 + \frac{k_{-2}}{k_3} + \frac{k_2}{k_3} + \frac{k_2}{k_4} \right] = 1.05 \left[1 + \frac{k_{-2}^*}{k_3^*} + \frac{k_2^*}{k_3^*} + \frac{k_2^*}{k_4^*} \right]$$

$$(2.40) \qquad \left[c + \frac{k_2}{k_4} \right] = 1.05 \left[c + \frac{k_2^*}{k_4^*} \right]$$

The equality in Eq. (2.40) can be true if k_2/k_4 is considerably larger than c, yielding Eq. (2.41) with k_4^* taken as equal to k_4 because a bond to C^{13} is not involved in the step described by this constant. Since k_2/k_2^* is ca. 1.06, Eq. (2.41) is correct, and V^*/V is approximately 1. Other more

$$(2.41) \qquad \left[\frac{k_2}{k_4} \right] = 1.05 \left[\frac{k_2^*}{k_4} \right] \qquad \frac{k_2}{k_2^*} = 1.05$$

complicated combinations of rate-constant relationships are clearly possible. It is thus rather difficult to arrive at conclusions about mechanism from studies of the isotope-rate effect on enzymatic reactions, primarily because so many unimolecular steps of comparable rate must occur in any reasonable chemical mechanism.

2.2-13. It is almost certain that the formation of isopentenyl pyrophosphate (Sec. 1.8) proceeds according to mechanism CD-3, decarboxylation being concerted with loss of a phosphate ion. The decarboxylation of orotidine-5'-phosphate to uridine-5'-phosphate may represent a decarboxylation like those of the pyridinium betaines. A mechanism for the reaction in Fig. 1.28 is given in Fig. 2.9. An interesting theoretical possibility exists for this particular decarboxylation since it might be regarded as a reaction in which a large dipole collapses to a small dipole by a decrease in the distance between the charges. A reaction of this type could be enormously accelerated by a reduction in the polarity of the medium around the dipole by, for example, two alkyl side chains of the enzyme displacing water from the region of the dipole.

Many biochemical decarboxylations have counterparts in the realm of organic chemistry. However, relatively little effort has been devoted

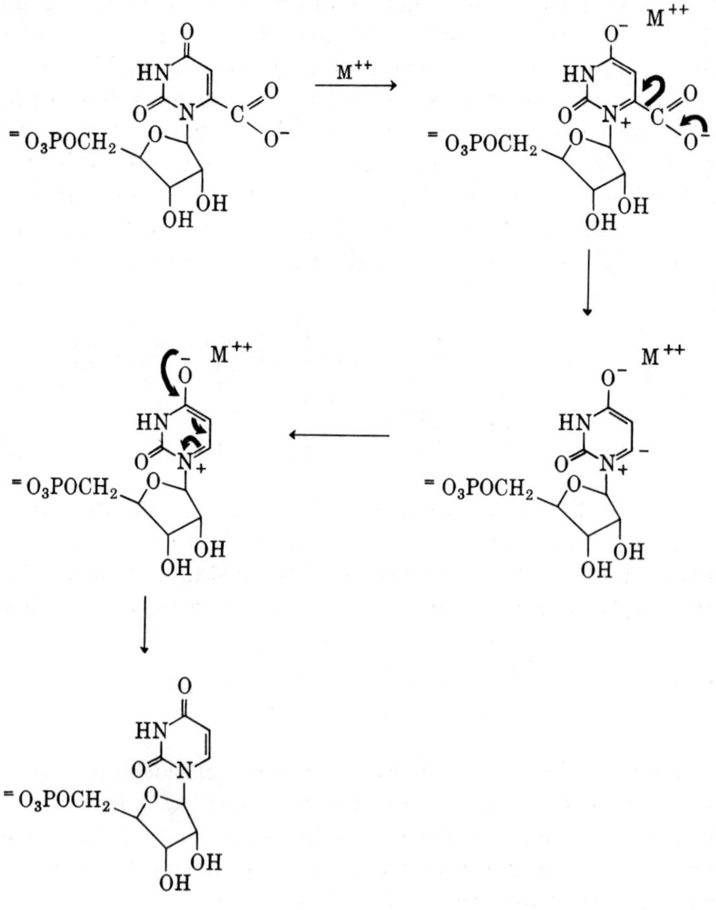

FIG. 2.9. Conversion of oritidine-5'-phosphate to uridine-5'-phosphate by decarboxylation.

to an investigation of the rates of decarboxylations, and except for a few β-keto acids, with and without metal ion catalysis, quantitative aspects of decarboxylation applicable to biochemical cases have not been examined. A need for such information exists so that the quantitative advantages of the various decarboxylation enzymes as catalysts can be understood.

2.3. ENOLIZATION AND ALDOL CONDENSATION

When I found myself on my Feet, I looked about me, and must confess I never beheld a more entertaining Prospect. The Country round appeared like a continued Garden. . . .

J. Swift

Enolization and aldol condensation of the enol with a carbonyl compound are important processes in both organic chemistry and biochemistry. Any treatment of these two topics must also include some consideration of the addition of hydroxyl groups to carbonyl groups. The enolization of acetaldehyde is shown in Eq. (2.42); the condensation of the enol of acetaldehyde with another molecule of acetaldehyde is given in Eq. (2.43).

$$(2.42) \quad CH_3CHO \underset{BH^+}{\overset{B}{\rightleftharpoons}} \left[{}^-CH_2CHO \longleftrightarrow CH_2=CH{\overset{O^-}{}} \right] \underset{B}{\overset{BH^+}{\rightleftharpoons}} CH_2=C{\overset{OH}{\underset{H}{}}}$$

$$(2.43) \quad CH_3\overset{O}{\overset{\|}{C}}H + CH_2=C{\overset{OH}{\underset{H}{}}} \rightleftharpoons CH_3\overset{OH}{\underset{H}{C}}CH_2CHO$$

The chemical properties of ethyl acetoacetate could not be ascribed to a unique structure and became the subject of a long controversy, which was only resolved by the realization that a mobile equilibrium between two forms could explain the results. The phenomenon of equilibrium between two isomeric forms was called *tautomerism,* and the forms themselves were called *tautomers.* The tautomers of ethyl acetoacetate are the *keto* and *enol* forms.[65]

2.3-1. The enol content of a mixture can be determined by titration with bromine, since the enol reacts rapidly, the keto form does not react and is transformed into the enol form relatively slowly.[66] A rapid-flow technique[67] permits the determination of very small enol contents. An improvement of the titration procedure[66] using iodine monochloride has been reported.[68] However, the results[68] are not

---

[65] An excellent survey of tautomerism, including its early history, may be found in C. K. Ingold, "Structure and Mechanism in Organic Chemistry," pp. 530–575, Cornell University Press, Ithaca, N.Y., 1953.

[66] K. H. Meyer, *Ann.,* **380,** 212 (1911).

[67] G. Schwarzenbach and C. Wittwer, *Helv. Chim. Acta,* **30,** 656 (1947).

[68] A. Gero, *J. Org. Chem.,* **19,** 469, 1960 (1954).

directly comparable to others because pure ketone was used and it is known that the enol-keto equilibrium is solvent-dependent.[69] Direct titration with barium hydroxide has indicated that the enol contents of methoxyacetone, s-dimethoxyacetone, and s-dihydroxyacetone are 1.1, 6.2, and 0.08%, respectively.[70] In contrast, DL-*epi-meso*-inosose (Fig. 2.10*a*) and *scyllo-meso*-inosose (Fig. 2.10*b*) contain no enediol in neutral

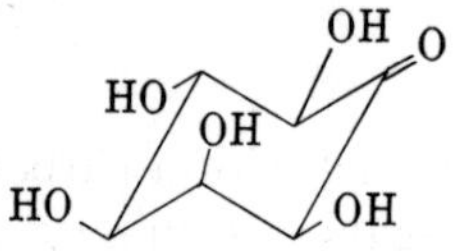

FIG. 2.10*a*. "DL-*epi-meso*-Inosose" (DL-*epi*-inosose-2).

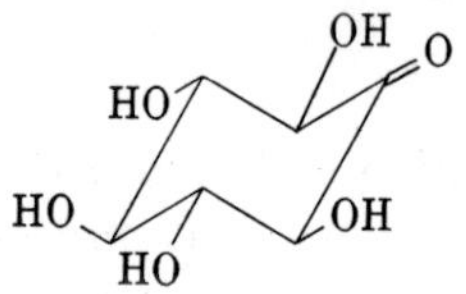

FIG. 2.10*b*. "*scyllo-meso*-Inosose" (*myo*-inosose-2).

aqueous solution.[71] A few equilibrium constants for enolization of carbonyl compounds are listed in Table 2.3-3. A list of biochemically important molecules which can undergo enolization is given in Table 2.3-1.

TABLE 2.3-1. ENOLIZABLE MOLECULES OF BIOCHEMICAL IMPORTANCE

α-Keto acids

1. α-Ketoglutaric acid
2. Oxalosuccinic acid
3. Oxaloacetic acid
4. Pyruvic acid
5. Hydroxypyruvic acid
6. 3-Phosphate of hydroxypyruvic acid
7. *p*-Hydroxyphenylpyruvic acid

Acids

8. Carboxylic acids, RCOOH
9. 2-Phosphoglyceric acid
10. 3-Phosphoglyceric acid

Thioesters

11. Acetyl coA
12. Malonyl coA
13. Butyryl coA

Aldehydes

14. Glyceraldehyde
15. Glyceraldehyde 3-phosphate
16. Ribose 5-phosphate
17. Acetaldehyde
18. Erythrose 4-phosphate
19. Glucose 6-phosphate
20. Glucose
21. Galactose

Ketones

22. Acetoacetic acid
23. Dihydroxyacetone phosphate
24. Acetoacetyl coA
25. Ribulose 5-phosphate
26. Ribulose 1,5-diphosphate
27. Xylulose 5-phosphate
28. Sedoheptulose 7-phosphate
29. Fructose
30. Fructose 6-phosphate

2.3-2. The transformation of a keto compound into an enol involves the removal of a hydrogen bound to carbon as a proton. Chemical experience, however, suggests that hydrogens bound to carbon are usually removed with difficulty as protons. The pK_a of methane, for

---

[69] E. M. Kosower, *J. Am. Chem. Soc.*, **80**, 3267 (1958).

[70] J. Kenner and G. N. Richards, *J. Chem. Soc.*, 2240 (1953).

[71] H. von Euler and A. Glaser, *Arkiv Kemi*, **8**, 61 (1954).

example, has been variously estimated as 40 or 58.[72]   The ionization reaction is indicated in Eq. (2.44).   Presumably, the alkide ion cannot

$$(2.44) \qquad\qquad CH_4 \rightleftharpoons CH_3^- + H^+$$

accommodate the negative charge.[74]   Negative charge can be accommodated by a carbanion in decarboxylation (Sec. 2.2) if appropriate groups replace the hydrogen or alkyl group in the carbanion [Eq. (2.44)].   The list of pK_a values in Table 2.3-2 indicates that one electron-attracting

TABLE 2.3-2. EFFECT OF GROUPS ON pK_a[75]

Compound	pK_a
CH_4	40 (58)
CH_3NO_2	11
$CH_2(NO_2)_2$	4
$CH(NO_2)_3$	0
CH_3COCH_3	20
$CH_2(COCH_3)_2$	9
$CH(COCH_3)_3$	6[a]
$CH_3SO_2CH_3$	23
$CH_2(SO_2CH_3)_2$	14
$CH(SO_2CH_3)_3$	0
CH_3CN	25
$CH_2(CN)_2$	12
$CH(CN)_3$	0

[a] $CH(CHO)_3$ has been reported to have a pK_a of approximately 2.3.[76]

substituent has a marked effect upon the acidity of methane.   Compounds with one such substituent may be referred to as *singly activated carbon acids*.   A second and third substituent also have large effects, and many of the *triply activated carbon acids* are fairly strong acids.[75]

[72] R. P. Bell, "The Proton in Chemistry," p. 87, Cornell University Press, Ithaca, N.Y., 1959, after a treatment suggested by Schwarzenbach.[73]

[73] G. Schwarzenbach, *Z. physik. Chem. (Leipzig)*, **176A**, 133 (1936).

[74] It is difficult to make valid comparisons between familiar dissociation constants for acids in dilute aqueous solution, and those which cannot be measured under these conditions due to the "leveling effect," i.e., that below a certain acid strength, all weak acids appear to be un-ionized in water.   While the range covered can be extended somewhat by the use of hydroxylic organic solvents, there is a limit to the solvent polarity which can serve the purpose of measuring dissociation constants comparable to those measured in water.   The reason for the lower limit is the occurrence of ion pairing in low-polarity solvents.   Ion pairing may be regarded as a specific type of solvation which cannot be evaluated at present.   In summary, we should really like to know the dissociation constant of methane in aqueous solution, so as to include solvation of the dissociated species, but the acidity of methane is unfortunately below the range in which we could hope to obtain a constant applicable to aqueous solution.

[75] R. G. Pearson and R. L. Dillon, *J. Am. Chem. Soc.*, **75**, 2439 (1953).

[76] Z. Arnold and J. Žemlička, *Collection Czechoslov. Chem. Commun.*, **25**, 1319 (1960).

Molecules of biochemical interest which are capable of enolization belong to the group of singly activated carbon acids, although there are a few important *doubly activated* compounds (acetoacetic acid, acetoacetyl coA, malonyl coA). Since most molecules in the singly activated group fall into an inconveniently weak class of acids, and possess rather low enol contents, most chemical studies of enols and enolization have been made with doubly activated carbon acids like acetylacetone.[77]

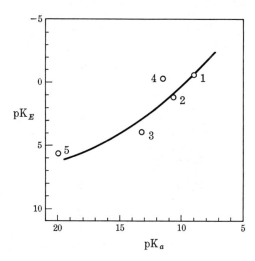

FIG. 2.11. pK_E versus pK_a (cf. Table 2.3-3).

It has just been stated that very weak carbon acids also possess low enol contents. It would not be expected that a precise parallelism would exist, but a comparison of pK_E [Eq. (2.45)] with pK_a (Fig. 2.11) for the

$$(2.45) \qquad\qquad pK_E = -\log \frac{(E)}{(K)}$$

few data which are available (Table 2.3-3) suggests that the relationship may be approximately true.

2.3-3. The *rate of ionization* of weak carbon acids is a property which depends very much on structure. An approximate empirical relationship has been found between the rate constant for ionization, k_1, and the equilibrium constant for ionization, K_a.[75] In general, the lower the dissociation constant, the more slowly a compound ionizes.

[77] G. S. Hammond, W. G. Borduim, and G. A. Guter, *J. Am. Chem. Soc.*, **81**, 4682 (1959).

TABLE 2.3-3. COMPARISON OF K_E WITH K_{diss}

Compound	Point in Fig. 2.11	K_{diss}[75]	K_E[68]	pK_E
$CH_3COCH_2COCH_3$	(1)	1×10^{-9}	3.24	-0.51
CH_3COCH_2COOEt	(2)	2.1×10^{-11}	0.087	1.26
CH_3COCH_3	(5)	10^{-20}	2×10^{-6}	5.7
$CH_2(CO_2Et)_2$	(3)	5×10^{-14}	7.7×10^{-5}	4.11
![O COOEt cyclohexanone]	(4)	3×10^{-12}	1.6	-0.2

Selected values for both constants are tabulated in Table 2.3-4, and the relationship is illustrated graphically in Fig. 2.12.

Most of the enolizable compounds of biochemical interest are singly activated and are therefore compounds which have small enol contents and which ionize rather slowly. *In those biochemical reactions for which the enol of a carbonyl compound is the substrate, the enzyme must catalyze the enolization.* If enolization were not catalyzed, it would be a rate-limiting step in the reactions concerned, and there is no evidence that this is correct.

TABLE 2.3-4. RATES AND EQUILIBRIA OF IONIZATION FOR CARBON ACIDS [75]

No.[a]	Compound	K_a[b]	k_1, sec^{-1}
1	CH_3COCH_3	10^{-20}	4.7×10^{-10}
2	CH_3COCH_2Cl	3×10^{-17}	5.5×10^{-8}
3	$CH_3COCHCl_2$	10^{-15}	7.3×10^{-7}
4	CH_3COCH_2COOEt	2.1×10^{-11}	1.2×10^{-3}
5	$CH_3COCH_2COCH_3$	1.0×10^{-9}	6.6×10^{-2}
6	$CH_3COCH(CH_3)COCH_3$	1×10^{-11}	8.3×10^{-4}
7	![O COOEt cyclopentanone]	3×10^{-11}	2.3×10^{-3}
8	![O COOEt cyclohexanone]	3×10^{-12}	9.7×10^{-6}
9	$CH_2(CN)_2$	6.5×10^{-12}	1.5×10^{-2}
10	$CH_2(COOEt)_2$	5×10^{-14}	2.5×10^{-5}

[a] See Fig. 2.12.
[b] Uncorrected for enol content (gross acidity).

Although it is true that the enol-keto equilibrium is solvent-depend-ent,[69] the change in the constant for a typical carbonyl compound, ethyl acetoacetate, is less than a factor of 1000 over the solvent range from hexane to water. Nonpolar media favor the enol, which is internally hydrogen-bonded. It seems unlikely that an enzyme catalyzes enoliza-tion merely through a medium effect.

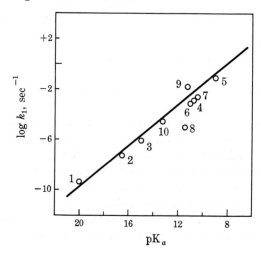

FIG. 2.12. Relationship between k_1 and pK_a for ionization of carbon acids.[75] (The numbers on the points correspond to the entries in Table 2.3-4.)

2.3-4. The solution of a carbonyl compound in water or another hydroxylic solvent may contain a proportion of 1,1-diol or hemiacetal, i.e., compounds derived from the addition of water or alcohol to the carbonyl group. Aqueous formaldehyde does not contain sufficient free formaldehyde (HCHO) to be observed by its $n \rightarrow \pi^*$ transition of the carbonyl group in the ultraviolet at room temperature.[78] The equi-

$$(2.46) \qquad\qquad HCHO + HOH \rightleftharpoons CH_2(OH)_2$$

librium in Eq. (2.46) is almost entirely to the right. Replacement of the hydrogen attached to the carbonyl group by a methyl group causes the position of the equilibrium to lie farther to the left; acetaldehyde is substantially but not completely hydrated in water. Electron-with-drawing substituents attached to the carbonyl favor hydration, as shown by the example of chloral hydrate (2,2,2-trichloro-1,1-ethanediol).

[78] This ultraviolet light absorption can be observed at elevated temperatures (53 to 64°C) in a very long cell.[79]

[79] R. Bieber and G. Trümpler, Helv. Chim. Acta, 30, 1860 (1947).

Many of the biologically important carbonyl compounds must exist in aqueous solution in equilibrium with their hydrated forms, except for the ketones. Their measured reactivities are thus, under these aqueous conditions, lower than the "true" reactivities for the carbonyl compound in such reactions as enolization or aldol condensation.[79a]

If the carbonyl compound contains an alcoholic hydroxyl group either three or four carbon atoms away, intramolecular addition to form a

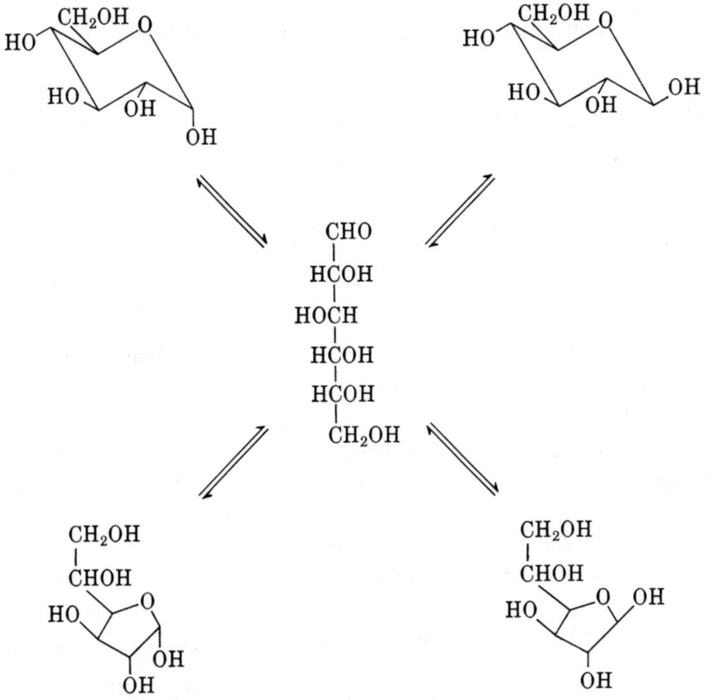

Fig. 2.13. Equilibria involving D-glucose in water.

hemiacetal occurs. The free aldehyde content of D-glucose in water has been estimated as only 0.0026% by polarographic means.[80] (The figure is not corrected for possible contributions from hydrated open-chain forms.[80]) The equilibria for D-glucose shown in Fig. 2.13 are acceptable for explaining the mutarotation of the glucose anomers in neutral solution since it has been found that oxygen (labeled with O^{18}) of the hemiacetal hydroxyl group is not exchanged with water during mutarotation.[81]

[79a] Cf., for example, the consideration of the rates of hydration and dehydration of α-keto acids presented by H. Strehlow, Am. Chem. Soc. Abstr., 140, 9T (1961).

[80] J. M. Los, L. B. Simpson, and K. Wiesner, J. Am. Chem. Soc., 78, 1564 (1956).

[81] R. Bentley and D. S. Bhate, J. Biol. Chem., 235, 1225 (1960).

2.3-5.   The rate of hydration of acetaldehyde at 0°C is somewhat slower than that of carbon dioxide (Sec. 2.1-3), with a rate constant of 7.2×10^{-4} sec^{-1} (ref. 82).   Ring closure of the aldehyde form of glucose to the hemiacetal is much faster.   The rate constants corresponding to the mechanism indicated in Eq. (2.47) are listed in Table 2.3-5.

$$(2.47) \qquad \alpha \underset{k_{-1}}{\overset{k_1}{\rightleftharpoons}} \gamma \underset{k_{-2}}{\overset{k_2}{\rightleftharpoons}} \beta$$

($\alpha = \alpha$-D-glucose, $\beta = \beta$-D-glucose, γ = aldehyde form)

Although the ring-closure and ring-opening reactions are reasonably fast, they are probably too slow to explain the rates observed for enzymatic

TABLE 2.3-5. RATE CONSTANTS FOR "CYCLIZATION" AND "DECYCLIZATION" OF D-GLUCOSE[80]

k_1	7.6×10^{-3} sec^{-1}
k_2	2.7×10^{-3} sec^{-1}
k_{-1}	1.08×10^2 sec^{-1}
k_{-2}	6.6×10^1 sec^{-1}

reactions (see Fig. 1.3, Sec. 1.1-1).   It is probably true in general that ring opening or dehydration of "masked" carbonyl groups must be enzyme-catalyzed.

2.3-6.   Enolization of a carbonyl compound in deuterium oxide leads to exchange of hydrogen for deuterium.   Many of the biologically interesting molecules listed in Table 2.3-1 should not exchange rapidly in uncatalyzed reactions because the rates of ionization are so low. Even under basic conditions, moderate alkalinity is required to produce reasonable rates of exchange.[83]   The interconversion of aldose and ketose is shown in Eq. (2.48).   It is of interest that the enolization of acetone is

[82] Y. Pocker, *Proc. Chem. Soc.*, 17 (1960).

[83] "Mild" conditions for the aldose-ketose interconversion (the "Lobry de Bruyn-Alberda van Ekenstein transformation") utilize 0.04 N calcium hydroxide.[84]

[84] J. C. Speck, Jr., *Advances in Carbohydrate Chem.*, **13**, 63 (1958).

promoted by the amino acids, glycine, and β-alanine, although pyridine and piperidine are inactive.[85]

2.3-7. Enzymatic catalysis of hydrogen exchange with deuterium (or tritium) oxide is usually interpreted as evidence for enolization of a carbonyl compound. However, lack of exchange is *not* firm evidence against enolization (see Sec. 3.1 and below). A number of enzymatically catalyzed exchanges require "irrelevant" coenzymes, that is, molecules which serve no obvious chemical function in the enolization. Thus, exchange of tritium from tritiated pyruvic acid with pyruvic kinase requires ATP, magnesium ion, and potassium ion. Oxygen labeling suggests that covalent bonds to the ATP are not formed.[86] The exchange of a β-hydrogen of α-ketoglutaric acid catalyzed by isocitric dehydrogenase is stereospecific and requires TPNH and magnesium ion. In the presence of carbon dioxide, isocitric acid is produced.[87]

A crystalline enzyme which catalyzes the isomerization shown in Eq. (2.49) has been isolated. When the enzyme was equilibrated with deuterium oxide and the isomerization carried out in deuterium oxide, *no deuterium was found* in the product.[88]

An intramolecular hydride transfer was suggested to explain the lack of exchange, but no simple chemical analogy to such a transformation exists. A simple explanation consistent with the enolizability of β,γ-unsaturated

(2.49)

ketones and the lack of exchange with solvent is possible if it is postulated that a basic group which contains no hydrogens (alkoxyl, carbonyl, etc.) removes the appropriate hydrogen from the substrate and that the resulting ion pair (BH^+K^-) is shielded from the solvent by the steroid molecule. Thus, a reaction which proceeds through enolization does not necessarily result in exchange of hydrogen with the solvent.

Enzymatic reactions for which a good (*congruent*, see Sec. 3.1) model reaction is known, and which show no hydrogen uptake from the medium in both the model and the enzymatic reactions, probably proceed by pathways which do not include enolization. No isotopic hydrogen from the medium is found in S-lactylglutathione formed from pyruvaldehyde

[85] E. A. Shilov and A. A. Yasinikov, *Ukrain. Khim. Zhur.*, **23**, 215 (1957); *Chem. Abstr.*, **51**, 14553*b* (1957).

[86] I. A. Rose, *J. Biol. Chem.*, **235**, 1170 (1960).

[87] Z. B. Rose, *J. Biol. Chem.*, **235**, 928 (1960).

[88] F. S. Kawahara and P. Talalay, *J. Biol. Chem.*, **235**, PC 1 (1960).

and glutathione in the presence of glyoxalase.[89],[90] Parallel observations regarding the lack of introduction of isotopic hydrogen from the medium are obtained with hydroxide ion[91] or 2-diethylaminoethanethiol.[92] The hydrogen which appears on the α carbon of the lactyl moiety must arise by an intramolecular transfer, probably a hydride shift [Eq. (2.50)].

(2.50)

$$CH_3C \overset{O}{\underset{SG}{\overset{\|}{C}}} \overset{H}{\underset{}{\overset{|}{C}}} O^- \longrightarrow CH_3C \overset{OH}{\underset{H}{\overset{|}{C}}} \overset{O}{\underset{}{\overset{\|}{C}}} SG$$

G = Glutathione

2.3-8. The conversion of glyceraldehyde-3-phosphate to dihydroxyacetone phosphate catalyzed by triose phosphate isomerase results in stereospecific acquisition of a hydrogen from the medium.[93] The enzyme aldolase also catalyzes a stereospecific hydrogen exchange of dihydroxyacetone phosphate with the medium, although the hydrogen which is exchanged is the one which is not removed by the triose phosphate isomerase.[94] Spectroscopic evidence (an increase in light absorption between 2330 and 2500 Å) for an enzyme-bound enediol intermediate has been found.[95] The enzyme has a high specificity for dihydroxyacetone phosphate but will catalyze aldol condensation with a variety of aldehydes. It seems likely that aldolase catalyzes the ring-opening reaction (see Sec. 1.1-1) for its usual substrate, fructose-1,6-diphosphate.

Another aldolase (deoxyribose aldolase) exhibits a high specificity for acetaldehyde, but will also catalyze aldol condensation with a variety of aldehydes.[96]

Aldolase action thus consists of the enolization of a carbonyl compound to form an enzyme-bound enol or enolate, the catalysis of the addition of the enol or enolate ion to a carbonyl group of an aldehyde, and probable catalysis of the ring-closure reaction for those products which have an alcoholic hydroxyl group in a suitable relation to the carbonyl group. Magnesium ion may be involved in aldolase action, possibly by stabilizing the enolate ion.[97] Condensations which are mechanistically similar to

[89] V. Franzen, *Chem. Ber.*, **89**, 1020 (1956).

[90] I. A. Rose, *Biochim. et Biophys. Acta*, **25**, 214 (1957).

[91] W. v. E. Doering, T. I. Taylor, and E. F. Schoenewaldt, *J. Am. Chem. Soc.*, **70**, 455 (1948).

[92] V. Franzen, *Chem. Ber.*, **88**, 1361 (1955).

[93] S. V. Rieder and I. A. Rose, *J. Biol. Chem.*, **234**, 1007 (1959).

[94] I. A. Rose and S. V. Rieder, *J. Biol. Chem.*, **231**, 315 (1958).

[95] Y. J. Topper, A. H. Mehler, and B. Bloom, *Science*, **126**, 1287 (1957).

[96] W. E. Pricer, Jr., and B. L. Horecker, *J. Biol. Chem.*, **235**, 1292 (1960).

[97] W. J. Rutter, in "The Enzymes," vol. 5, chap. 20, Academic Press, Inc., New York, 1961.

the aldol condensation are catalyzed by thiamine pyrophosphate. The anionic center in "active acetaldehyde" (Fig. 1.10) adds to a carbonyl group in the same fashion as the enolate ion of a ketone or aldehyde.

2.3-9. The aldol condensation is relatively difficult to study even in the nonenzymatic case because (a) the steps are all reversible, (b) it is difficult to evaluate the effects of different parameters on single steps, and (c) subsequent reactions often obscure the experimental results. A detailed mechanism for the aldol condensation of acetaldehyde will illustrate these points [Eqs. (2.51) to (2.55)].

(2.51) $\qquad$ $B + CH_3CHO \underset{k_{-1}}{\overset{k_1}{\rightleftharpoons}} \bar{C}H_2CHO + BH^+$

(2.52) $\qquad$ $CH_3CHO + \bar{C}H_2CHO \underset{k_{-2}}{\overset{k_2}{\rightleftharpoons}} CH_3\overset{O^-}{\underset{H}{\overset{|}{\underset{|}{C}}}}-CH_2CHO$

(2.53) $\qquad$ $CH_3\overset{O^-}{\underset{H}{\overset{|}{\underset{|}{C}}}}-CH_2CHO + BH^+ \underset{k_{-3}}{\overset{k_3}{\rightleftharpoons}} CH_3\overset{OH}{\underset{H}{\overset{|}{\underset{|}{C}}}}-CH_2CHO + B$

(2.54) $\qquad$ $CH_3\overset{OH}{\underset{H}{\overset{|}{\underset{|}{C}}}}-CH_2CHO + B \underset{k_{-4}}{\overset{k_4}{\rightleftharpoons}} CH_3\overset{OH}{\underset{H}{\overset{|}{\underset{|}{C}}}}-\bar{C}HCHO + BH^+$

(2.55) $\qquad$ $CH_3\overset{OH}{\underset{H}{\overset{|}{\underset{|}{C}}}}-\bar{C}HCHO \underset{k_{-5}}{\overset{k_5}{\rightleftharpoons}} CH_3CH{=}CHCHO$

With 10 M acetaldehyde in deuterium oxide and a catalyst, no detectable amount of deuterium is bound to carbon in the aldol, and therefore $k_2(CH_3CHO) \gg k_{-1}$,[98] but deuterium is introduced at lower acetaldehyde concentrations.[99] In the case of acetone, $k_2(CH_3COCH_3)$ is always smaller than k_{-1}, and a 1 M solution of acetone in alkaline deuterium oxide exchanges hydrogen with the solvent about 1000 times faster than condensation occurs.[98]

Although enolization can be readily described in general terms, it is much more difficult to make precise statements about the relevant transition states including the base and solvent.[100] A comparison of the

[98] K. F. Bonhoeffer and W. D. Walters, Z. physik. Chem. (Leipzig), 181, 441 (1938).
[99] R. P. Bell and M. J. Smith, J. Chem. Soc., 1691 (1958).
[100] C. G. Swain, E. C. Stivers, J. F. Reuwer, Jr., and L. J. Schaad, J. Am. Chem. Soc., 80, 5885 (1958).

kinetic parameters for enzymatic and nonenzymatic enolization reactions might be valuable.

2.4. NUCLEOPHILIC DISPLACEMENTS

There is a willow grows aslant a brook,
That shows his hoar leaves in the glassy stream;
There with fantastic garlands did she come
Of crow-flowers, nettles, daisies, and long purples,
That liberal shepherds give a grosser name,
But our cold maids do dead men's fingers call them:
There, on the pendent boughs her coronet weeds
Clambering to hang, an envious sliver broke;
When down her weedy trophies and herself
Fell in the weeping brook.

W. Shakespeare

Replacements of groups attached to carbon by other groups are reasonably well understood,[101] but the chemistry of replacements on other atoms like sulfur, phosphorus, and metal atoms is one for which only rough mechanistic formulations are available. Biochemical pathways proceed through replacement reactions much less frequently than addition reactions (aldol condensations, carboxylations), but replacement reactions are of sufficient importance to make their chemistry worth consideration.

2.4-1. The two general mechanisms of replacement reactions on carbon are ionization (S_N1) and displacement (S_N2). These are written in Eqs. (2.56) to (2.58) for a nucleophile N. The kinetic expressions used

$$(2.56) \qquad\qquad RX \rightarrow R^+ + X^-$$
$$(2.57) \qquad\qquad R^+ + N^- \rightarrow RN$$
$$(2.58) \qquad\qquad N^- + RX \rightarrow NR + X^-$$

to identify these mechanisms are given in Eq. (2.59), S_N1, and Eq. (2.60), S_N2. The stereochemistry of replacement through ionization in the

$$(2.59) \qquad\qquad v = k(RX)$$
$$(2.60) \qquad\qquad v = k(RX)(N)$$

simplest cases is indiscriminate; that is, the nucleophile can react with either side of the intermediate carbonium ion. Displacement (S_N2)

---

[101] A. Streitwieser, Jr., *Chem. Revs.*, **56**, 571 (1956).

normally leads to inversion of configuration at the carbon to which the group being displaced was attached. The latter group is often called a "leaving group."[102] Complications which affect the stereochemical results are mentioned in the next subsection.

The rates of both S_N1 and S_N2 reactions vary with solvent polarity;[103] the effect of solvent can usually be rationalized in terms of the relative solvation of the ground and transition states. Thus, S_N1 reactions are much more sensitive to the polarity of the solvent than S_N2 reactions because the transition state to ionization is much more highly charged than that for displacement.[106]

2.4-2. Many molecules react in a way not interpretable in the simple terms of the preceding subsection. If the nucleophile is attached to the molecule with the leaving group and geometric requirements are satisfied, intramolecular reaction will occur. The intervention of an "internal" nucleophile in a replacement reaction is known as the "neighboring group effect." The "neighboring group," in many instances, can provide "driving force" for the reaction (i.e., lower the transition-state free energy) as "anchimeric acceleration" of an intramolecular displacement reaction. The stereochemical result of the reaction is determined by the fate of the reaction intermediate, and this may vary with the reaction conditions. The solvolysis of *trans*-2-acetoxycyclohexyl *p*-toluenesulfonate (tosylate) in acetic acid containing sodium acetate yields

---

[102] No word of Greek origin seems to have been coined for this awkward expression. An opportunity to utilize Minoan B is therefore available to the chemical scholar.

[103] "Polarity" with respect to replacement reactions refers to solvating ability of the solvent. The usual parameter quoted is dielectric constant, but the latter refers to behavior of solvent molecules in an electric field over *macroscopic* distances, and is unsuitable for correlating the effects of solvent polarity operating on the *microscopic* level. Two empirical parameters useful at the microscopic level are **Y**, the log of the rate of solvolysis of *t*-butyl chloride[104] and **Z**, the position of the charge-transfer band of 1-ethyl-4-carbomethoxypyridinium iodide.[105,105a]

[104] A. H. Fainberg and S. Winstein, *J. Am. Chem. Soc.*, **78**, 2770 (1956).

[105] E. M. Kosower, *J. Am. Chem. Soc.*, **80**, 3253 (1958).

[105a] A new empirical parameter, Ω, based on the *endo/exo* ratio of the Diels-Alder product formed from cyclopentadiene and methyl acrylate, is linear in both **Z** and **Y**. It is useful in nonpolar media and in certain solvents not readily measurable by other methods.[105b]

[105b] J. A. Berson, Z. Hamlet, and W. A. Mueller, *J. Am. Chem. Soc.*, **84**, 297 (1962).

[106] The reaction of amines with alkyl halides (the "Menschutkin reaction") is often quoted as an example of a solvent-sensitive reaction, but the rate for a typical example only changes by a factor of ca. 10^2 for a solvent change, *t*-butyl alcohol (**Z** 71.3) to water (**Z** 94.6) in contrast to *t*-butyl chloride solvolysis, which changes in rate by a factor of ca. 10^7 over the same range. Many of the somewhat larger rate effects noted in the Menschutkin reaction are due to specific interaction of the solvent molecules with the leaving group or the nucleophile or both.[69]

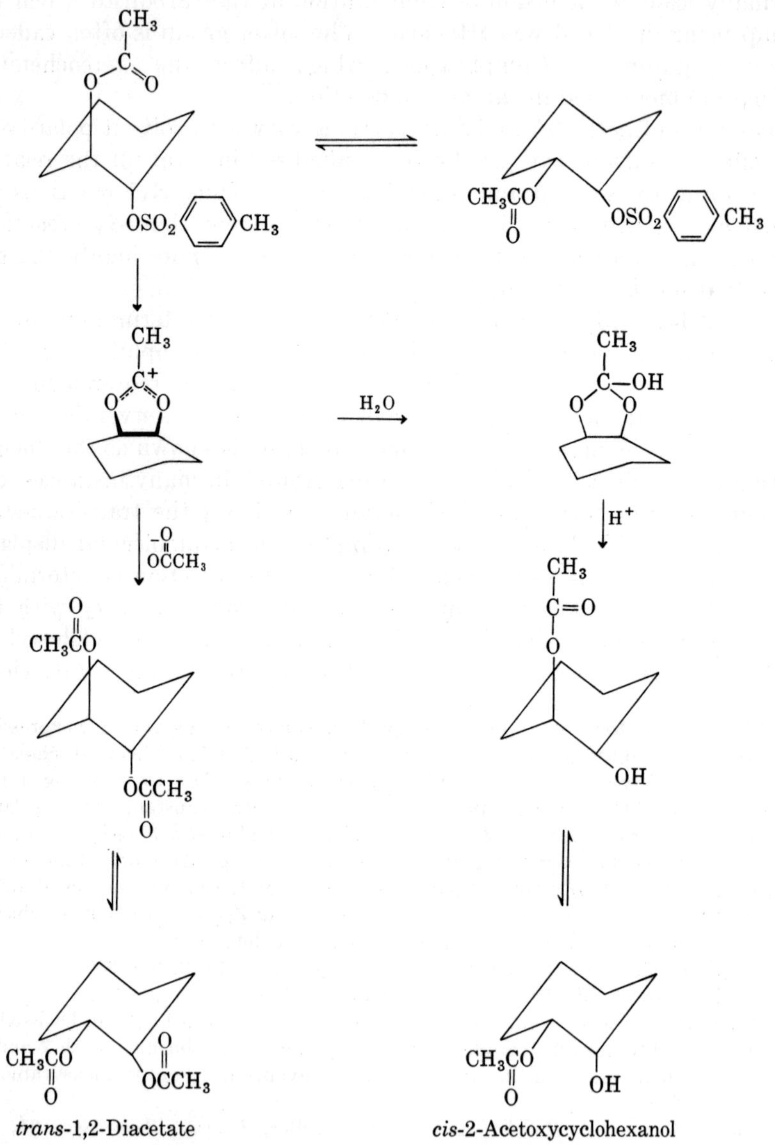

FIG. 2.14. Solvolysis of *trans*-2-acetoxycyclohexyl tosylate.

trans-1,2-diacetoxycyclohexane, but in acetic acid containing some water, the product is *cis*-2-acetoxycyclohexanol[107,108] (Fig. 2.14).

[107] S. Winstein, H. V. Hess, and R. E. Buckles, *J. Am. Chem. Soc.*, **64,** 2796 (1942).
[108] S. Winstein and R. E. Buckles, *J. Am. Chem. Soc.*, **64,** 2780, 2785 (1942); **65,** 613 (1943).

Ionization reactions may also have results unforeseen by Eq. (2.56). Alcohols can be converted to chlorides with thionyl chloride under special conditions first deduced for 3,5-cyclocholestan-6β-ol ("*i*-cholesterol") with *retention* of configuration[109,110] (Fig. 2.15). In contrast, methanolysis

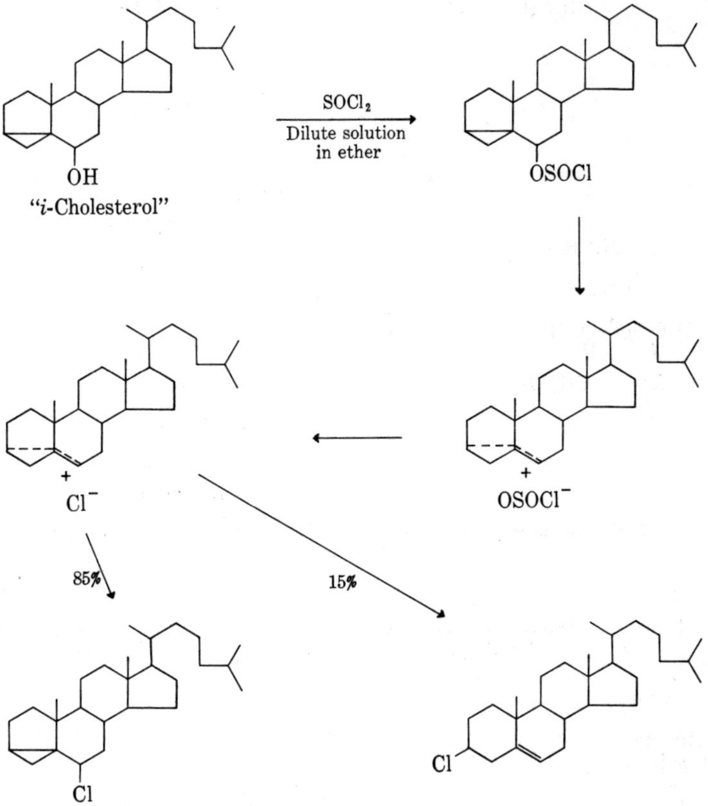

Fig. 2.15. Formation of 3,5-cyclocholestan-6β-yl chloride. The chlorine in both products is attached to the same side (β) of the molecule as the hydroxyl group in the starting alcohol (*retention*).

of 2,4-dimethyl-4-hexyl hydrogen phthalate produces methyl ether with substantial *inversion* of configuration[111] (Fig. 2.16). A more sophisticated version of Eq. (2.56) which clarifies some of these results and many others is illustrated in annotated form in Fig. 2.17.[112]

[109] E. M. Kosower, Ph.D. Thesis, University of California (Los Angeles), 1952.
[110] E. M. Kosower and S. Winstein, *J. Am. Chem. Soc.*, **78**, 4347 (1956).
[111] W. v. E. Doering and H. H. Zeiss, *J. Am. Chem. Soc.*, **75**, 4733 (1953).
[112] S. Winstein, P. E. Klinedinst, Jr., and G. C. Robinson, *J. Am. Chem. Soc.*, **83**, 885 (1961).

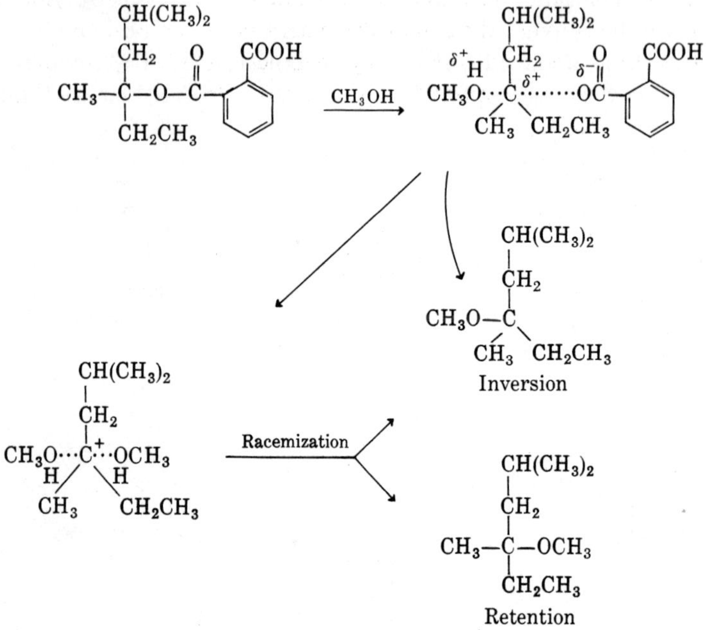

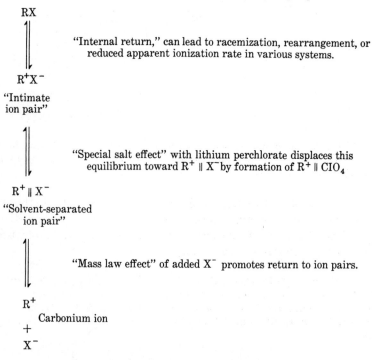

Fig. 2.16. Methanolysis of 2,4-dimethyl-4-hexyl hydrogen phthalate.

RX

"Internal return," can lead to racemization, rearrangement, or reduced apparent ionization rate in various systems.

R^+X^-

"Intimate
ion pair"

"Special salt effect" with lithium perchlorate displaces this equilibrium toward $R^+ \parallel X^-$ by formation of $R^+ \parallel ClO_4$

$R^+ \parallel X^-$

"Solvent-separated
ion pair"

"Mass law effect" of added X^- promotes return to ion pairs.

R^+

Carbonium ion

$+$

X^-

Fig. 2.17. Intermediates in ionization reactions.

The lesson of this discussion is that *an over-all stereochemical result cannot uniquely define the molecular process by which a reaction proceeded without a considerable amount of additional information.* Classification of enzyme mechanisms as "single displacements," "double displacements," etc.,[113] on the basis of stereochemical results of reactions is therefore premature.

2.4-3. Biochemical investigations usually lead to the stoichiometry of reactions. If these transformations have the appearance of replacement reactions, then it is worth evaluating the possible pathways which might be written.[114] Does the substrate possess a reasonable leaving group? Is an enzyme-substrate compound formed as an intermediate? Is the substrate a molecule that would be expected to ionize or to undergo nucleophilic displacement? Are there neighboring groups present in the molecule?

A table of probable leaving groups (such as Table 2.4-1[115–119]) can be constructed on the basis of certain reaction stoichiometries. Biochemically important leaving groups are rather different from those usually encountered in organic chemistry and there is little quantitative information on most of the groups listed. There is, however, a rough rule that is of qualitative value: The stronger the acid (HX) from which a leaving group (X) is derived, the better the leaving group. A reactivity sequence of leaving groups in displacement reactions is: $-N\equiv N^+ >$ $OSO_2R > I \sim Br > NO_3 \sim Cl > OH_2^+ > SMe_2^+ > F > OSO_3^- > NR_3^+ >$ $OR > NR_2$.[120]

2.4-4. Only three types of R group are represented in the reactions for which the leaving groups are listed. These groups are methyl,

[113] D. E. Koshland, Jr., "Mechanism of Enzyme Action," Johns Hopkins Press, Baltimore, 1954, pp. 608–624; and in "The Enzymes," vol. 1, chap. 7, Academic Press, Inc., New York, 1959.

[114] Apparent replacements which are catalyzed by DPN are assumed to proceed through oxidation followed by reduction, as in the transformation of UDP-galactose to UDP-glucose.

[115] N. O. Kaplan, in "The Enzymes," vol. 3, chap. 12, pp. 165–169, Academic Press, Inc., New York, 1960.

[116] D. E. Metzler, in "The Enzymes," vol. 2, chap. 9, pp. 309–311, Academic Press, Inc., New York, 1960.

[117] G. L. Cantoni, *J. Am. Chem. Soc.*, **74**, 2942 (1952).

[117a] F. Challenger and M. I. Simpson, *J. Chem. Soc.*, 1591 (1948).

[117b] G. L. Cantoni and D. G. Anderson, *J. Biol. Chem.*, **222**, 171 (1956).

[117c] F. Challenger, "Aspects of the Organic Chemistry of Sulfur," pp. 174–177, Butterworth & Co. (Publishers) Ltd., London, 1959.

[118] F. Shafizadeh, *Advances in Carbohydrate Chem.*, **13**, 37–43 (1958).

[119] M. M. Kreevoy and R. W. Taft, Jr., *J. Am. Chem. Soc.*, **77**, 3146, 5590 (1955).

[120] J. Hine, "Physical Organic Chemistry," p. 167 (also previous discussion), McGraw-Hill Book Company, Inc., New York, 1956.

TABLE 2.4-1. BIOCHEMICALLY IMPORTANT LEAVING GROUPS

Group	*Notes*
X^+ [pyridine ring with $\overset{+}{N}$ and $CONH_2$]	DPNase reactions[115,a] NMNase phosphorolysis[115,b]
[thiazolium ring: CH_3, $-\overset{+}{N}$, S, $CH_2CH_2OP(O)(O^-)OP(O)(O^-)O^-$]	Sulfite reaction[116] Thiaminase[116]
[structure: $CH_2CH_2\overset{NH_2}{\overset{|}{C}}HCOOH$ attached to $\overset{+}{S}$, $\overset{|}{C}H_2$, ribose with OH, OH, linked to adenine (NH_2)]	Possible methyl donation[117a,117b,117c]
[structure: $-\overset{+}{S}\overset{CH_3}{\diagdown}(CH_2)_2COO^-$]	
$-OH_2^+$	Sugar reactions[118] Acetal hydrolysis[119]
$-N(CH_3)_3^+$	Reactions of choline
X^- $-O\overset{O}{\overset{\|}{P}}(O^-)-O-\overset{O}{\overset{\|}{P}}(O^-)-O^-$	Terpene biogenesis-propagation[c] Purine and pyrimidine biosynthesis[d]

[a] Cleavage of DPN.
[b] Cleavage of nicotinamide mononucleotide.
[c] Sec. 1.8.
[d] Sec. 1.7.

α-hydroxy (or alkoxy) methyl, and allyl (or benzyl). In nucleophilic displacement reactions (e.g., displacement of chloride by iodide ion in acetone solution), all these structures are roughly of the same reactivity.[120] (Steric hindrance to nucleophilic attack in a particular example could very much reduce the observed displacement rate). It can be estimated that methyl halide will be 10^2 to 10^3 faster than a glucopyranosyl halide in a *displacement* reaction.[120] A far greater range of reactivities with structural variation is found for ionization reactions,[101] as Table 2.4-2 demonstrates. It appears safe to conclude that methyl transfer will occur through a displacement reaction rather than ionization since methyl derivatives are so low in the scale of ionization reactivities. The methyl groups of methionine are transferred almost[121] intact as the C_{24} methyl group of ergosterol.[122] Presumably, the reactive methylating agent in the biochemical system is S-adenosylmethionine (see Sec. 2.15).

TABLE 2.4-2. Comparison of Ionization Rates

Structure	Relative rate	Notes
CH_3OCH_2-	10^{13}	
CH_3CH_2OCH- $\qquad\quad|$ $\qquad\ CH_2OH$	10^{10}	a
$(CH_3)_3C-$	10^{8-9}	c
ϕCH_2-	10^3	
$CH_3CH_2CH_2-$	1	b

a Based on a comparison in the rates of hydrolysis of acetaldehyde diethyl acetal and glycolaldehyde diethyl acetal.[119]

b The rate used for the saturated alkyl chloride was the rate of reaction with the solvent. It is highly unlikely that this rate is anything but that of displacement by solvent (ethanol). The "true ionization rate" may be as little as 10^{-2} to 10^{-6} of the rate of bimolecular reaction, based on a figure of 10^3 to 10^6 often used to estimate the effect of a methyl group when substituted at the reaction center in an ionization.

c Note that the comparison of the t-butyl group with the glucopyranosyl group indicates that a derivative of the former should have an ionization rate ca. 10^3 greater than the latter (cf. Sec. 2.15B-3).

A decision between ionization or displacement by a group on the enzyme to explain the replacement reactions catalyzed by DPNase and thiaminase does not now seem possible, the indication of an enzyme-ribosyl intermediate in DPNase reactions[123,124] not being sufficient to prove a chemical bond between a group on the enzyme and the ribosyl carbonium ion formed by ionization. Electrostatic attraction could easily be sufficient to "solvate" the ribosyl carbonium ion in the transition state (see Fig. 1.29 and Sec. 2.15).

Considerable effort could be directed toward evaluating in a quantitative fashion the reactivities of biochemically important molecules in replacement reactions.

[121] A double labeling experiment with tritium and carbon-14 indicates that 86–91% of the tritium is transferred with the carbon.[122]

[122] G. J. Alexander and E. Schwenk, *J. Am. Chem. Soc.*, **79**, 4554 (1957).

[123] L. J. Zatman, N. O. Kaplan, and S. P. Colowick, *J. Biol. Chem.*, **200**, 197 (1953).

[124] S. G. A. Alivisatos, *Nature*, **183**, 1034 (1959).

2.5. HYDRATION AND DEHYDRATION

O wie ist alles fern
und lange vergangen
Ich glaube, der Stern,
von welchem ich Glanz empfange,
ist seit Jahrtausenden tot. . . .
                                    R. M. Rilke

The addition of water to double bonds, and its elimination, are reactions
that occur in several key biochemical sequences.   Simple alkenes do not
react with water at an appreciable rate at room temperature to form
alcohols, nor do alcohols readily eliminate under these conditions.   The
equilibrium of Eq. (2.61) is only established at reasonable rates in the
presence of catalysts.   It is true, however, that electrically asymmetric

$$(2.61) \qquad {>}C{=}C{<} + HOH \rightleftharpoons {>}\overset{\displaystyle H}{\underset{\displaystyle OH}{C{-}C}}{<}$$

double bonds undergo addition more rapidly than alkenes; the extent of
bond polarization is an important factor in determining the rate of water
addition to a double bond.   [Compare the rate of addition of water to
acetaldehyde (Sec. 2.3) to the unreactivity of a simple alkene.]

   2.5-1.   Acid-catalyzed hydration of alkenes yields the product
expected from the most stable carbonium ion derived by addition of a
proton to the double bond [Eq. (2.62)].   If the rate of hydration of
isobutene is measured in solutions of different acid concentration, the rate

$$(2.62) \qquad CH_2{=}\overset{\displaystyle CH_3}{\underset{}{C}}{-}CH_3 \xrightarrow[H_2O]{H^+} CH_3{-}\overset{\displaystyle CH_3}{\underset{\displaystyle OH}{C}}{-}CH_3$$

constant is found to be linear in the acidity function H_0 (Sec. 2.5-2) and
not in the concentration of acid (H_3O^+).[125]   The reverse reaction, the
dehydration of *t*-butyl alcohol, also provides rate constants which are
linear in H_0, rather than (H_3O^+).[126]   The exchange between *t*-butyl
alcohol and H_2O^{18}, catalyzed by acid, is 27 times faster than dehydration

   [125] R. W. Taft, Jr., *J. Am. Chem. Soc.*, **74**, 5372 (1952).
   [126] R. H. Boyd, R. W. Taft, Jr., A. P. Wolf, and D. R. Christman, *J. Am. Chem. Soc.*, **82**, 4729 (1960).

at 55°C in 0.45 M sulfuric acid[127] and also has rate constants which are linear in H_0, rather than the acid concentration[126] [Eq. (2.63)]. Although

$$\text{(2.63)} \quad \underset{\overset{|}{CH_3}}{\overset{CH_3}{\overset{|}{CH_3\underset{}{C}-OH}}} + H_2O^{18} \;\underset{}{\overset{H^+}{\rightleftharpoons}}\; \underset{\overset{|}{CH_3}}{\overset{CH_3}{\overset{|}{CH_3\underset{}{C}-O^{18}H}}} + H_2O$$

it was at one time believed that correlation of a rate with acid concentration meant that a water molecule was involved in the transition state, and correlation with H_0 suggested that no water molecule was significantly involved in the transition state,[128] criticism,[129] modification,[130] and skepticism[126] concerning the interpretation of the rate-H_0 correlations now mark recent publications.

The simplest statement about the isobutene–t-butyl alcohol results is that the activities of the transition states and initial states respond to the acid medium in a manner parallel to the activities of the protonated indicator and the indicator. A detailed mechanism which seems reasonable can be written after consideration of certain facts about H_3O^+ (see Sec. 2.5-3).

2.5-2. The acidity function $H_0{}^{131,132}$ is defined in terms of an experimentally measurable ratio of indicator and indicator conjugate acid, derived from examining the extent of reaction [Eq. (2.64)] and expressed as Eq. (2.65). The limiting value of H_0 as acidity falls is, of course, the

$$\text{(2.64)} \quad \text{Indicator (B)} + H^+ \rightleftharpoons \text{conjugate acid of indicator (BH}^+)$$

$$\text{(2.65)} \quad H_0 \equiv -\log h_0 \equiv pK_{BH}{}^+ - \log \frac{[BH^+]}{[B]}$$

$$\text{(2.66)} \quad H_0 \to pH \qquad \text{as } (H_3O^+) \to 0.1\ M$$

pH [Eq. (2.66)]. Thus, H_0 measures the proton-donating ability of an acid toward a particular base as well as the proton-accepting ability of the acid medium toward the proton donor BH^+. If the natures of B and BH^+ were not important in determining the value of H_0 for a particular acid medium, then the acidity function would be generally applicable for evaluating such ratios for any molecule which could act as a base. However, the indicators used to obtain H_0 are almost all members of a limited class of weak aromatic bases, and since, even within this class, "specific

[127] I. Dostrovsky and F. S. Klein, *J. Chem. Soc.*, 791, 4401 (1955).

[128] L. Zucker and L. P. Hammett, *J. Am. Chem. Soc.*, **61**, 2779, 2785, 2791 (1939).

[129] C. Eaborn, to be published.

[130] J. F. Bunnett, *J. Am. Chem. Soc.*, **82**, 499 (1960).

[131] M. A. Paul and F. A. Long, *Chem. Revs.*, **57**, 1 (1957), review the function suggested in ref. 132.

[132] L. P. Hammett and A. J. Deyrup, *J. Am. Chem. Soc.*, **54**, 2721 (1932).

effects" (i.e., deviations from linear correlations) are found, the "adequate generality"[131] of the acidity function has limitations. In media of high polarity and high ionic concentrations like strong acids, the acidity function is a valuable empirical method for determining the position of base–conjugate acid equilibrium to be expected. Its application to problems of reaction mechanisms is "a somewhat temporary expedient."[133]

As the mechanism for the hydration of isobutene will illustrate (Sec. 2.5-3), it is perhaps not surprising that the rates of the measurable reactions (hydration, dehydration, and exchange) correlate with H_0, since the transition states correspond to BH^+ and the initial states to B.

2.5-3. The hydroxonium ion, H_3O^+, in water is strongly hydrated, and must be considered a trihydrate on the basis of a variety

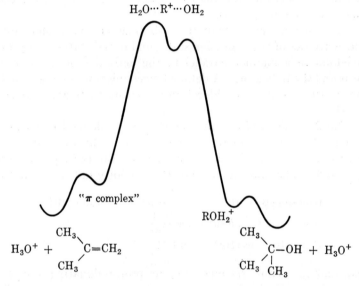

FIG. 2.18. Energy versus reaction coordinate in hydration of isobutene. (The intermediates corresponding to minima are labeled.)

of properties.[134] Reactions which lead to positively charged species, either oxonium ions or carbonium ions, in aqueous solution must therefore be explained in terms which include strong hydration of the positive center.[135] The mechanism for the hydration of isobutene is written in Eqs. (2.67) to (2.70), an energy versus reaction coordinate diagram for the reaction is given in Fig. 2.18, and details on the hydration of the "π

[133] F. A. Long and M. A. Paul, *Chem. Revs.*, **57**, 935 (1957).

[134] Ref. 72, pp. 83–84.

[135] The term, "encumbered carbonium ion," has been used[126] to indicate some solvation of the carbonium ion in aqueous acid. "Solvated carbonium ion" is used in this book.

complex" and its rearrangement product, the solvated carbonium ion, are shown in Fig. 2.19. The hydrated hydroxonium ion is shown in Fig. 2.20.

$$
(2.67) \quad CH_3-\underset{\underset{CH_3}{|}}{C}=CH_2 + (H_3O^+)_{aq} \;\rightleftharpoons\; \left(CH_3\underset{\underset{\overset{\cdot\cdot}{H^+}}{|}}{C}\!\rightleftharpoons\! CH_2 \right)_{aq} \quad (\text{"}\pi\text{ complex"})
$$

$$
(2.68) \quad \left(CH_3\underset{\underset{\overset{\cdot\cdot}{H^+}}{|}}{C}\!\rightleftharpoons\! CH_2 \right)_{aq} \;\rightleftharpoons\; \left(CH_3\underset{\underset{CH_3}{|}}{C^+} \right)_{aq}
$$

$$
(2.69) \quad \left(CH_3\underset{\underset{CH_3}{|}}{\overset{\overset{CH_3}{|}}{C^+}} \right)_{aq} \;\rightleftharpoons\; \left(CH_3\underset{\underset{CH_3}{|}}{\overset{\overset{CH_3}{|}}{C}OH_2{}^+} \right)_{aq}
$$

$$
(2.70) \quad \left(CH_3\underset{\underset{CH_3}{|}}{\overset{\overset{CH_3}{|}}{C}OH_2{}^+} \right)_{aq} \;\rightleftharpoons\; (H_3O^+)_{aq} + \left(CH_3\underset{\underset{CH_3}{|}}{\overset{\overset{CH_3}{|}}{C}OH} \right)_{aq}
$$

The water proximate to the positive center is strongly attracted and is, therefore, *primary* hydration, while more distantly located water can be called *secondary* hydration.[136,136a] A comparison of the entropy of activation for hydration of isobutene (ca. $+2$ e.u.)[125] with the entropy of activation for acid-catalyzed hydration of β,β-dimethylacrolein (ca. -23 e.u.)[137] suggests that the latter transition state is more highly organized with respect to the initial state than the former. The hydration of acrolein is illustrated in Fig. 2.21. The failure of the hydration rates of β,β-dimethylacrolein to correlate with H_0 is probably not good evidence

[136] The structure of the solvent (water and acid) should also be considered in these descriptions (see Sec. 3.0). As given in Figs. 2.19 and 2.21, the changes in solvent organization are qualitative attempts to describe the chemical reactions on the molecular level.

[136a] It has been deduced that the number of water molecules close to the carbonium ion center in the acid-catalyzed oxygen exchange and isomerization of 2-butanol is *two*.[136b] Other considerations lead to the suggestion that there is considerable covalent character[136b] in the bonding of what has been labeled *primary* water of hydration (in the text) to the central carbon of the carbonium ion. While this suggestion is plausible, it is perhaps simpler at this time to remain noncommittal about the precise nature of the intermediate.

[136b] J. Manassen and F. S. Klein, *J. Chem. Soc.*, 4203 (1961).

[137] H. J. Lucas, W. T. Stewart, and D. P. Pressman, *J. Am. Chem. Soc.*, **66**, 1818 (1944).

for a "different mechanism"[125] but, rather, a reflection of different solvation patterns and different degrees of bonding of water oxygen to the organic molecule in the transition state.

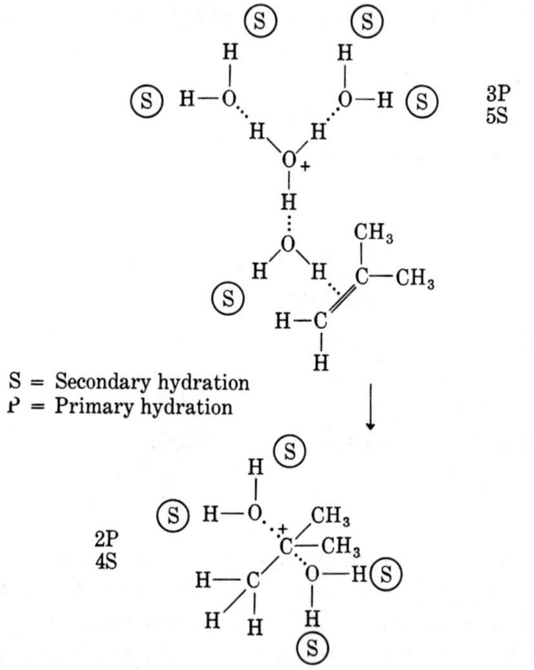

S = Secondary hydration
P = Primary hydration

FIG. 2.19. "π complex" to solvated carbonium ion (*including solvent*). Each S in product (and transition state) is probably more tightly bound than S in initial state because it is closer to positive center (2 atoms versus 3).

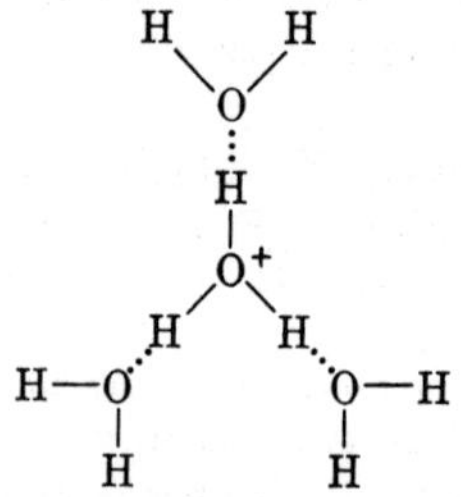

FIG. 2.20. Hydrated hydroxonium ion.

2.5-4. Base-catalyzed addition of water occurs with polarized double bonds, like those of α,β-unsaturated ketones. The β-hydroxyketone product of addition is susceptible to base-catalyzed cleavage, and the rate of such cleavage is, under certain conditions, greater than the rate of water addition.   The rate constants for hydration of benzalacetone and mesityl oxide are compared in Fig. 2.22 for a hydroxide ion concentration of 0.1 M.[138]   Base-catalyzed addition is of interest because it is

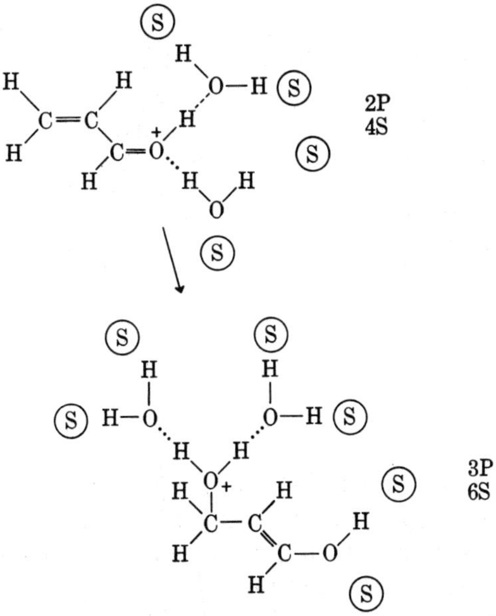

Fig. 2.21. Hydration of the α,β-unsaturated aldehyde, acrolein (*including solvent*).

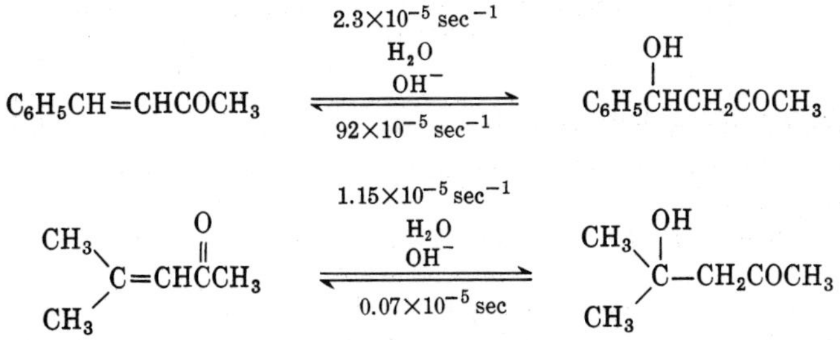

Fig. 2.22. Hydration of benzalacetone and mesityl oxide. Rate constants are pseudo-first-order constants at $(OH^-) = 0.1$ M.

effective with α,β-unsaturated systems and all the biochemical cases of hydration represent the addition of water to such conjugated systems (Table 2.5-1).

2.5-5.   The alkenes and hydroxy compounds which are related by the hydration of the former to the latter in biochemical systems are

[138] D. S. Noyce and W. L. Reed, *J. Am. Chem. Soc.*, **81**, 624 (1959).

listed in Table 2.5-1.[139]   All the alkenes are α,β-unsaturated systems.
The pathways catalyzed by the enzymes may be different, since the
cofactor requirements vary from none for fumarase, crotonase, and
5-dehydroquinase to magnesium (or other divalent cation) for enolase
and iron(II) for aconitase.

TABLE 2.5-1. ALKENES SUBJECT TO HYDRATION BY ENZYMES

Alkene	Hydroxy compound
Fumaric acid	D(−)-Malic acid[b]
cis-Aconitic acid	Citric acid[c]
Phosphoenolpyruvic acid	D-2-Phosphoglyceric acid[d]
trans-Crotonyl coA[a]	L(+)-β-hydroxybutyryl coA[e]
5-Dehydroshikimic acid	5-Dehydroquinic acid[f]

[a] Other α,β-unsaturated acyl coA derivatives are hydrated by enzymes, e.g.,
β-methylglutaconyl coA.

[b] Fumarase.

[c] Aconitase.

[d] Enolase.

[e] Crotonase.

[f] 5-Dehydroquinase.

The *minimum* values for the rate of combination of fumaric acid and
malic acid with the enzyme fumarase are of the order of 10^9 l mole^{-1} sec^{-1},
which is only consistent with a diffusion-controlled combination step[140]
(see Sec. 3.1).   The hydration of fumaric acid is stereospecific and *trans*
in character [Fig. 3.1 and Eq. (2.71)].[141]   The synthesis of stereospecifi-

$$\text{(2.71)} \quad \underset{\overset{|}{H}}{\overset{\overset{H}{|}}{HOOCC}}=\underset{\overset{|}{H}}{\overset{}{CCOOH}} \quad \xrightarrow[\text{Fumarase}]{H_2O} \quad \underset{\overset{|}{H}}{\overset{\overset{H}{|}}{HOOCC}}-\underset{\overset{|}{H}}{\overset{\overset{OH}{|}}{C}}-COOH$$

cally labeled monodeuteromalic acids is shown in Fig. 2.23.[141−143,143a]

[139] B. G. Malmström, in "The Enzymes," vol. 5, chap. 28, Academic Press, Inc.,
New York, 1961.

[140] R. A. Alberty, in "The Enzymes," vol. 5, chap. 32, Academic Press, Inc., New
York, 1961.

[141] Examination of a monodeuteromalic acid with hydrogens *cis* (carboxylic acid
groups are taken as *trans*) by NMR spectroscopy shows a coupling constant between
these hydrogens, J_{12} of 4.4 ± 0.2 cps.   Monodeuteromalic acid prepared by the
hydration of fumaric acid in deuterium oxide has a coupling constant J_{12} between the
hydrogens on adjacent carbons of 7.3 cps.[142,143]   It is known both experimentally[144]
and theoretically[145] that the coupling constants of *trans*-hydrogens are greater than
those of *cis*-hydrogens, and that, in general, the coupling constants of hydrogens in
NMR are dependent upon the angle between the carbon-hydrogen bonds.

[142] O. Gawron and T. P. Fondy, *J. Am. Chem. Soc.*, **81**, 6333 (1959).

[143] F. A. L. Anet, *J. Am. Chem. Soc.*, **82**, 994 (1960).

[143a] O. Gawron, A. J. Glaid III, and T. P. Fondy, *J. Am. Chem. Soc.*, **83**, 3634 (1961).

[144] R. V. Lemieux, R. K. Kullnig, H. J. Bernstein, and W. G. Schneider, *J. Am.
Chem. Soc.*, **79**, 1006 (1957).

[145] M. Karplus, *J. Chem. Phys.*, **30**, 11 (1959).

Enzymatically prepared monodeuteromalic acid is dehydrated in ordinary water by fumarase with the same maximal initial velocity and Michaelis constant as ordinary malic acid. Furthermore, malic acid recovered from a reaction with fumarase in deuterium oxide which had been allowed to proceed only to a small extent contained no deuterium other than that which would be expected from the reverse reaction

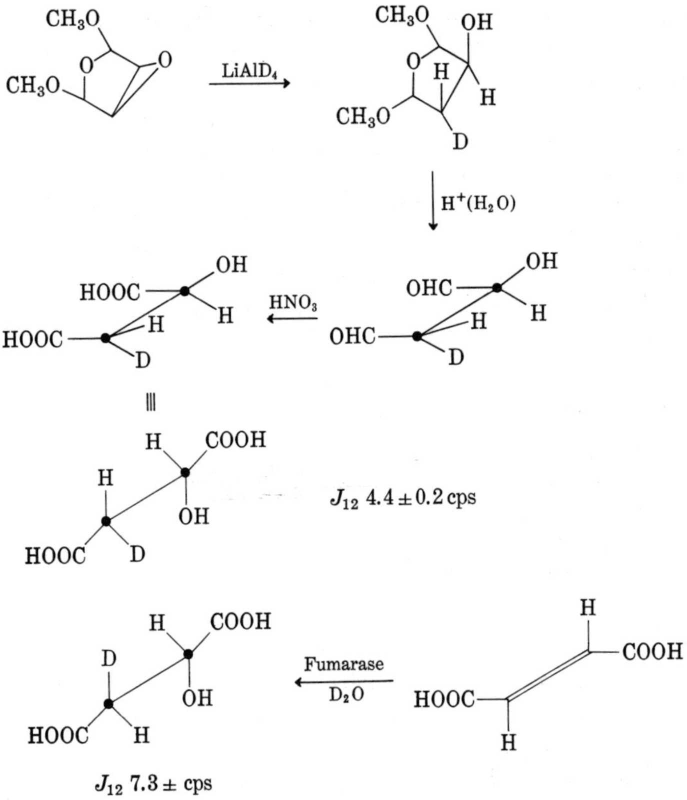

FIG. 2.23. Synthesis of monodeuteromalic acids.

(hydration of fumaric acid). No exchange, therefore, of the hydrogen which is eventually removed in the dehydration is catalyzed by the enzyme. Malic acid with O^{18} in the hydroxyl group did not exchange with water except by formation of fumaric acid and rehydration.[140] The lack of exchange, the lack of an isotope effect, and the possibility that hydration (or its reverse) is not a concerted reaction all suggest that an additional intermediate is involved between the enzyme–fumaric acid and the enzyme–malic acid complexes.[140] (See Sec. 2.2 for discussion on the lack of isotope effects in multi-intermediate enzyme-catalyzed reactions.) A simplified mechanism is written in Eq. (2.72). (The additional complications arising from protonation are discussed in ref. 140.)

$$F + E \rightleftharpoons EF \rightleftharpoons EX \rightleftharpoons EM \rightleftharpoons M + E \qquad (2.72)$$

There may, in fact, be more than one unidentified intermediate on the pathway between EF and EM, F and M being fumaric and malic acids, respectively.

The participation of two imidazole groups in the hydration of fumaric acid by fumarase has been tentatively suggested on the basis of the pH-rate profile for the enzymatic reaction.[140,145a] The use of such information is not reliable, as the discussion in Sec. 3.1 indicates. Nevertheless, it is curious, and possibly significant, that the V_{max} for hydration (at least a minimum value for the hydration-step rate constant) is on the order of $2 \times 10^3 \ sec^{-1}$ (ref. 140), while the rate constant for the reaction of imidazole with water is ca. $2.3 \times 10^3 \ sec^{-1}$ (ref. 146).

The hydration of *cis*-aconitic acid is also *trans* in stereochemistry.[147] (The mechanism is briefly discussed in ref. 17, Sec. 1.2.)

2.6. IMINES

> Не надо тебя!
> Не хочу!
> Все равно
> Я знаю
> Я скоро сдохну.
>
> *V. Mayakovsky*

The intermediates in transamination are imines; imines are probable intermediates in the oxidation of α-aminoacids to α-keto acids in reactions which do not involve pyridoxal phosphate as a cofactor (see Sec. 1.6). The imine derivatives derived from pyridoxal phosphate are capable of a large variety of reactions.[148]

2.6-1. It was common belief that kinetic data on the rate of formation of semicarbazides from semicarbazine and ketones in acidic

---

[145a] The monoanion of fumaric acid undergoes uncatalyzed hydration at 175°C in a manner attractively interpreted as a result of the cooperative action of the —COOH and —COO⁻ groups.[145b]

[145b] M. L. Bender and K. A. Connors, *J. Am. Chem. Soc.*, **83**, 4099 (1961).

[146] M. Eigen, G. G. Hammes, and K. Kustin, *J. Am. Chem. Soc.*, **82**, 3482 (1960).

[147] O. Gawron, A. J. Glaid III, A. LoMonte, and S. Gary, *J. Am. Chem. Soc.*, **80**, 5856 (1958).

[148] A. E. Braunstein, in "The Enzymes," vol. 2, chap. 6, Academic Press, Inc., New York, 1960.

media led to the mechanism outlined in Eqs. (2.73) to (2.75).[149]   How-

(2.73) $\quad$ >=O + HA $\rightleftharpoons$ $\quad$ >O$\cdots$HA

(2.74) $\quad$ >=O$\cdots$HA + NH$_2$NHCONH$_2$ $\xrightarrow{\text{Slow}}$ $\quad$ X(OH)(NHNHCONH$_2$)

(2.75) $\quad$ X(OH)(NHNHCONH$_2$) $\longrightarrow$ >=NNHCONH$_2$

ever, spectroscopic examination of the reaction of furfural and semi-carbazine at pH 7 revealed that an initial very fast reaction led to the disappearance of the ketone absorption band, and only a slow subsequent reaction produced the light-absorbing semicarbazone.[150] The fast reaction must have been addition of the nucleophile to the carbonyl double bond, and the slow reaction was the elimination reaction [Eqs. (2.76) to (2.80)]. Analogous observations were made for hydroxyl-

(2.76) $\quad$ >=O + NH$_2$NHCONH$_2$ $\xrightarrow{\text{Fast}}$ $\quad$ X(O$^-$)($\overset{+}{\text{N}}$H$_2$NHCONH$_2$)

(2.77) $\quad$ X(O$^-$)($\overset{+}{\text{N}}$H$_2$NHCONH$_2$) $\rightleftharpoons$ X(OH)(NHNHCONH$_2$)

(2.78) $\quad$ X(OH)(NHNHCONH$_2$) + HA $\rightleftharpoons$ X($\overset{\text{H}}{\text{O}}\cdots$HA)(NHNHCONH$_2$)

(2.79) $\quad$ X($\overset{\text{H}}{\text{O}}\cdots$HA)(NHNHCONH$_2$) $\longrightarrow$ >=$\overset{+}{\text{N}}\overset{}{(\text{H})}$NHCONH$_2$ + H$_2$O + A$^-$

(2.80) $\quad$ >=$\overset{+}{\text{N}}\overset{}{(\text{H})}$NHCONH$_2$ + A$^-$ $\rightleftharpoons$ >=NNHCONH$_2$ + HA

amine and a number of ketones, including pyruvic acid, acetone, and cyclohexanone.[150]

[149] Ref. 120, pp. 246–250.
[150] W. P. Jencks, *J. Am. Chem. Soc.*, **81**, 475 (1959).

Addition of a nitrogen nucleophile to an imine double bond would not be as rapid as to a carbonyl group. However, the addition of a positive charge (with a proton) to the imine nitrogen would increase its electronegativity to that of oxygen. Rapid addition of a nitrogen nucleophile should be expected for a protonated imine. The intermediate thus formed might also decompose readily if the proton were removed at the same time that the carbon-nitrogen bond was broken. The reaction of an amine with an imine to give another imine and a second amine is illustrated in Fig. 2.24.

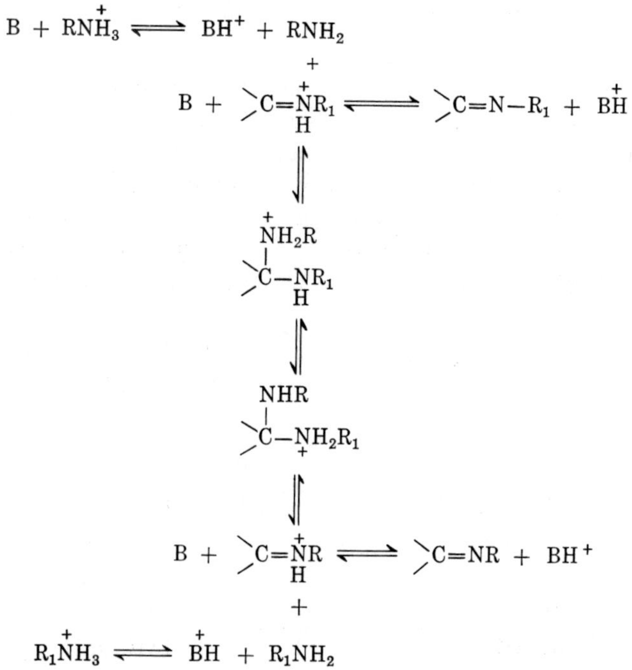

$$B + R\overset{+}{N}H_3 \rightleftharpoons BH^+ + RNH_2$$

$$B + \underset{H}{\overset{+}{>}C}\!=\!\overset{+}{N}R_1 \rightleftharpoons {>}C\!=\!N\!-\!R_1 + B\overset{+}{H}$$

$$\underset{H}{\overset{+}{>}C}\!-\!\overset{NH_2R}{N}R_1$$

$$\underset{+}{>}C\!-\!\overset{NHR}{N}H_2R_1$$

$$B + \underset{H}{\overset{+}{>}C}\!=\!\overset{+}{N}R \rightleftharpoons {>}C\!=\!NR + BH^+$$

$$+$$

$$R_1\overset{+}{N}H_3 \rightleftharpoons \overset{+}{B}H + R_1NH_2$$

FIG. 2.24. The reaction of an amine with an imine.

2.6-2. The coenzyme of transaminases is pyridoxal phosphate; the relatively strong binding between the coenzyme and the enzyme found in many cases suggests that a covalent bond has been formed.[148] It is assumed that this covalent compound is an imine ("Schiff base") resulting from the reaction of the aldehyde function with an ε-amino group of a lysine (see Sec. 1.6). A highly purified transaminase does not contain an appreciable amount of a metal ion, and in general, there seems to be no metal-ion requirement for transaminases.[151] The formation of the first intermediate in transamination might therefore be represented as in Fig. 2.25, as the reaction of an amine with an imine (Fig. 2.24). An

[151] B. E. C. Banks and C. A. Vernon, *J. Chem. Soc.*, 1698 (1961).

indication of how the enzyme might control specificity is also shown in Fig. 2.25. The hydrolysis of the imine derived from the amino acid and pyridoxal is given in Fig. 1.26, with an isomeric imine as the intermediate derived from proton transfer. The isomeric imine intermediate may also

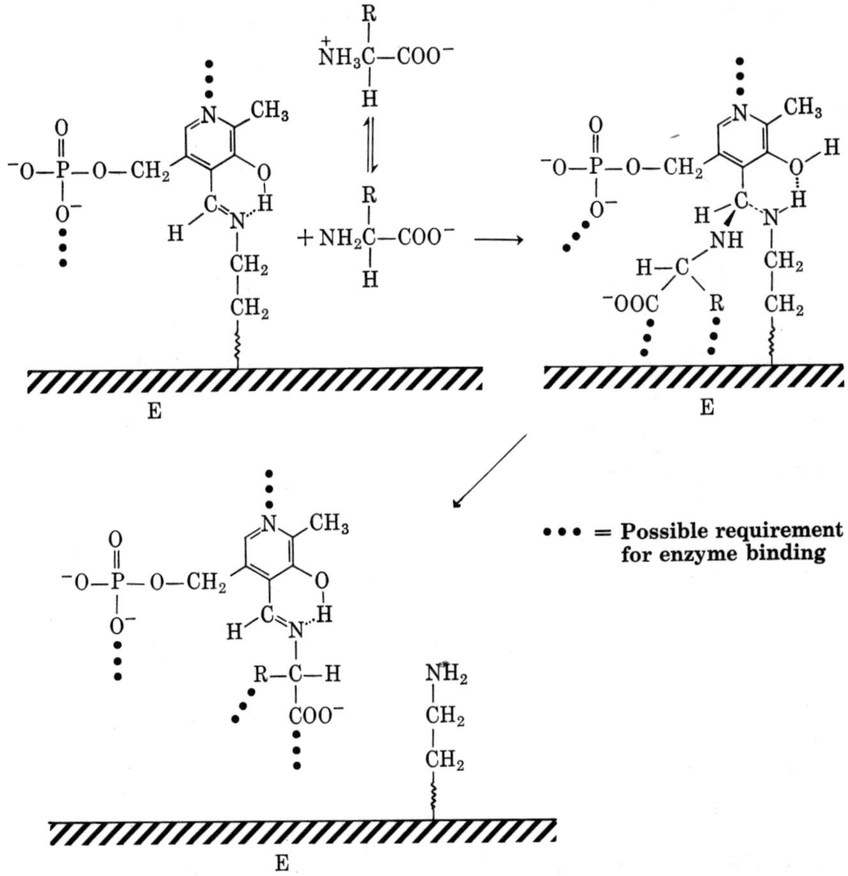

Fig. 2.25. Formation of Schiff base from pyridoxal and amino acid.

react with a proton to revert to the initial amino acid–pyridoxal imine in a nonstereospecific manner. The amino acid produced by hydrolysis of the latter imine is racemized (Fig. 2.26). The isomeric imine intermediate may act as a nucleophile toward a carbonyl compound to form such compounds as the imines of threonine or serine (Fig. 2.26).

An isomeric imine intermediate can be formed by decarboxylation as well as by proton transfer, thus leaving the hydrogen which was the α-hydrogen of the amino acid unaffected.[152] Hydrolysis of the isomeric

[152] S. Mandeles, R. Koppelman, and M. E. Hanke, *J. Biol Chem.*, **209**, 327 (1954).

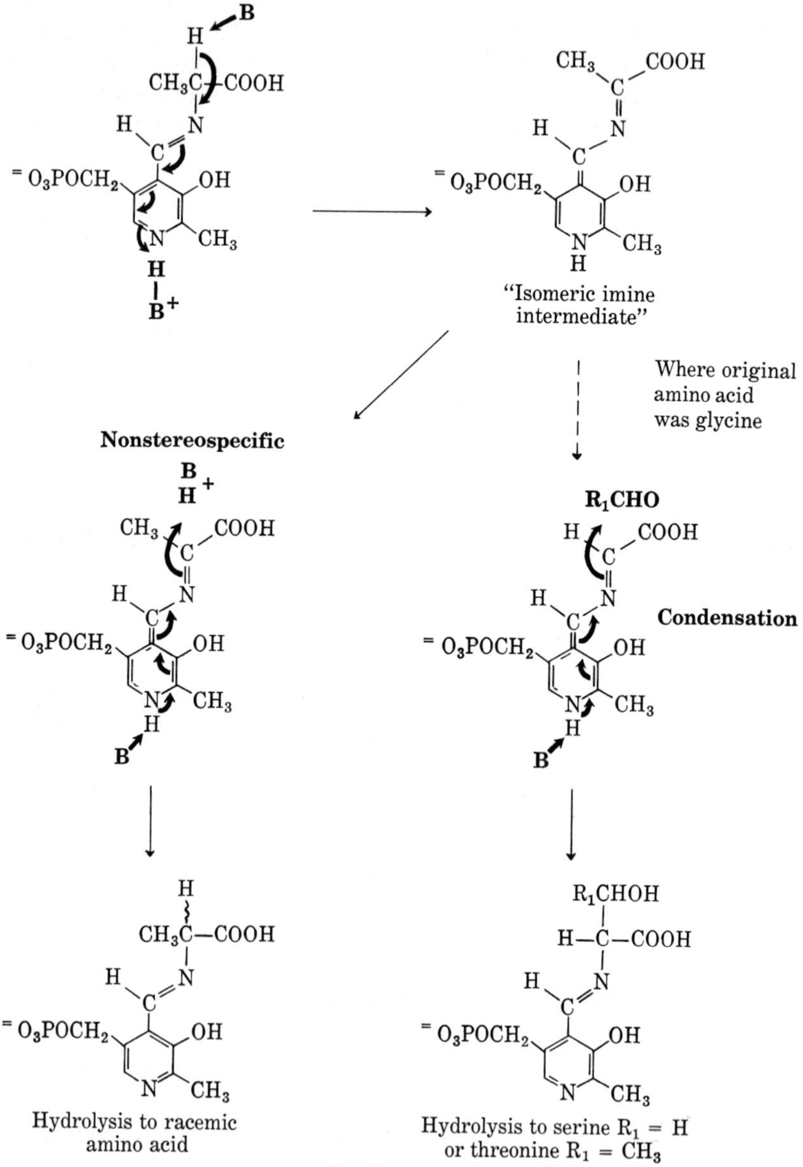

FIG. 2.26. Racemization and condensation of amino acids.

imine leads to aldehyde, while proton transfer with formation of a new imine yields, after hydrolysis, an amine (Fig. 2.27). The reported decarboxylations of o- and p-aminobenzoic acids[153] may be written

[153] W. G. McCullough, J. T. Piligian, and I. J. Daniel, *J. Am. Chem. Soc.*, **79**, 628 (1957).

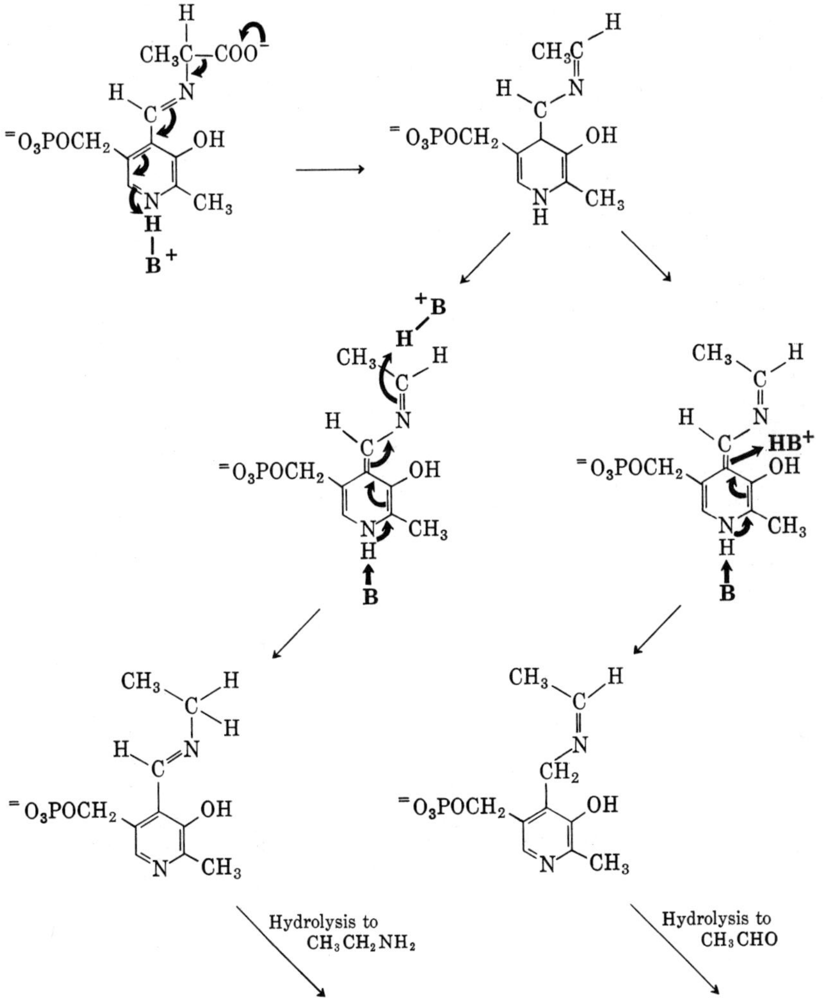

Fig. 2.27. Decarboxylation of amino acids.

formally in an analogous way, although they are somewhat surprising (Fig. 2.28).

2.6-3. The imine derived from amino acids like serine and tryptophan and pyridoxal can undergo an enzyme-catalyzed reaction leading to loss of the substituent β to the carboxyl group.[154] The inter-

---

[154] One example of an enzymatic activity of this type, that of the formation of α-ketobutyric acid from threonine by L-threonine dehydrase, is apparently an artifact.[155]

[155] D. H. Russell, E. M. Thain, and C. A. Vernon, *Proc. Chem. Soc.*, 255 (1960).

mediate formed in the elimination may add a nucleophile to give the original or a different β-substituted α-amino acid, or it may be hydrolyzed to an α-keto acid, possibly through the α-aminoacrylic acid (Fig. 2.29).

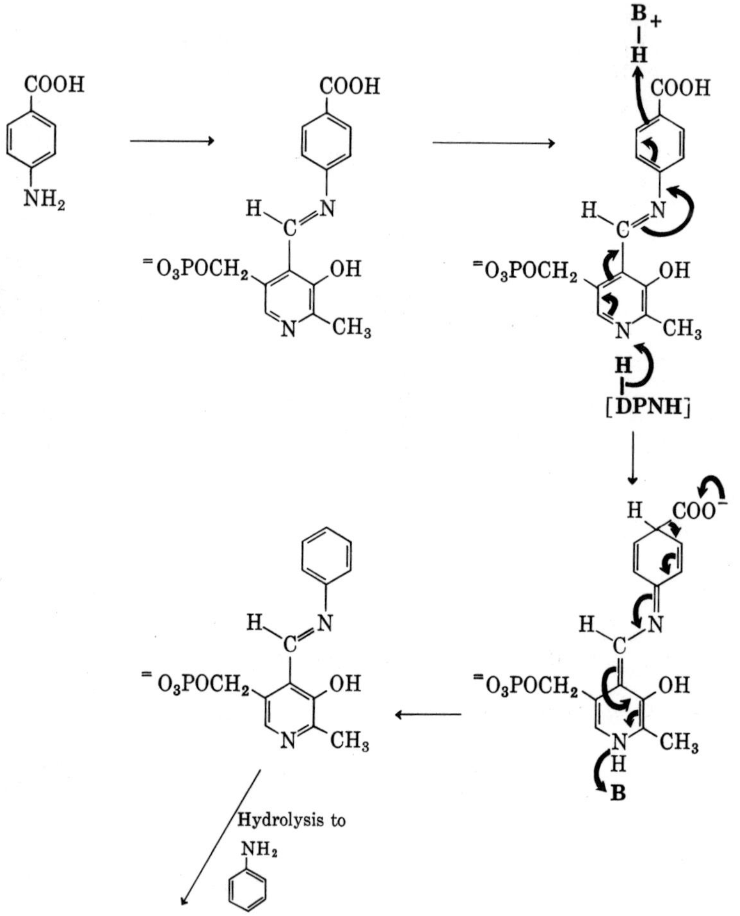

FIG. 2.28. Decarboxylation of p-aminobenzoic acid.

It is unnecessary to postulate "front-side displacement"[148] to account for such conversions as serine to tryptophan.

If the chemical rationalizations of the observed transformations are indeed applicable to enzymatic reactions, it would seem that the specificity of a particular conversion is "arranged" by the availability of proton donors and acceptors. Thus, an understanding of pyridoxal phosphate-catalyzed reactions may depend upon detailed knowledge about the "active sites" of these enzymes.[155a]

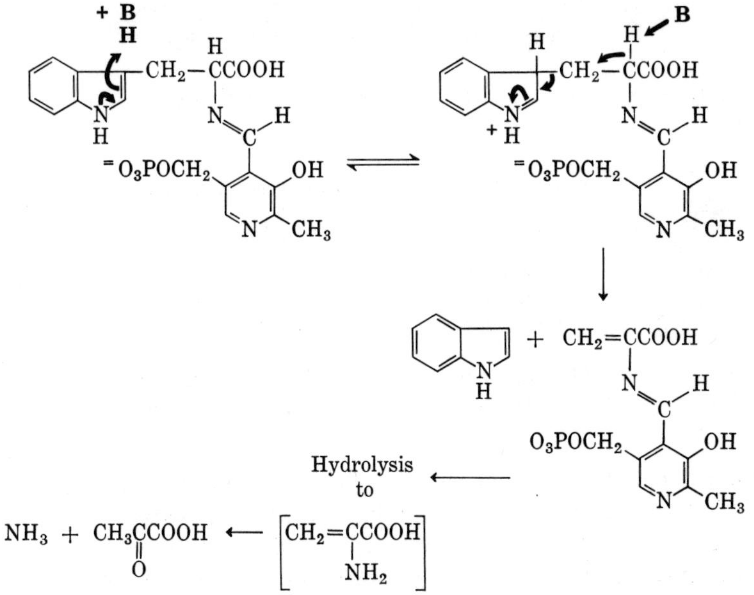

FIG. 2.29. Removal of indole from tryptophan.

2.7. HYDROLYSIS: ESTERS

Pretty butterflies . . .
  Be careful of pine-needle points
in this gusty wind!

Shusen

The hydrolysis of the ester acetylcholine by acetylcholinesterase is intimately connected with the process of recovery of nerve cells after they have been triggered to send an impulse. An ester hydrolysis is therefore one of the most important biochemical reactions in organisms with a nervous system.

[155a] In the formation of alanine from pyridoxamine and pyruvic acid (in vitro), it has been found that the imine derivative (the Schiff base) forms rapidly and that the rate-determining step is the conversion of that imine to its isomer by proton transfer. "The primary function of the protein in enzymatic reactions must be to catalyze the interconversion of the imine intermediates."[155b]

[155b] B. E. C. Banks, A. A. Diamantis, and C. A. Vernon, *J. Chem. Soc.*, 4235 (1961).

2.7-1.   Ester hydrolyses [Eq. (2.81)] can be classified according

$$
\text{(2.81)} \qquad \underset{\text{R'COR}}{\overset{\text{O}}{\overset{\|}{}}} + \text{HOH} \; \rightleftharpoons \; \underset{\text{R'COH}}{\overset{\text{O}}{\overset{\|}{}}} + \text{ROH}
$$

to whether they occur with "acyl fission" or "alkyl fission"[156] (Table 2.7-1).

TABLE 2.7-1. TYPES OF ESTER HYDROLYSIS

Acyl fission	*Alkyl fission*
Bimolecular	Bimolecular
Basic catalysis	Basic catalysis
Acidic catalysis	Acidic catalysis
Monomolecular	Monomolecular
Acidic catalysis	Acidic catalysis

Ester hydrolyses which occur with alkyl-oxygen cleavage ("alkyl fission") are simply solvolysis reactions of alkyl derivatives in which the leaving group is a carboxylate ion or carboxylic acid.[157]   Such hydrolyses do not appear to be of great biochemical importance and are not further considered because they do not illustrate to any degree the special characteristics of the ester group.

Alkaline hydrolysis of ethyl acetate was shown to be second-order many years ago,[160] but only recently did exchange evidence provide proof of an intermediate in these hydrolyses.[161]   If ethyl benzoate-*carbonyl*-O^{18} is hydrolyzed in ordinary water, ester reisolated from the reaction mixture contains less than the initial quantity of oxygen-18.   In other words, an intermediate is formed which (*a*) can give rise to either the original ester or hydrolysis products, and (*b*) contains oxygen-16 from the water in a form chemically equivalent to the oxygen-18 of the ester.   The intermediate, illustrated in Eq. (2.82), is often called the "tetrahedral intermediate."

---

[156] A comprehensive review of chemical and biochemical ester hydrolyses has been published by M. L. Bender, *Chem. Revs.*, **60**, 53 (1960).

[157] A carboxylate ion like *p*-nitrobenzoate [158] and trichloracetate[159] is adequate as a leaving group only when the alkyl group readily yields the corresponding carbonium ion.   Cf., however, ref. 166.

[158] H. Hart and J. M. Sandri, *J. Am. Chem. Soc.*, **81**, 320 (1959).

[159] E. M. Kosower and S. Winstein, *J. Am. Chem. Soc.*, **78**, 4347 (1956).

[160] R. B. Warder, *Ber.*, **14**, 1361 (1881).

[161] M. L. Bender, *J. Am. Chem. Soc.*, **73**, 1626 (1951).

(2.82)

2.7-2. It is the occurrence of "additional relationships to things directly accessible that constitute our reasons for believing in the reality of the unstable intermediates."[162] Stable addition compounds are formed by the addition of alkali methoxides to a number of ethyl haloacetates. The equilibrium between addition product and alkali methoxide and ethyl trifluoroacetate is 99% on the side of the addition product [Eq. (2.83)].

$$(2.83) \qquad CH_3O^- + CF_3\overset{\overset{\displaystyle O}{\|}}{C}OEt \;\rightleftharpoons\; CF_3\underset{\underset{\displaystyle CH_3}{\overset{\displaystyle |}{O}}}{\overset{\overset{\displaystyle O^-}{|}}{C}}\!\!-OEt$$

Compounds with three alkoxy groups bound to the same carbon are well known (e.g., the orthoformates, the orthoacetates) and are quite reactive.

Ester hydrolysis can be regarded as a substitution at an unsaturated center. In most cases, excepting those in which an acylium ion is generated by the use of a strong Lewis acid, an intermediate is required by the evidence[163] (as in many examples of aromatic nucleophilic substitution[164]) or is involved in the most reasonable explanation for a reaction. Even when steric hindrance to the formation of a "tetrahedral intermediate" might be expected, as in the hydrolysis of methyl 2,4,6-trimethylbenzoate, the rate of hydrolysis was in the same proportion to the rate of exchange of oxygen-18 out of the carbonyl group of the ester as was found for other esters.[165] However, alkyl-oxygen fission by attack of hydroxide ion on methyl can be observed if the carbonyl group of the ester is even more sterically hindered, i.e., in the case of methyl 2,4,6-tri-t-butylbenzoate.[166]

[162] J. E. Leffler, "The Reactive Intermediates of Organic Chemistry," Interscience Publishers, Inc., New York, 1956.

[163] J. F. Bunnett and G. T. Davis, J. Am. Chem. Soc., **82**, 665 (1960).

[164] J. F. Bunnett, Quart. Revs. (London), **12**, 1 (1958).

[165] M. L. Bender and R. S. Dewey, J. Am. Chem. Soc., **78**, 317 (1956).

[166] L. R. C. Barclay, G. A. Cooke, and N. D. Hall, Chem. & Ind. (London), 346 (1961).

2.7-3.   The complex character of the mechanism for most ester hydrolyses[167] makes difficult the evaluation of ester reactivities.   Taking a general equation for ester hydrolysis [Eq. (2.84)], three factors important

$$
(2.84) \qquad
\underset{\substack{\parallel\\ \text{O}}}{\text{RCX}} + \text{Y}^- \underset{k_2}{\overset{k_1}{\rightleftharpoons}}
\underset{\substack{\mid\\ \text{X}}}{\overset{\substack{\text{O}^-\\ \mid}}{\text{RC}}}-\text{Y} \xrightarrow{k_3}
\underset{\substack{\parallel\\ \text{O}}}{\text{RCY}} + \text{X}^-
$$

in the reactivity of an ester can be distinguished.   These are: (a) The *susceptibility* of the carbonyl group of the ester to attack, which would be measured by k_1.   An approximate correlation between the ester carbonyl stretching frequency in deuterium oxide and reactivity has been reported.[169]   (b) The *nucleophilicity* of Y toward the ester carbonyl.

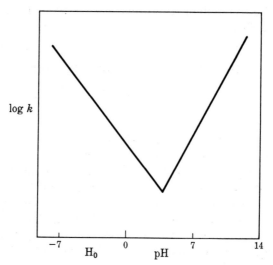

FIG. 2.30. pH-rate profile for ester hydrolysis.

(c) The relative "leaving-ability" of X and Y from the "tetrahedral intermediate."   Each of these three factors would vary with the nature of the medium used in the hydrolysis, and might also be sensitive to the presence of appropriate cations.

---

[167] Ester hydrolyses which proceed through (a) alkyl-oxygen fission or (b) acylium ion formation are not, of course, included within the area covered by this generalization.   There are excellent examples in which the tendency to form acylium ion is an important clue in the assignment of mechanism.[168]

[168] H. K. Hall, Jr., *J. Am. Chem. Soc.*, **77,** 5993 (1955).

[169] W. P. Jencks, F. Perini, and J. Roberts, *Arch. Biochem. Biophys.*, **88,** 193 (1960).

Ester hydrolysis through a tetrahedral intermediate can be expressed as the sum of three reactions, one with water alone, a second with hydroxide ion, and a third with acid. The expression for the rate constant for hydrolysis is given in Eq. (2.85). The rate-pH profile for a

$$(2.85) \qquad k = k_0 + k_{H^+}(H^+) + k_{OH^-}(OH^-)$$

"typical" ester hydrolysis is shown in Fig. 2.30. The protonated ester is usually written as an intermediate in acid-catalyzed hydrolysis, with formation of the tetrahedral intermediate resulting from nucleophilic attack by water [Eq. (2.86)]. Objections to this mechanism are based on the low basicity of esters, and a cyclic transition state has been proposed[170] which in one step forms the tetrahedral intermediate from the ester, a water molecule, and a hydroxonium ion. A related cyclic transition has been advanced to explain the formation of polyaminoacids from aminoacyl fluorides in anhydrous hydrogen fluoride[171] [Eq. (2.87)].

$$(2.86) \qquad R'\overset{\overset{O}{\|}}{C}OR + H^+ \rightleftharpoons R'\overset{\overset{+}{\overset{OH}{\|}}}{C}OR \overset{H_2O}{\rightleftharpoons} R\overset{\overset{OH}{|}}{\underset{\underset{+}{O}H_2}{C}}OR \longrightarrow products$$

$$(2.87)$$

$$\longrightarrow R\overset{+}{N}H_2\overset{\overset{O}{\|}}{C}R + 2HF$$

The fact that the ester group has numerous possible conformations around the bond connecting the alkoxy oxygen to the carbonyl group has led to the suggestion that *s-cis* conformations are more reactive than *s-trans* conformations, presumably because the former arrangement is electrostatically less stable than the latter.[172] Small ring lactones hydrolyze much more rapidly than large ring lactones, and this reactivity difference has been explained as a result of the *s-cis* conformation of the ester group of the small ring lactones.[172] It has been suggested that ester hydrolysis by α-chymotrypsin derives considerable rate advantage by acting only on the *s-cis* conformation of the substrate ester [cf. Eq. (2.88)].[173]

[170] Y. K. Syrkin and I. I. Moiseev, *Uspekhi Khim.*, **27**, 717 (1958), quoted in ref. 156.
[171] K. D. Kopple and J. J. Katz, *J. Am. Chem. Soc.*, **78**, 6199 (1956).
[172] R. Huisgen and H. Ott, *Tetrahedron*, **6**, 253 (1959).
[173] T. C. Bruice, *J. Polymer Sci.*, **49**, 100 (1961).

$$(2.88) \qquad \underset{s\text{-}trans}{\overset{O}{\underset{}{\overset{\|}{C}}}\!\!\diagdown_{O}\!\diagup^{R}} \quad \rightleftharpoons \quad \underset{s\text{-}cis}{\overset{O}{\underset{}{\overset{\|}{C}}}\!\!\diagdown_{O}\diagup_{R}}$$

2.7-4. Ester hydrolysis may be catalyzed in several ways, which are usually referred to as "nucleophilic catalysis," general base catalysis, and general acid catalysis. Intramolecular general acid catalysis has been proposed for a number of ester hydrolyses in which the ester molecule has a hydroxyl group suitably juxtaposed to the ester group.[174,175] However, simple compounds with the apparently correct relationship of the ester and hydroxyl groups do not exhibit greatly enhanced hydrolysis rates,[176] although p-nitrophenyl salicylate hydrolyzes approximately 400 times faster than p-nitrophenyl o-methoxybenzoate at pH 7 in 60% ethanol-water.[177]

The relationship of nucleophilic to general base catalysis can be most easily seen in a comparison of the reactions of two esters, RCOY and RCOZ, with N as a nucleophile [Eqs. (2.89) to (2.94)]. For reasons that are not understood, nucleophilic species differ widely in their tendency to add to the carbonyl group. The attack of any nucleophile on the carbonyl group has a rate constant k_N, except for water which is assigned the rate constant k_O. It is presumed that the concentration of the tetrahedral intermediate can vary over a considerable range from case to case, but will, in most instances, be fairly low. The difference between the magnitudes of k_N and k_O will probably depend upon the electrophilicity of the ester carbonyl group; the more electrophilic (or reactive) the carbonyl group, the smaller should be the difference between k_N and k_O.

$$(2.89) \quad N + R\overset{O}{\overset{\|}{C}}Y \quad \underset{k_{-N}^{Y}}{\overset{k_{N}^{Y}}{\rightleftharpoons}} \quad R\overset{O^{-}}{\underset{N^{+}}{\overset{|}{C}}}Y \quad \underset{k_{Y}^{N^{+}}}{\overset{k_{-Y}}{\rightleftharpoons}} \quad RC N^{+} + Y^{-}$$

$$(2.90) \quad \underset{H}{H O} + R\overset{O}{\overset{\|}{C}}Y \quad \underset{k_{-O}^{Y}}{\overset{k_{O}^{Y}}{\rightleftharpoons}} \quad R\overset{O^{-}}{\underset{\underset{+}{HOH}}{\overset{|}{C}}}Y \quad \overset{k_{-Y}}{\longrightarrow} \quad RC O^{-} + Y^{-}$$

---

[174] W. S. Johnson and S. M. Kupchan, *J. Am. Chem. Soc.*, **78**, 3864 (1956).
[175] H. B. Henbest and B. J. Lovell, *J. Chem. Soc.*, 1965 (1957).
[176] Ref. 173, pp. 98–99.
[177] M. L. Bender and B. Zerner, quoted in ref. 178.
[178] M. L. Bender, G. R. Schonbaum, and G. A. Hamilton, *J. Polymer Sci.*, **49**, 75 (1961).

$$(2.91) \quad N + R\overset{\overset{\displaystyle O}{\|}}{C}N^+ \underset{k_{-N}^{N^+}}{\overset{k_N^{N^+}}{\rightleftharpoons}} \begin{matrix} O^- \\ | \\ R C N^+ \\ | \\ N^+ \end{matrix}$$

$$(2.92) \quad \underset{H}{HO} + R\overset{\overset{\displaystyle O}{\|}}{C}N^+ \underset{k_{-O}^{N^+}}{\overset{k_O^{N^+}}{\rightleftharpoons}} \begin{matrix} O^- \\ | \\ R C - N^+ \\ | \\ HOH \\ + \end{matrix} \xrightarrow{k_{-N}} R\overset{\overset{\displaystyle O}{\|}}{C}-O^- + N$$

$$(2.93) \quad N + R\overset{\overset{\displaystyle O}{\|}}{C}Z \underset{k_{-N}^{Z}}{\overset{k_N^{Z}}{\rightleftharpoons}} \begin{matrix} O^- \\ | \\ R C Z \\ | \\ N^+ \end{matrix} \xrightarrow{k_{-Z}} R\overset{\overset{\displaystyle O}{\|}}{C}N^+ + Z^-$$

$$(2.94) \quad \underset{H}{HO} + R\overset{\overset{\displaystyle O}{\|}}{C}Z \underset{k_{-O}^{Z}}{\overset{k_O^{Z}}{\rightleftharpoons}} \begin{matrix} O^- \\ | \\ R C Z \\ | \\ HOH \\ + \end{matrix} \xrightarrow{k_{-Z}} R\overset{\overset{\displaystyle O}{\|}}{C}O^- + Z^-$$

If $k_N^Y \gg k_O^Y$ and $k_{-N}^Y \sim k_{-Y}$, then the formation of $RCON^+$ will take precedence over hydrolysis. In many instances, but not all, $k_O^{N^+} \gg k_O^Y$ and $k_O^{N^+} \sim k_N^Y$, resulting in nucleophilic catalysis, that is, acceleration of hydrolysis by the attack of a nucleophile other than water on the ester carbonyl. If $k_{-N}^Z \gg k_{-Z}$, but $k_N^Z > k_O^Z$, then the rate of formation of $RCON^+$ will be very low. If, in addition, $k_{-O}^Z \sim k_{-Z}$, then general base catalysis will be observed.[179]

An enormous range in the rate of production of p-nitrophenol from p-nitrophenyl acetate has been found for different nucleophiles.[180] Correlations of nucleophilicity exist, i.e., correlations of reaction rates with properties of the nucleophile like electrode potential and basicity,[181,182] (Table 2.7-2).

Electron-withdrawing groups should favor attack on the ester carbon group, and thus increase k_1 [Eq. (2.84)], but except for the indirect evidence provided by the correlations of ester hydrolysis with the substituent constant σ,[183] direct observations of k_1 are not available.[184]

[179] A slightly different description of these phenomena has been given by W. P. Jencks and J. Carriuolo, J. Am. Chem. Soc., 83, 1743 (1961).

[180] W. P. Jencks and J. Carriuolo, J. Am. Chem. Soc., 82, 1778 (1960).

[181] J. O. Edwards, J. Am. Chem. Soc., 76, 1540 (1954).

[182] C. G. Swain and C. B. Scott, J. Am. Chem. Soc., 75, 141 (1953).

[183] H. H. Jaffé, Chem. Revs., 53, 191 (1953).

[184] According to ref. 156, M. L. Bender has undertaken such measurements.[185]

[185] Although the rates of hydrolysis of a series of p-substituted methyl benzoates correlate very well with σ ($\rho = 1.93$), the ratio $k_{hydrol}/k_{exchange}$ varies from 30 for the p-amino group to 2.8 for the p-nitro group.[185a]

[185a] M. L. Bender and R. J. Thomas, Am. Chem. Soc. Abstr., 140, 50T (1961). Cf. M. L. Bender and R. J. Thomas, J. Am. Chem. Soc., 83, 4189 (1961).

TABLE 2.7-2. NUCLEOPHILIC ACTIVITY TOWARD p-NITROPHENYL ACETATE

Nucleophile	k_2, l $mole^{-1}$ min^{-1} [a]
N,N-dimethylhydroxylamine	10.7
Trimethylamine N-oxide	8.8×10^{-4}
N-hydroxyphthalimide	28.9
Isonitrosoacetone	2000
Potassium hypochlorite	1670
Methyl hydroperoxide	1.08×10^5
Aniline	0.015
Mercaptoethanol	620
Hydroxide ion	890
Water	6×10^{-7}

[a] The pH at which the rate constants were measured is given in the table of ref. 180 along with pK_a data for the nucleophile conjugate acids (except for certain compounds as indicated in the reference). The data in Table 2.7-2 is presented only to illustrate the range of ester reaction rates obtainable through a variation in the nucleophile.

2.7-5. The pH-rate profile for the hydrolysis of esters by α-chymotrypsin suggested that a basic group with a pK_a of ca. 7 was involved in the reaction. (See, however, discussion of pH-rate profiles in Sec. 3.1.) The imidazole ring of histidine was postulated as a participant in the process of esterase action, and, for this reason, considerable effort has been spent on the investigation of the reaction of imidazoles with esters.[186-188]

The reaction between imidazole and p-nitrophenyl acetate has been shown to proceed with intermediate formation of N-acetylimidazole [Eqs. (2.95) and (2.96); cf. Eqs. (2.89) and (2.90)]. The nucleophilicity of

(2.95)

(2.96)

imidazoles in the hydrolysis of p-nitrophenyl acetate is parallel to their basicity as shown by the Brønsted correlation observed, $k_{hydrol} = c(pK_a)$. As might have been expected for $k_{-Im}^{OEt} \gg k_{-OEt}$ and $k_{-Im}^{SEt} \sim k_{-SEt}$ [cf. Eqs. (2.89) to (2.95)], imidazole catalyzes the hydrolysis of ethyl thiol-

[186] M. L. Bender and B. W. Turnquest, *J. Am. Chem. Soc.*, **79**, 1652, 1656 (1957).

[187] T. C. Bruice and G. L. Schmir, *J. Am. Chem. Soc.*, **79**, 1663 (1957); **80**, 148 (1958).

[188] W. P. Jencks and J. Carriuolo, *J. Biol. Chem.*, **234**, 1280 (1959).

acetate[186] and acetyl thiocholine[189] but not the hydrolysis of ethyl acetate or acetyl choline.[186]

The occurrence of acylimidazoles as intermediates in ester hydrolysis created interest in evaluating the factors responsible for the reactivity of N-acylheterocyclic compounds. The N-acyl derivatives of pyrrole, imidazole, pyrazole, 1,2,4-triazole, tetrazole, indole, benzimidazole, and benztriazole were prepared and their hydrolysis rates in neutral solution compared with the position of the carbonyl stretching band[190,191] (cf. ref. 169). Reactivity of N-acylheterocyclics (Table 2.7-3) increases with an increasing number of nitrogens in the ring. It is worth noting that the reaction product of phosgene and imidazole, carbonyldiimidazole, has proved of great utility in many synthetic reactions.[192]

2.7-6. If particular functional groups are involved in enzymatic hydrolysis, their relationship to the ester group must be roughly analogous to the relationship of a neighboring group to a leaving group in solvolysis. On this basis, a number of model systems which exhibit intramolecular catalysis of ester hydrolysis were of interest. Another feature of interest was the possibility of directly comparing the first-order rate constants for the models to the rates observed with α-chymotrypsin, in order to ascertain whether or not the neighboring group relationship with a nucleophilic catalyst was sufficient to cause hydrolysis at rates comparable to that of the enzyme.

The pH-rate profile for the hydrolysis of acetylsalicylic acid (aspirin) indicates the rate does not decrease continuously as the pH falls below 9, but remains roughly constant until pH 5, from which it decreases steadily as the carboxylate ion acquires a proton until pH 2. The occurrence of an acid-catalyzed hydrolysis causes the rate to increase steadily as the pH is lowered from 2.[156] The pH-rate profile for the hydrolysis of methyl hydrogen phthalate resembles that for aspirin except that the intrinsic rates are much lower[193] [Eq. (2.97)]. These reactions are illustrative of

(2.97)

[189] F. Bergmann, S. Rimon, and R. Segal, *Biochem. J.*, **68**, 493 (1958).

[190] H. A. Staab, W. Otting, and A. Ueberle, *Z. Elektrochem.*, **61**, 1000 (1957).

[191] H. A. Staab, *Ann.*, **622**, 31 (1959).

[192] H. A. Staab, personal communication.

[193] M. L. Bender, F. Chloupek, and M. C. Neveu, *J. Am. Chem. Soc.*, **80**, 5384 (1958).

TABLE 2.7-3. PROPERTIES OF *N*-ACETYLHETEROCYCLICS

Acetylheterocyclic	$t_{1/2}(H_2O)$, min 20°C	$\nu_{C=O}(CHCl_3)$, cm^{-1}
Pyrrole	∞	1732
Imidazole	40	1747
3,5-Dimethylpyrazole	~8600	1733
1,2,4-Triazole	6.2	1765
Tetrazole	<0.1	1779
Indole	∞	1711
Benzimidazole	1260	1729
Benzotriazole	115	1735

the behavior of the carboxylate group as an intramolecular nucleophilic catalyst.

The p-nitrophenyl ester of γ-(4-imidazolyl)-butyric acid[194] and 2-(4-imidazolyl)-ethyl acetate[195] hydrolyze with participation of imidazole. The former ester forms a cyclic acyl derivative (Fig. 2.31) at a rate (3.3 sec^{-1}) comparable to that which characterizes the acetylation of α-chymotrypsin by p-nitrophenyl acetate (3.0 sec^{-1}). The further hydrolysis of the cyclic acylimidazole is much slower (rate constant at

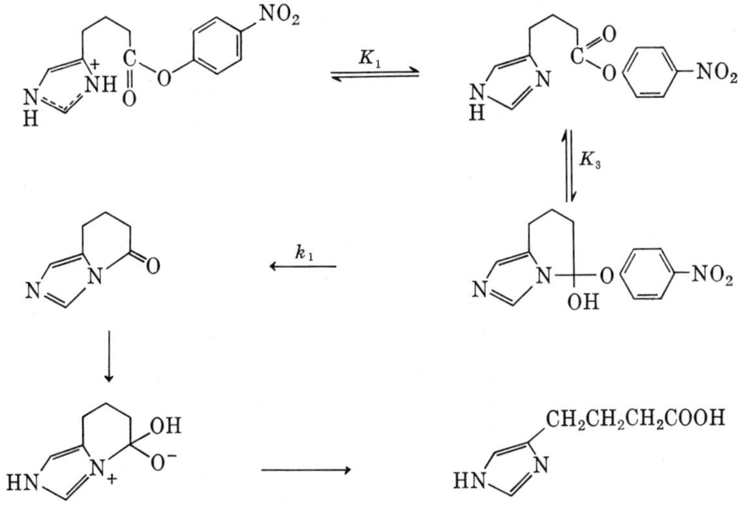

Fig. 2.31. Anchimeric assistance in p-nitrophenyl ester hydrolysis.

pH 7, 2×10^{-4} sec^{-1}) than the hydrolysis ("deacylation") of acetyl-α-chymotrypsin (2.5×10^{-2} sec^{-1} above pH 8).

Mercaptide ion can function in both *inter*- and *intra*molecular nucleophilic catalysis of ester hydrolysis, as illustrated by the reaction of o-mercaptobenzoic acid and p-nitrophenyl acetate to form thioaspirin, which subsequently hydrolyzes to o-mercaptobenzoic acid and acetate ion.[196]

2.7-7. Previous allusions in this section will have made it abundantly clear that one of the most carefully studied esterases is α-chymotrypsin. The enzyme also hydrolyzes certain peptide bonds as its chief biological function. Not only can the enzyme be readily obtained in pure and reproducible form, but its molecular weight (ca. 25,000) is low enough so that a complete determination of the amino acid

[194] T. C. Bruice and J. M. Sturtevant, *J. Am. Chem. Soc.*, **81**, 2860 (1959).
[195] U. K. Pandit and T. C. Bruice, *J. Am. Chem. Soc.*, **82**, 3386 (1960).
[196] G. R. Schonbaum and M. L. Bender, *J. Am. Chem. Soc.*, **82**, 1900 (1960).

sequence, although difficult, is feasible and may be completed within the near future. It might thus be possible to relate to the actual protein structure some of the deductions based on models, although it should be recognized that the enormous number of possible arrangements of a particular primary peptide sequence will make unambiguous identification of the "active site" difficult.

Chymotrypsin reacts with p-nitrophenyl acetate to form acetyl-chymotrypsin, which is, in turn, hydrolyzed to acetic acid and chymotrypsin. At pH 5, the acetylenzyme can be isolated from the reaction. When the acetylchymotrypsin is degraded, the acetyl group is found bonded to the hydroxyl group of a serine.[197] Reaction of chymotrypsin with diisopropyl phosphorofluoridate (DFP) leads to a phosphoryl derivative of the enzyme which is enzymatically inactive.[198] Degradation of the phosphorylated enzyme yields a peptide containing a serine phosphate. Chymotrypsin reacts with diphenyl phosphorochloridate to yield a phosphorylated enzyme, presumably analogous to the one isolated from DFP treatment. This phosphorylated enzyme releases phenol at a moderate rate in neutral solution.[199] Since alkyl diphenyl phosphates are normally hydrolyzed slowly in strongly basic solution,[200] there is a strong presumption that *a second nucleophilic group is present at the "active site" of chymotrypsin*, in addition to the serine hydroxyl group.[201] It has been suggested that the second group at the "active site" is imidazole, primarily on the basis of the pH-rate profile, which suggests that both acylation and deacylation depend on a basic group with a pK_a of ca. 7.[178] (Cf. Sec. 3.1 for discussion of the use of pH-rate profiles in this way.) The formation of the acyl enzyme in the hydrolysis of any ester (and not only those susceptible to nucleophilic catalysis) is supported by the fact that chymotrypsin catalyzes the exchange of methanol with acetyl-L-phenylalanine methyl-C^{14} ester.[202]

The acyl chymotrypsin, cinnamoyl-α-chymotrypsin, has an absorption maximum at 2880 Å, at longer wavelengths than methyl cinnamate (2790 Å).[178] An investigation of the solvent effect on absorption spectra of cinnamate esters over the polarity range from isoöctane to 10 M lithium chloride[203] indicated that the difference between cinnamoylchymotrypsin and the esters could not be completely accounted for by a solvent effect

[197] R. A. Oosterbaan and M. E. van Adrichem, *Biochim. et Biophys. Acta,* **27**, 423 (1958).

[198] E. F. Jansen, M. D. F. Nutting, and A. K. Balls, *J. Biol. Chem.,* **179**, 201 (1949).

[199] W. Lee and J. H. Turnbull, *Experientia,* **17**, 360 (1961).

[200] G. J. Durant, J. H. Turnbull, and W. Wilson, *Chem. & Ind. (London),* 157 (1958).

[201] It would be of considerable interest to degrade the product of the reaction of the second nucleophilic group in the hope that it was still bonded to the phosphorus atom.

[202] M. L. Bender and W. A. Glasson, *J. Am. Chem. Soc.,* **82**, 3336 (1960).

[203] E. M. Kosower and G.-S. Wu, *J. Am. Chem. Soc.,* **83**, 3142 (1961).

exerted by the enzyme.[204]   However, assuming that the second group at the "active site" is imidazole, and taking into account the fact that the spectrum of cinnamoyl chymotrypsin was measured at pH 4.05, a strong hydrogen bond between the imidazolium ion and the carbonyl group of the serine cinnamate might account for the unusually long wavelength maximum of the acyl chymotrypsin (Fig. 2.32).

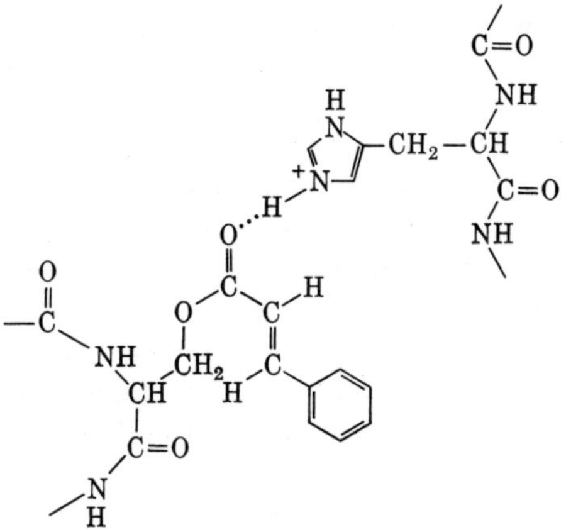

Fig. 2.32. Cinnamoyl chymotrypsin at pH 4.05.

2.7-8.   Chymotrypsin hydrolyses have been interpreted according to Eq. (2.98); some of the rate constants are listed in Table 2.7-4.

Table 2.7-4. Chymotrypsin Hydrolyses

Ester	Acylation,[a,b] k_1, sec^{-1}	Deacylation,[a,b] k_2, sec^{-1}
p-Nitrophenyl acetate	3.0	2.5×10^{-2}
p-Nitrophenyl ester of N-benzoyloxycarbonyl-L-tyrosine	>1000	300
p-Nitrophenyl trimethylacetate	0.37	1.33×10^{-4}
o-Nitrophenyl trans-cinnamate	ca. 0.14	1.18×10^{-2}

[a] Rate constants correspond to Eq. (2.98).
[b] Taken from ref. 178.

Not surprisingly, the rate of acylation is very much dependent on struc-

[204] M. L. Bender, Paper presented at the Seventh Reaction Mechanisms Conference, September 7–10, 1960, Princeton, N.J.

$$(2.98) \qquad \text{Chy} + \overset{\overset{\text{O}}{\|}}{\text{RCOR}'} \; \rightleftharpoons \; \text{Chy} \overset{\overset{\text{O}}{\|}}{\text{RCOR}'}$$

$$\Big\downarrow k_1$$

$$\text{Chy} + \overset{\overset{\text{O}}{\|}}{\text{RCOH}} \; \overset{k_2}{\longleftarrow} \; \text{Chy}{-}\overset{\overset{\text{O}}{\|}}{\text{CR}} + \text{R}'\text{OH}$$

ture; large rate differences also exist in the deacylation step, and seem too large to be ascribed to differing susceptibilities of the carbonyl group to attack by whatever mechanism the enzyme uses for deacylation.[205] Part of the catalytic activity must then depend upon interactions between the enzyme and the substrate which are not considered in a discussion of functional groups alone. In this connection, it is interesting to note the reasonable conclusion that trypsin and α-chymotrypsin have similar mechanisms of catalytic action based on the observations that the deacylation rates of cinnamoyl trypsin and cinnamoyl-α-chymotrypsin are the same and that difference spectra (light absorption by acyl enzyme minus enzyme light absorption) for both acyl enzymes are quite similar.[205a]

The mechanism of Eq. (2.98) makes no provision for tetrahedral intermediates which almost certainly intervene in both the acylation and deacylation steps. The relationship of the rate constants to particular processes is thus uncertain; if other intermediates occur (e.g., an *s-cis* conformer of the ester in equilibrium with the *s-trans*), the meaning of the rate constants becomes even more obscure.

A variety of mechanisms has been proposed for chymotrypsin action,[178,206] but although some seem to be mechanistically reasonable pathways for ester hydrolysis, none of them are based on compelling evidence.[207]

Inhibition of the enzyme acetylcholinesterase by "nerve gases" (compounds related to DFP) results in the phosphorylation of a serine hydroxyl group. Assuming that imidazole was the "basic site" at the

---

[205] H. Neurath, *J. Polymer Sci.*, **49**, 101 (1961).

[205a] M. L. Bender, E. T. Kaiser, and B. Zerner, *J. Am. Chem. Soc.*, **83**, 4656 (1961).

[206] M. L. Bender, G. R. Schonbaum, G. A. Hamilton, and B. Zerner, *J. Am. Chem. Soc.*, **83**, 1256 (1961).

[207] The notion that methanol is a "water analogue"[202,208] is involved in one of the lines of reasoning used for a chymotrypsin mechanism. This does not seem correct. If the hydroxyl group of methanol is hydrogen-bonded to the enzyme, then the orientation of the methyl group *cannot* be analogous to that of the hydrogen which a water molecule hydrogen-bonded to the enzyme would present. The methyl group might interact with a hydrocarbon side chain of the protein, whereas the water molecule would not.

[208] D. E. Koshland, Jr., and E. B. Herr, Jr., *J. Biol. Chem.*, **228**, 1021 (1957).

"active site," and utilizing some of the geometric conclusions derived from studies of acetylcholinesterase inhibition, a functional group arrangement for the "active site" of acetylcholinesterase has been constructed.[209]   No detailed mechanism for the hydrolytic action of the enzyme is given, and the assumptions and extrapolations used in developing the picture of the "active site" are such that it is probably best viewed as an interesting hypothesis.

2.8. HYDROLYSIS: AMIDES

> Chide, chide no more away
> The fleeting daughters of the day,
> Nor with impatient thoughts outrun
> The lazy sun. . . .
> *T. Stanley*

The hydrolysis of amide linkages is the critical step in the degradation of proteins.   Amino acid sequence determinations for proteins depend upon controlled hydrolysis of peptide bonds, mostly by enzymes.[210]

2.8-1.   The hydrolysis of amides resembles that of esters.   Oxygen exchange accompanies the hydrolysis in alkaline solution, thus providing evidence for the occurrence of a "tetrahedral intermediate" (see Sec. 2.7) in amide hydrolysis[211] [Eq. (2.99)].   However, exchange is not observed in acid hydrolysis.   It is conceivable that acid hydrolysis might occur through a mechanism different from that found in alkaline solution, e.g. direct displacement as in Eq. (2.100), but a simpler explanation is that the tetrahedral intermediate decomposes in acid solution by only one route, with $k_{-NH_3^+} \gg k_{-OH}$.   A comparison of exchange and

$$
(2.99) \quad \underset{\substack{\| \\ RCNH_2}}{O} \underset{k_2}{\overset{k_1}{\rightleftarrows}} \underset{\substack{| \\ OH}}{\overset{OH}{\underset{|}{RC-NH_2}}} \rightleftarrows \underset{\substack{| \\ OH}}{\overset{O^-}{\underset{|}{RC-NH_3}}} \longrightarrow \underset{\substack{\|}}{\overset{O}{RCOH}} + NH_3
$$

$$
(2.100) \quad \underset{\substack{| \\ R}}{\overset{O}{\underset{|}{H_2O\cdots C\cdots NH_3}}} \longrightarrow RCOOH_2^+ + NH_3
$$

hydrolysis rates for a series of *p*-substituted acetanilides revealed that the

---

[209] R. M. Krupka and K. J. Laidler, *J. Am. Chem. Soc.*, **83**, 1458 (1961).

[210] F. Sanger, *J. Polymer Chem.*, **49**, 3 (1961).

[211] M. L. Bender and R. D. Ginger, *J. Am. Chem. Soc.*, **77**, 348 (1955).

addition of hydroxide ion was favored by electron-withdrawing substituents on the ring ($\rho = 1.1$ for k_1) but that electron-supplying substituents favored dissociation of the intermediate to products (k_2/k_3 had ρ ca. -1).[212]

2.8-2. The basic atom of a peptide bond is the oxygen atom. Complex formation between dimethylacetamide and iodine in carbon tetrachloride is detected by a shift to longer wavelength for the carbonyl stretching band and a shift to shorter wavelength for the carbon-nitrogen stretching band. These changes are consistent with interaction through oxygen; combination of an electron-acceptor with the oxygen would weaken the carbon-oxygen bond and strengthen the carbon-nitrogen bond.[213]

An investigation of the NMR spectrum of dimethylformamide in acid solution indicated that the proton acquired in acid solution was bonded to the oxygen. Furthermore, acquisition of the proton increased the barrier to rotation from 9.6 ± 1.5 kcal/mole to 12.7 ± 1.5 kcal/mole.[214] The hydrogen-bonding between peptide bonds in helical structures must therefore produce an appreciable degree of stiffening of the peptide bond itself [Eq. (2.101)].

(2.101)

$$
\begin{bmatrix}
\mathrm{CH_3}\!\!\diagdown & & & \mathrm{O} \\
& \mathrm{N}\!-\!\mathrm{C} & & \\
\mathrm{CH_3}\!\!\diagup & \updownarrow & & \mathrm{H} \\
\mathrm{CH_3}\!\!\diagdown & & & \mathrm{O^-} \\
& \overset{+}{\mathrm{N}}\!\!=\!\!\mathrm{C} & & \\
\mathrm{CH_3}\!\!\diagup & & & \mathrm{H}
\end{bmatrix}
+ \mathrm{H^+} \rightleftharpoons
\begin{bmatrix}
\mathrm{CH_3}\!\!\diagdown & & & \overset{+}{\mathrm{O}}\mathrm{H} \\
& \mathrm{N}\!-\!\mathrm{C} & & \\
\mathrm{CH_3}\!\!\diagup & \updownarrow & & \mathrm{H} \\
\mathrm{CH_3}\!\!\diagdown & & & \mathrm{OH} \\
& \overset{+}{\mathrm{N}}\!\!=\!\!\mathrm{C} & & \\
\mathrm{CH_3}\!\!\diagup & & & \mathrm{H}
\end{bmatrix}
$$

2.8-3. Amides, like esters, are susceptible to *intra*molecular nucleophilic catalysis of hydrolysis. The hydrolysis rate of phthalamic acid (Fig. 2.33) rises rapidly as the pH decreases from 6 to 3. From pH 3 to 1, the rate is relatively independent of pH, but increases at still lower pH values. In contrast, the hydrolysis rate of benzamide increases with acid concentration in a simple linear fashion until other factors disturb the linearity at high acid concentrations (i.e., decrease in water activity). The pH-rate profile reveals that the reactive species in the case of phthalamic acid is the undissociated acid. Its hydrolysis is some 75,000 times faster than that of benzamide at pH 3.[215] The reaction and a possible mechanism are shown in Fig. 2.33.

Direct proof that phthalic anhydride is an intermediate in the hydrolysis of phthalamic acid at pH 3 is not available because the anhydride

[212] M. L. Bender and R. Thomas, *Am. Chem. Soc. Abstr.*, **137**, 510 (1960). Cf. M. L. Bender and R. J. Thomas, *J. Am. Chem. Soc.*, **83**, 4183 (1961).

[213] C. D. Schmulbach and R. S. Drago, *J. Am. Chem. Soc.*, **82**, 4484 (1960).

[214] G. Fraenkel and C. Franconi, *J. Am. Chem. Soc.*, **82**, 4478 (1960).

[215] M. L. Bender, Y.-L. Chow, and F. Chloupek, *J. Am. Chem. Soc.*, **80**, 5380 (1958).

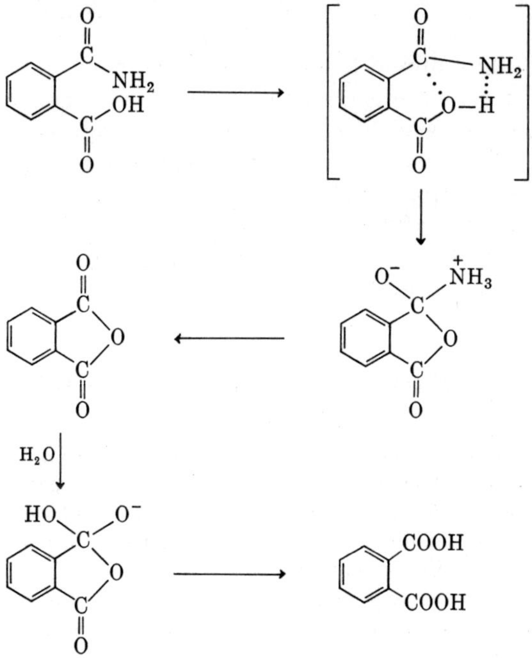

FIG. 2.33. Hydrolysis of phthalamic acid.

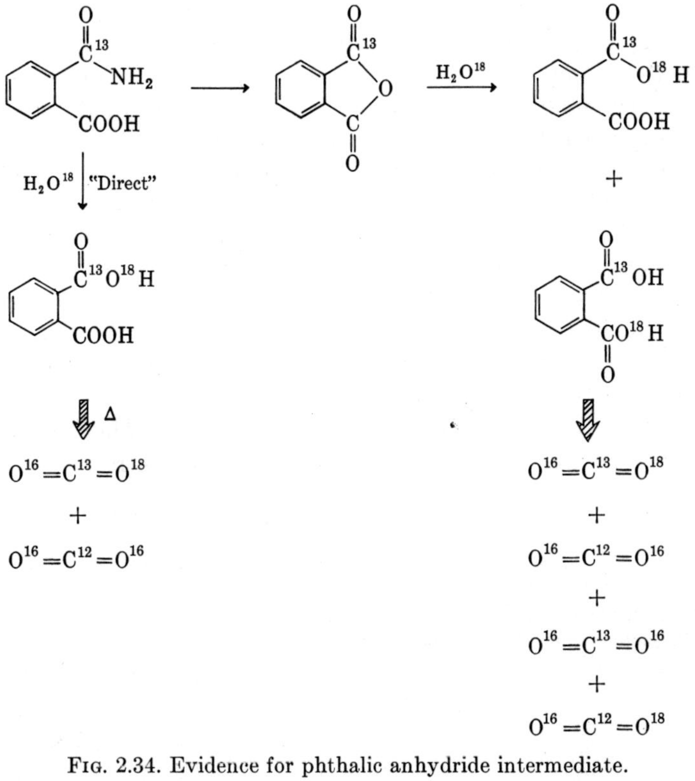

FIG. 2.34. Evidence for phthalic anhydride intermediate.

itself is rapidly hydrolyzed to o-phthalic acid under the reaction conditions. Indirect evidence is obtained with a double-labeling experiment in which phthalamic acid–*carboxamide*-C^{13} is hydrolyzed in the presence of water-O^{18}. The resulting phthalic acid yielded the quantity of $O^{16}C^{13}O^{18}$ expected from a phthalic anhydride intermediate, and only half of that expected for "direct" hydrolysis of the amide group (Fig. 2.34).

An enzyme which hydrolyzes amide linkages (α-chymotrypsin) has already been discussed in Sec. 2.7.

2.9. OXIDATION-REDUCTION: PRINCIPLES

It was obviously being played by someone with an imperfect command over it; it squeaked and yipped, started a line over again, only to founder once more in squeals. The music was punctuated by a series of shattering disconnected observations in a roaring bass voice of such power that one could feel the sympathetic vibrations from a set of copper cauldrons standing somewhere in the innermost recesses of Clito's cave. Bursts of helpless laughter and a labored altercation also played an intermittent part in the proceedings.

L. Durrell

Oxidation and reduction reactions of both organic and inorganic compounds are important in the operations of living systems. There are relatively few good model reactions for those transformations of most interest to biochemistry, but a resurgence of interest in these reactions, expecially those of inorganic chemistry, promises to improve the situation.[216–219]

2.9-1. The most convenient classification of oxidation-reduction reactions is based on the number of equivalents transferred from the reducing agent to the oxidizing agent. The number of electrons transferred in an elementary step may not be the same as the *net* number of equivalents transferred in the over-all reaction. Four categories can be established on this basis and the additional circumstance that atom (or group) transfer often accompanies electron transfer. These are (*a*) one-electron transfer, (*b*) two-electron transfer, (*c*) one-electron transfer with

[216] International Conference on Coordination Chemistry, London, April 6–11, 1959, *Chem. Soc. (London), Spec. Publ. No. 13,* 1959.

[217] H. Taube, Mechanisms of Redox Reactions of Simple Chemistry, *Advances in Inorg. Chem. and Radiochem.,* **1,** 1–53 (1959).

[218] "Modern Coordination Chemistry," ed. by J. Lewis and R. G. Wilkins, Interscience Publishers, Inc., New York, 1960.

[219] Oxidation-Reduction Reactions in Ionizing Solvents, *Discussions Faraday Soc.,* **29,** 1960.

atom (or group) transfer, and (*d*) two-electron transfer with atom (or group) transfer.

2.9-2. On the basis of the prevalence of one-electron transfer reactions between the molecules of a limited class of organic compounds, the suggestion was made that all oxidation-reduction reactions *must* proceed by one-electron steps.[220]   Despite wide acceptance of the idea of "compulsory one-electron transfer" in biochemical circles, it is not generally valid.   Operationally, electrons could be transferred successively (transfer time, 10^{-15} to 10^{-13} sec) and be observed as a simultaneous two-electron transfer because the solvent "cage" (the solvent molecule arrangement around the reactant species) would persist for 10^{-12} to 10^{-11} sec.[221]   There are, in addition, many displacement reactions which result in a two-equivalent change in oxidation state (e.g., reaction of hydride ion with alkyl halide) and are therefore best considered two-electron transfer reactions.

2.9-3. The "principle of equivalence change"[222] states that rapid electron transfer is much more likely between complementary reactants than between noncomplementary reactants.   Complementarity in this connection refers to the identity of the net change in the oxidation states of both oxidant and reductant.   Thus, cerium(IV) reacts rapidly with titanium(III) to form cerium(III) and titanium(IV), whereas thallium(III) reacts slowly with iron(II) to form thallium(I) and iron(III).   However, the implications of the "principle" that 2-equivalent complementarity will always lead to a 2-equivalent reaction, or that such reaction will be rapid, are not borne out by all data.[223]   Some of the factors which vitiate the generality of "principle" are the occurrence of unstable, but not inaccessible, oxidation states [e.g. chromium(IV), chromium(V), magnesium(I)], the enormous influence of ligands upon oxidation-reduction reaction rates, the possibility of atom (or group) transfer reactions, and the geometric difference between ions of different *d*-electron configurations.

2.9-4. The approach of two charged reactants will be favored if they are of opposite charges, or disfavored if they are of the same charge type.   It can be calculated from Eq. (2.102) that the repulsion between iron(II) and iron(III) at 2 Å separation in a vacuum is ca. 1000 kcal/mole. The approach of two ions of like charge can be greatly facilitated if an ion

$$(2.102) \qquad E \text{ (kcal/mole)} = 333 \cdot \frac{z_a z_b}{D r_{ab}}$$

[220] L. Michaelis, *Cold Spring Harbor Symposia Quant. Biol.*, **7**, 33 (1939).

[221] F. H. Westheimer, in "Mechanism of Enzyme Action," pp. 321–322, ed. by W. D. McElroy and B. Glass, Johns Hopkins Press, Baltimore, 1954.

[222] P. A. Shaffer, *J. Phys. Chem.*, **40**, 1021 (1936).

[223] J. Halpern, *Can. J. Chem.*, **37**, 148 (1959).

of opposite charge is placed in between. The attractive force for the linear system, iron(II)-chloride-iron(III), can be estimated as ca. 300 kcal/mole.

In solution, both repulsion and attraction are reduced in magnitude since the interaction takes place through a medium of high dielectric constant (water, $D = 78$). At great distances, the macroscopic dielectric constant is a reasonable parameter for the calculation of ionic interactions, but at distances on the order of ionic sizes, it is no longer satisfactory. At moderate distances, the changed dielectric constant of the water coordinated to charged species must be taken into account.[224]

2.9-5. If the products of electron transfer between ionic species are appreciably different in solvation from the original reactants, the restrictions imposed by the Franck-Condon principle will seriously affect the rate of the over-all reaction.[225] The principle states that electronic motions are much faster than nuclear motions; an electron transfer would be complete before the solvent shell could accommodate the product of the electron transfer. For example, the bond distances and solvent arrangement of $Fe(H_2O)_6^{+2}$ are different from those of $Fe(H_2O)_6^{+3}$; the latter ion, with a higher charge, would attract the atoms of the first coordination shell more strongly than the former ion. If an electron transfer were to occur between these two iron species, the resulting iron(III) would have a solvent arrangement suitable for iron(II), i.e. *expanded*, and the iron(II) would have a solvent arrangement suitable for iron(III), i.e. *compressed*. A lower energy pathway for the reaction could be brought about by partial rearrangement of the solvent shells *before* electron transfer; the required vibrational excitation energy is called the Franck-Condon rearrangement energy.[226]

2.9-6. If electron transfer occurs with no change in the inner coordination shells of the ions, the transition state is said to be an "outer-sphere activated complex." If the ligands lack π electrons, the barrier through which the electron must be transferred is high, and the electron transfer may proceed at a low rate. Ligands which contain π-electron systems "transmit" d-orbital character to the outer regions of the complex ions (as shown by hyperfine electron-spin resonance studies[237a]) and lead to fast electron-transfer reactions. The effect of ligands is illustrated briefly by the rate constants tabulated in Table 2.9-1.[217]

Many inorganic ions possess "labile" coordination shells; that is, substitution of one group for another in the first coordination shell occurs rapidly. A number of ions have "inert" coordination shells, and substitution is relatively slow. If an "inert" ion of the type $(NH_3)_5Co(III)X$

[224] J. A. Schellman, *J. Chem. Phys.*, **26**, 1225 (1957).
[225] W. F. Libby, *J. Phys. Chem.*, **56**, 863 (1952).
[226] J. Halpern and L. E. Orgel, in ref. 219, p. 17.

is reacted with Cr_{aq}^{+2}, the product chromium(III) species which is "inert" is found to contain X in the inner coordination shell. The kinetics and products are in agreement with a "bridged" transition state of the type:

$$(NH_3)_5Co\text{----}X\text{----}Cr(H_2O)_5$$

The atom (or group) X is called a "bridging" atom (group).[227] Not only are such reactions of possible importance in connection with some of the

Table 2.9-1. Electron Exchange Rates of Cobalt Complexes

Reactants	T, °C	Second-order rate constant, l mole^{-1} sec^{-1}
$Co(phen)_3^{++}$ | $Co(phen)_3^{3+}$	0^a	3.5
$Co(en)_3^{++}$ | $Co(en)_3^{3+}$	25^b	6×10^{-4}
$Co(NH_3)_6^{++}$ | $Co(NH_3)_6^{3+}$	45	7×10^{-6}
$Co(en)_3^{++}$ | $Co(NH_3)_6^{3+}$	25	2×10^{-2}

^{a} phen = 1,10-phenanthroline.
^{b} en = ethylene diamine.

key reactions in photosynthesis (see Sec. 1.4), but they have many aspects of fundamental and useful import (see Sec. 2.12).

2.9-7. The theory of outer-sphere reactions has been developed to a considerable extent by a consideration of electrostatic repulsion (or attraction) and the Franck-Condon rearrangement energy.[228-231]

The rate of electron transfer through bridged transition states is probably dependent upon the nature of the pontal[227] group, and the theoretical problem becomes one of understanding the manner in which the pontal group can affect the rate of electron transfer.[232] In a simple model system, in which A transfers an electron to the corresponding ion A$^+$ (labeled B$^+$ to avoid confusion) through the pontal group X, the rate of electron transfer is derivable from a consideration of the two states (I and II) involved[232] [Eqs. (2.103) to (2.105)]. Use of the steady-

(2.103) $$A + X^-B^+ \underset{k_{-1}}{\overset{k_1}{\rightleftharpoons}} (AX^-B^+)$$

[227] Consideration might be given to the use of the adjective "pontal," from the Latin, *pontus*, bridge, to describe atoms or groups which serve in a bridging capacity.

[228] R. A. Marcus, *J. Chem. Phys.*, **24**, 966 (1956).
[229] R. A. Marcus, *J. Chem. Phys.*, **26**, 867, 872 (1957).
[230] R. A. Marcus, *Can. J. Chem.*, **37**, 155 (1959).
[231] R. A. Marcus, in ref. 219, p. 21.
[232] J. Halpern and L. E. Orgel, in ref. 219, p. 32.

$$(2.104) \qquad (AX^-B^+) \underset{k_{-2}}{\overset{k_2}{\rightleftharpoons}} (A^+X^-B)$$
$$\qquad\qquad\qquad I \qquad\qquad\qquad II$$

$$(2.105) \qquad (A^+X^-B) \overset{k_3}{\longrightarrow} A^+X^- + B$$

state approximation leads to a bimolecular rate constant for the over-all reaction, k_0, given by Eq. (2.106). If the probability of electron transfer

$$(2.106) \qquad k_0 = \frac{k_1}{1 + \dfrac{k_{-1}k_{-2}}{k_2 k_3} + \dfrac{k_{-1}}{k_2}}$$

is small, $k_{-1} \gg k_2$, k_0 is approximately $k_1 k_2 / k_{-1}$, and the lifetime of the intermediate is of the order of $1/k_{-1}$. The probability of the transition from I to II then determines the rate of the reaction.

These probabilities have been estimated for the transition for I to II through a treatment which emphasizes direct exchange of electrons between orbitals of A and B and "double exchange," in which an electron is transferred to X from A at the same time an electron from X moves to B.[232] Another treatment, which utilizes certain excited states of the intermediate complex (e.g., $A^+X^-B^+$), is called "superexchange."[233]

The theory is insufficiently developed to evaluate quantitatively the role of the pontal groups in electron transfer.[232] The rate of the substitution step [Eq. (2.103)] and the influence on the rate of the Franck-Condon rearrangement energy for I [Eq. (2.104)] cannot be separated from the over-all rate, and there is thus no good way in which the predictions of the theory can be tested. Some exceptions to the latter statement may exist for organic ligands, in which it is possible to make small changes in certain properties without affecting greatly geometry and solvation of the complex ions.

2.9-8. One approach which is particularly helpful in understanding some of the chemistry and much of the visible spectra of transition metal ions is ligand field theory.[234] The basic idea of the theory[235] is that the presence of ligand electrons[237] along some or all of the coordi-

[233] P. George and J. S. Griffith, in "The Enzymes," vol. 1, chap. 8, Academic Press, Inc., New York, 1959.

[234] L. E. Orgel, "An Introduction to Transition Metal Chemistry: Ligand Field Theory," Methuen & Co., Ltd., London, 1960.

[235] The application of the electrostatic principle to the energy levels of transition metal ions was made many years ago[236] as crystal field theory.

[236] H. Bethe, *Ann. Physik*, (5) **3**, 133 (1929).

[237] Ligands are those groups or molecules which are coordinatively associated with a central metal ion; the electrons are those present in the orbitals directed toward the metal ion. Effects also arise from ligand electrons or acceptor orbitals which are not directed toward the metal ion.

nate axes based on a transition metal ion results in a preference of the metal ion d electrons for directions away from such axes. The result of the electrostatic repulsion is to divide the d orbitals into at least two groups, those with probabilities away from the ligands being known as t_{2g}, and those with probabilities closer to the ligands as e_g. Many of the transition metal ions of interest are listed along with their electron configurations in strong octahedral fields (where the electrostatic repulsion is strong) and weak octahedral fields in Table 2.9-2. The d orbitals are illustrated in Fig. 2.35.[237a]

Table 2.9-2. Electronic Configurations of Transition Metal Ions

Ion	Orbital Arrangement	Configuration in octahedral field			
		Weak ligand field		Strong ligand field	
		t_{2g}	e_g	t_{2g}	e_g
V(III)	$(1s)^2(2s)^2(2p)^6(3p)^6(3d)^2$	↑ ↑ —	— —	↑ ↑ —	— —
V(II)	$\cdots (3d)^3$ }	↑ ↑ ↑	— —	↑ ↑ ↑	— —
Mn(IV)	$\cdots (3d)^3$ }				
Mn(III)	$\cdots (3d)^4$	↑ ↑ ↑	↑ —	↑↓ ↑ ↑	— —
Mn(II)	$\cdots (3d)^5$ }	↑ ↑ ↑	↑ ↑	↑↓ ↑↓ ↑	— —
Fe(III)	$\cdots (3d)^5$ }				
Fe(II)	$\cdots (3d)^6$ }	↑↓ ↑ ↑	↑ ↑	↑↓ ↑↓ ↑↓	— —
Co(III)	$\cdots (3d)^6$ }				
Co(II)	$\cdots (3d)^7$	↑↓ ↑↓ ↑	↑ ↑	↑↓ ↑↓ ↑↓	↑ —
Cu(II)	$\cdots (3d)^9$	↑↓ ↑↓ ↑↓	↑↓ ↑	↑↓ ↑↓ ↑↓	↑↓ ↑
Cu(I)	$\cdots (3d)^{10}$ }	↑↓ ↑↓ ↑↓	↑↓ ↑↓	↑↓ ↑↓ ↑↓	↑↓ ↑↓
Zn(II)	$\cdots (3d)^{10}$ }				

2.9-9. A value Δ represents the separation between the t_{2g} and e_g orbitals and is derived by an analysis of the visible spectra of various metal ion–ligand combinations. (In other words, the orbital separations correspond to 40 to 70 kcal/mole in energy.) Electrons tend to occupy the maximum number of separate orbitals, due to electron-electron repulsion and the stabilization which arises by electron exchange. In the absence of ligand effects, the "high-spin" arrangement would be favored. Ligands vary in their ability to overcome the favored arrangement. Iodide is a "weak-field" ligand, and cyanide is a "strong-field" ligand. The field produced by the ligands is evaluated from the visible

[237a] A concise discussion of bonding in coordination compounds may be found in C. J. Ballhausen, in "Advances in the Chemistry of the Coordination Compounds," p. 3, The Macmillan Company, New York, 1961.

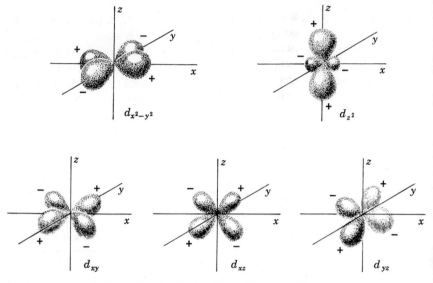

FIG. 2.35. d orbitals of transition metal ions.

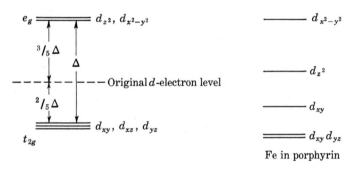

FIG. 2.36. Energy levels for d orbitals in octahedral fields.

spectra, giving rise to the order of ability to produce a "strong field" as follows:

$$I^-, Br^-, Cl^-, C_2H_5OH, H_2O, NH_3, NH_2CH_2CH_2NH_2, NO_2^-, CN^-$$

The energy levels for the d orbitals in an octahedral field are shown in Fig. 2.36; also illustrated is the energy-level arrangement for an ion like iron complexed within a porphyrin, for which the two ligands along the z axis (Fig. 2.37) are different from those on the x and y axes.[238]

[238] A tetrahedral ligand arrangement exists for some iron species (e.g. $FeCl_4^-$),[239] but the rigid porphin ring precludes any but a distorted octahedral arrangement.

[239] Raman spectroscopy was used to confirm the tetrahedral arrangement of the ligands in $FeCl_4^-$ by L. A. Woodward and M. J. Taylor, *J. Chem. Soc.*, 4473 (1960).

2.9-10. Oxidation-reduction potentials reflect the thermo-dynamic relationship between the oxidized and reduced forms of a species. The standard potential with reference to the hydrogen electrode for an oxidation of M^{++} [Eq. (2.107)] is given in Eq. (2.108).

(2.107) $$M^{++} = M^{3+} + e^- \qquad E_0 = E_1$$

(2.108) $$E = E_0 - \frac{0.059}{n} \log \frac{(M^{3+})}{(M^{++})}$$

The oxidation-reduction potential of a metal ion is very much affected by the nature of the ligands bonded to it. Writing another equation for the

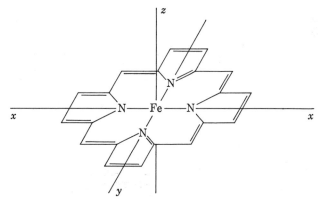

Fig. 2.37. Porphyrin iron.

oxidation of LM^{++} [Eq. (2.109)], the position of the equilibrium for a

(2.109) $$LM^{++} = LM^{3+} + e^- \qquad E_0 = E_2$$

reaction between M^{++} and LM^{3+} can be evaluated from a knowledge of the standard potentials and the concentrations [Eq. (2.110)]. The fact

(2.110) $$M^{++} + LM^{3+} = LM^{++} + M^{3+} \qquad E_0 = E_1 - E_2$$

that an equilibrium is unfavorable does not imply that a product of the reaction cannot serve as an intermediate in a reaction. If the electron transfer catalyzed by the product is a diffusion-controlled reaction for both of the other reactants, as little as 10^{-6} M product would give a rate on the order of many enzymatic reaction rates. Thus, a form of iron which did not change in concentration appreciably upon total reduction of the electron transport system in mitochondria might go undetected and yet serve as an intermediate in electron transport between such molecules as flavoprotein and coenzyme Q or cytochrome c.

2.10. OXIDATION-REDUCTION:
ONE-ELECTRON TRANSFER

I have had playmates, I have had companions,
In my days of childhood, in my joyful school-days;
All, all are gone, the old familiar faces.

C. Lamb

One-electron transfer reactions are of considerable actual or potential importance in inorganic chemistry, organic chemistry, and biochemistry. A list of metal ions of biological interest, some of which may participate in oxidation-reduction reactions, is given in Table 2.10-1.

TABLE 2.10-1. SOME METAL IONS OF BIOLOGICAL INTEREST

Group	Ions	Occurrence
Oxidation-reduction catalysis	Fe(II)-Fe(III) Cu(I)-Cu(II) Mo(VI)[a] V(II)-V(III) Co(II)-Co(III)	Cytochrome c Cytochrome a Xanthine oxidase Ascidian blood chromogen Vitamin B_{12}
Capable of oxidation-reduction catalysis	Mn(II)[b]	Peptidase
Positive ions	Mg(II) Ca(II) Zn(II) K(I) Na(I)	ATPase Amylase Carbonic anhydrase, ADH[c] Nerve cells Plasma

[a] With flavin; possibly involved in a one-electron change (see p. 226).
[b] Oxidation-reduction of managanese has been suggested in photosynthesis.[240]
[c] It is highly unlikely that Zn(II) is involved in the oxidation-reduction reaction catalyzed by alcohol dehydrogenase, ADH.

2.10-1. Electron-transfer reactions which take place with no change in the inner coordination shell of the reactant ions proceed through "outer-sphere activated complexes." Reactants in which all of the ligands are saturated molecules (NH_3, $NH_2CH_2CH_2NH_2$, etc.) can react rather slowly (Table 2.9-1). Reactions in which one of the reactants has saturated ligands and one possesses ligand groups with π-electron systems can go much faster, and the rate constant can be correlated with

[240] H. A. Tanner, T. E. Brown, C. Eyster, and R. W. Treharne, *Ohio J. Sci.*, **60**, 231 (1960); *Chem. Eng. News*, Aug. 15, 1960, pp. 42–43.

the free-energy change for the reaction[241] (examples are given in Table 2.10-2).

TABLE 2.10-2. SECOND-ORDER RATE CONSTANTS FOR OXIDATION-REDUCTION REACTIONS[a,b]

Reactants	Medium	E_0, volts	k, F^{-1} sec^{-1}
$IrCl_6^-$ | $Fe(CN)_6^{4-}$	H_2O	0.66	1.20×10^6
$IrCl_6^-$ | $Fe(CN)_6^{4-}$	0.5 F HClO$_4$	0.34	4.1×10^5
MnO_4^- | $Fe(CN)_6^{4-}$	0.1 F NaOH	0.10	1.34×10^4
$OsCl_6^-$ | $Fe(CN)_6^{4-}$	H_2O	0.07	1.79×10^{-1}
$IrCl_6^-$ | $Os(dipy)_3^{+2}$ [c]	0.5 F HClO$_4$	0.23	$>10^8$

[a] Ref. 241.
[b] Measured in rapid-flow apparatus.[242]
[c] dipy = 2,2'-dipyridyl.

Reactants in which both ligand shells have extensive π-electron systems can react extremely rapidly, and may even react at diffusion-controlled rates (examples are shown in Table 2.10-3).[241] In contrast, a much lower rate is observed for the reaction of Co(phen)$_3^{++}$ and Co(phen)$_3^{3+}$ (Table 2.9-1) even though both reactants have ligands with π-electron systems. The most likely explanation is that the ligands are "strong-field" (Table 2.9-2) and electron transfer requires the transfer of an e_g electron from the Co(II) to the Co(III) and therefore a considerable change in the ionic dimensions. The electron-transfer reaction between ferricyanide and ferrocyanide is much slower than the other reactions listed in Table 2.10-3, probably because of the large electrostatic repulsion to be expected between ions of $3-$ and $4-$ charges, respectively.

TABLE 2.10-3. FAST ELECTRON-TRANSFER REACTIONS[a,b]

Reactants	Medium	E_0, volts	k, F^{-1} sec^{-1}
$Fe(phen)_3^{3+}$ [c] | $Fe(CN)_6^{4-}$	0.5 F HClO$_4$	0.23	$>10^8$
$Os(dipy)_3^{3+}$ | $Fe(CN)_6^{4-}$	0.5 F HClO$_4$	0.11	$>10^8$
$Ru(dipy)_3^{3+}$ | $Fe(t\text{-}phen)_3^{++}$ [d]	0.5 F H$_2$SO$_4$	0.46	$>10^8$
$Fe(phen)_3^{3+}$ | $Os(dipy)_3^{++}$	0.5 F HClO$_4$	0.23	$>10^8$
$Fe(CN)_6^{3-}$ | $Fe(CN)_6^{4-}$ [e]	H_2O		1×10^3 [f]

[a] Ref. 241.
[b] Measured in rapid-flow apparatus.[242]
[c] phen = 1,10-phenanthroline.
[d] t-phen = 3,4,7,8-tetramethyl-1,10-phenanthroline.
[e] Virtual reaction followed with radioactive iron.
[f] Ref. 217.

[241] B. M. Gordon, L. L. Williams, and N. Sutin, *J. Am. Chem. Soc.*, **83**, 2061 (1961).
[242] N. Sutin and B. M. Gordon, *J. Am. Chem. Soc.*, **83**, 70 (1961).

An interesting difference in rate has been observed for the reactions of ferricyanide with ferrohemoglobin[243] and ferrocytochrome c.[244] At 25°C in phosphate buffer of pH 6.0, the former reaction has a second-order rate constant of $7.0 \pm 0.5 \times 10^4$ l mole^{-1} sec^{-1} and the latter reaction, one of $1.6 \pm 0.1 \times 10^7$ l mole^{-1} sec^{-1}. It is thought that the sixth ligand coordinated to the iron in the case of hemoglobin is water, but that for the iron of cytochrome c, it is histidine. The imidazole ring of the histidine is a ligand with a π-electron system which should favor faster electron transfer than with a saturated molecule like water as the ligand. Electron transfer through peptide linkages is also a possibility, although probably not too likely (see Sec. 2.12). A more important factor, which cannot be evaluated, is the stereochemistry of the interaction permitted by the protein directly preceding electron transfer.

2.10-2. Many of the reactions of organic free radicals involve the transfer of an atom [Eq. (2.111)] or formation of a new radical by

$$(2.111) \qquad \text{R·} + \text{BH} \rightarrow \text{RH} + \text{B·}$$

addition to a multiple bond and of dimer by reaction with another radical [Eqs. (2.112) and (2.113)]. There are, however, reactions which are

$$(2.112) \qquad \text{R·} + \ce{>C=C<} \rightarrow \ce{R-\overset{|}{C}-\overset{|}{C}·}$$

$$(2.113) \qquad \text{2R·} \rightarrow \text{R—R}$$

"purely" electron-transfer in character, such as the formation of two radicals from an ion pair [Eq. (2.114)], reduction of a π-electron system to a free radical [Eq. (2.115)], and electron transfer from a radical to a π-electron system [Eq. (2.116)].

$$(2.114) \qquad \text{R}^+\text{X}^- \xrightarrow{e^-} \text{R· X·}$$

$$(2.115) \qquad \text{Ar}^+ \rightarrow \text{Ar·}$$

$$(2.116) \qquad \text{Ar}_1\text{·} + \text{Ar}_2 \rightarrow \text{Ar}_1 + \text{Ar}_2\text{·}$$

An ion pair can be transformed into a radical pair [Eq. (2.114)] either thermally or photochemically. The ionization of tris(p-nitrophenyl)methyl bromide in polar solvents leads to products explicable on the basis of intermediate carbonium ion formation, but in nonpolar solvents, radicals are formed. An ion pair would decrease in stability in comparison to a radical pair as the solvating power of the solvent decreased. For certain ion pairs, the decrease in stability would be sufficient to make the radical

[243] N. Sutin, *Nature*, **190**, 438 (1961).

[244] N. Sutin and D. R. Christman, *J. Am. Chem. Soc.*, **83**, 1773 (1961).

pair the thermodynamically stable form.[69,244a] Photochemical production of a radical pair from an ion pair is found in the case of 1-methylpyridinium iodides.[245]

2.10-3. Electrochemical reduction of 1-alkyl-4-substituted pyridinium ions in acetonitrile yields the corresponding free radical [Eq. (2.117)]. In the cases where the 4-substituent is a carbomethoxy or a

(2.117)

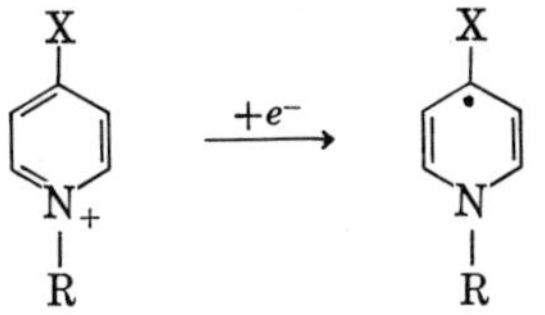

carbamido group, the free radicals are stable enough to be detected by electron-spin resonance spectroscopy.[246] In the case of a 4-cyano group, dimerization occurs, followed by ionization of the cyano groups as cyanide ion and a one-electron reduction to a "viologen"

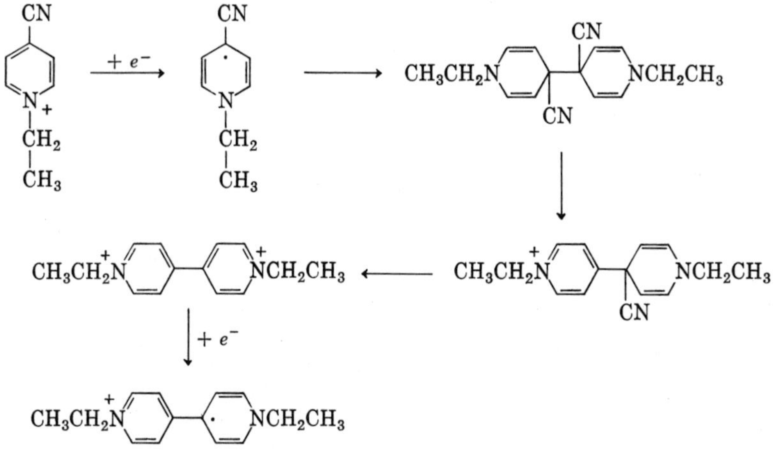

FIG. 2.38. Dimerization of 4-cyanopyridinyl radicals.

radical (Fig. 2.38). A similar reaction is observed if 1-methyl-4-cyanopyridinium ion is reduced in buffered aqueous solution with sodium dithionite[247] (see Sec. 2.13).

[244a] Another example of a solvent effect on an equilibrium between ion pairs and radical pairs is given by D. H. Anderson, R. M. Elofson, H. S. Gutowsky, S. Levine, and R. B. Sandin, *J. Am. Chem. Soc.*, **83**, 3157 (1961).

[245] E. M. Kosower, J. A. Skorcz, W. M. Schwarz, Jr., and J. W. Patton, *J. Am. Chem. Soc.*, **82**, 2188 (1960).

[246] W. M. Schwarz, E. M. Kosower, and I. Shain, *J. Am. Chem. Soc.*, **83**, 3164 (1961).

[247] E. M. Kosower and J. L. Cotter, unpublished results.

The reduction of 1-ethyl-3-carbamidopyridinium ion in acetonitrile using cyclic triangular wave voltammetry[248] at a hanging mercury drop electrode[249] shows that a moderately stable free radical intermediate can be detected in this manner.[250] Reduction of 1-propyl-, 1-benzyl-, or 1-(2,6-dichlorobenzyl)-pyridinium ion with chromium(II) ion produces the 6,6'-dimers[251,252] (Fig. 2.39). The dimers react rapidly with another

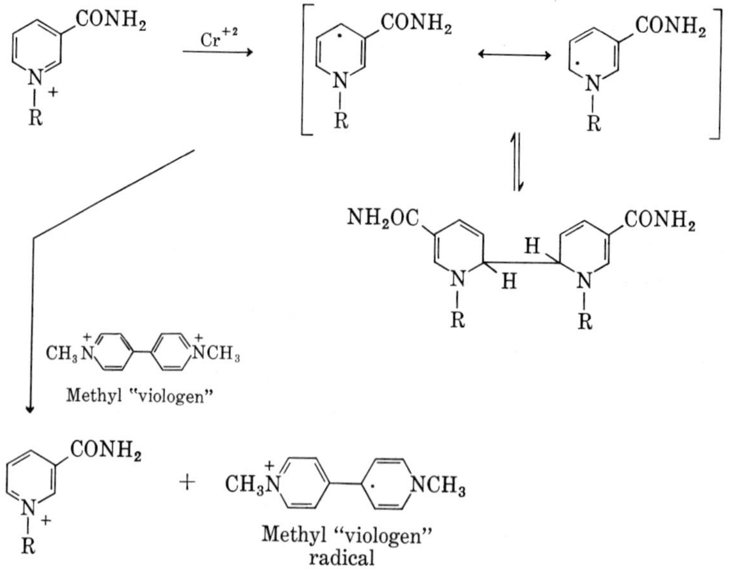

Fig. 2.39. Pyridinyl dimer formation and dissociation.

radical and not at all with malachite green, a dye which is readily reduced by "two-electron" reagents. The dimers are also oxidized to monomeric pyridinium ions by silver ion; presumably the preferred pathway for the dimers is dissociation to monomeric radicals. The formation of the dimers and their reactions are in agreement with the observations on the formation of relatively stable free radicals by reduction of 1-alkylnicotin-amide quaternary ions.

[248] Variation of the potential imposed on the electrodes in the cell in a cyclic fashion such that reduction is succeeded by oxidation. Control of the rate of the cycle thus offers a means for estimating the stability of radical intermediates when these can react further, e.g., dimerize.

[249] The measurements of ref. 248 should be carried out in such a way that the products of reduction can diffuse back to the electrode for reoxidation, i.e., at a stationary electrode.

[250] W. M. Schwarz, unpublished results.

[251] K. Wallenfels and M. Gellrich, *Ann.* **621**, 198 (1959).

[252] K. Wallenfels and M. Gellrich, *Chem. Ber.*, **92**, 1406 (1959).

Free radicals like those obtained by reduction of pyridinium ions have been suggested as intermediates in the photochemical reaction of 1,4-dihydropyridines with bromotrichloromethane to form pyridinium ions.[253]

2.10-4. Radicals which are sufficiently stable to survive without dimerization or disproportionation may transfer an electron to another system capable of forming a stable radical. Typical radicals of this type are those derived from aromatic rings by the addition of one electron [Eq. (2.116)]. (Although the pyridinyl radicals described in Sec. 2.10-3 should exchange electrons with pyridinium rings, no measurements with such a combination have been made.) Electron transfer between the

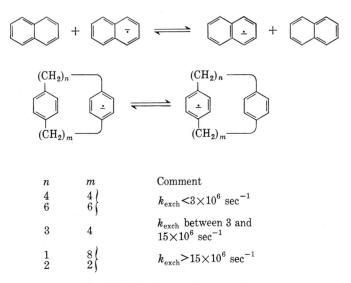

n	m	Comment
4 6	4 6	$k_{exch} < 3 \times 10^6$ sec^{-1}
3	4	k_{exch} between 3 and 15×10^6 sec^{-1}
1 2	8 2	$k_{exch} > 15 \times 10^6$ sec^{-1}

Fig. 2.40. Electron-exchange systems.

naphthalene anion radical and naphthalene can be measured by the line width of the electron-spin resonance absorption and is quite rapid, with a rate constant of ca. 10^6 l mole^{-1} sec^{-1} (ref. 254). If the aromatic rings are present in the same molecule and are forced into proximity by the structure as in the paracyclophanes, the exchange rate is dependent upon the precise geometric relationship of the aromatic rings (Fig. 2.40).[255]

It is of interest that such electron-exchange systems are responsible for the conductivity observed in complex salts composed of a cation (7,7,8,8-

[253] J. L. Kurz, R. Hutton, and F. H. Westheimer, *J. Am. Chem. Soc.*, **83**, 584 (1961).
[254] R. L. Ward and S. I. Weissman, *J. Am. Chem. Soc.*, **76**, 3612 (1954).
[255] S. I. Weissman, *J. Am. Chem. Soc.*, **80**, 6462 (1958).

tetracyanoquinodimethane) and the anion radical derived from the latter [Eq. (2.118)].[256]

(2.118)

$$
\begin{bmatrix} \text{structure} \end{bmatrix} \quad \cdots \quad \begin{bmatrix} \text{structure} \end{bmatrix} \rightleftharpoons \begin{bmatrix} \text{structure} \end{bmatrix} \quad \cdots \quad \begin{bmatrix} \text{structure} \end{bmatrix}
$$

The presence of nonheme iron in mitochondria suggests the possibility that electron transfer in terminal oxidation may be mediated by such iron without the necessity for proximity between the recognized components of the electron-transport system like flavoprotein and cytochrome c (see Sec. 1.3). The relationship of the nonheme iron to the "structural protein" of mitochondria remains to be elucidated.[257]

2.11. OXIDATION-REDUCTION: TWO-ELECTRON TRANSFER

Che fai tu, luna in ciel? dimmi, che fai,
silenziosa luna?

G. Leopardi

Well-authenticated cases of two-electron transfer which do not involve a pontal atom or group are difficult to find. Two-electron transfers according to Eq. (2.119) occur in the gas-phase with cross sections lower

(2.119)
$$ A + A^{++} \rightarrow A^{++} + A $$

than those for one-electron transfers. In solution, it would be expected that an ion which differed by two charges from another would also differ greatly in solvation, and that the Franck-Condon rearrangement energy would be considerable. Even in such "obvious" cases as the reaction of thallium(I) with thallium(III), it is not clear what portion of the exchange is to be understood on the basis of an outer-sphere activated complex, and therefore as a "pure" two-electron transfer.[258] The fact that the exchange rate decreases with increasing perchlorate-ion concentration might argue against an outer-sphere complex since it would be expected

[256] R. E. Benson, D. S. Acker, R. J. Harder, W. R. Hertler, W. Mahler, L. R. Melby, and W. E. Mochel, *J. Am. Chem. Soc.*, **82**, 6408 (1960).

[257] D. E. Green, H. D. Tisdale, R. S. Criddle, and R. M. Bock, *Biochem. Biophys. Research Comm.*, **5**, 1 (1961).

[258] S. W. Gilks and G. M. Waind, in ref. 219, p. 102.

that counter ions would favor electron transfer between ions of like charge.

2.11-1.   One type of two-electron transfer which may have general significance is the simultaneous one-electron transfer from two groups to two metal ions coupled to the formation of a covalent bond. The production of cystine from a dimeric complex of cysteine and ferric ion can be taken as an example of such a reaction [Eq. (2.120)].[259]

(2.120)

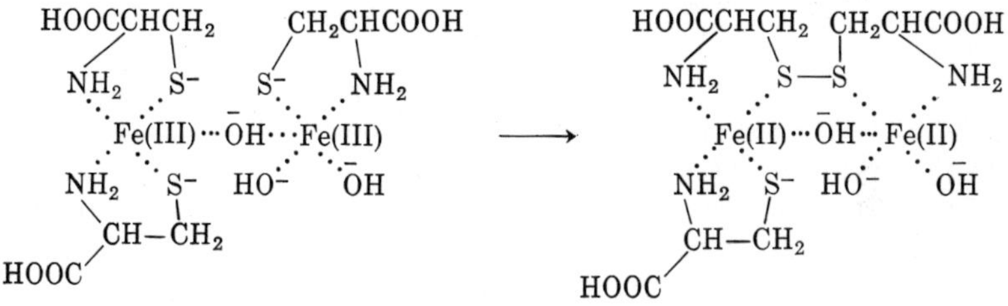

Another reaction which may be an example of two simultaneous one-electron transfers coupled to covalent bond formation is the copper(II)

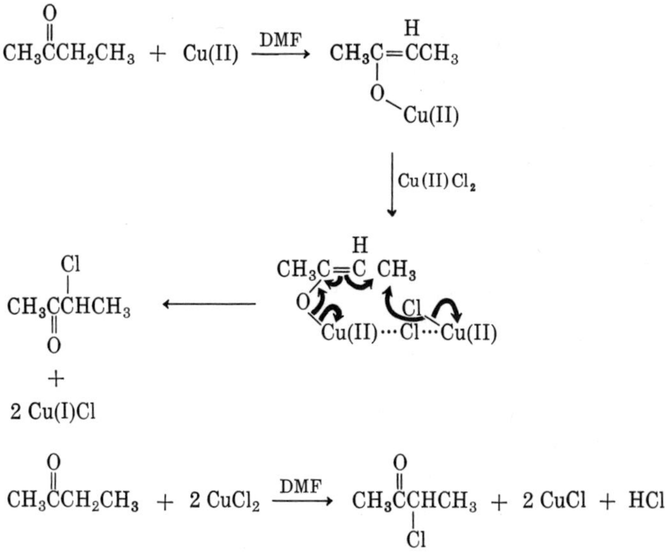

Fig. 2.41. Copper(II) chloride reaction with methyl ethyl ketone.

halide halogenation of enolizable compounds.[260] A mechanism which expresses this view of the reaction is shown in Fig. 2.41.

[259] D. L. Leussing and L. Newman, J. Am. Chem. Soc., 78, 5526 (1956).
[260] E. M. Kosower, W. J. Cole, G. Meisters, and G.-S. Wu, unpublished results. Cf. also Am. Chem. Soc. Abstr. (September, 1960).

2.12. OXIDATION-REDUCTION: ATOM (OR GROUP) TRANSFER

Ímajen alta y tierna del consuelo,
aurora de mis mares de tristeza,
lis de paz con olores de pureza,
¡premio divino de mi largo duelo!
J. R. Jiménez

Many oxidation-reduction reactions do not proceed by "pure" electron transfer, but rather by a route in which a group Z serves as a bridge between the two reactants A and B. In many cases, the group Z (or the atom Z) is transferred from A to B as part of the reaction.

2.12-1. Transition states in which a pontal group Z (ref. 227) participates, can be described loosely as one-electron [Eq. (2.121)] or two-electron [Eq. (2.122) or (2.123)], the number signifying the net change in the oxidation state of the reactants A and B in the electron-transfer step.

(2.121) $AZ + B \rightarrow A \ldots \dot{Z} \ldots B$

(2.122) $AZ + B \rightarrow A \ldots Z^+ \ldots B$

(2.123) $AZ + B \rightarrow A \ldots Z^- \ldots B$

A whole variety of organic and inorganic reactions can be classified according to the atom or group which serves as the pontal group. A selection of such reactions for both one- and two-electron transfer is presented in Table 2.12-1.

2.12-2. An aqueous solution of chloropentaminocobalt(III) perchlorate is relatively stable and replacement of the groups which constitute the inner coordination shell around the cobalt is slow. In contrast, the water of the inner coordination shell of chromium(II) ion exchanges rapidly with the solvent water; in such cases, the coordination shell is termed *labile*. Cobalt(II) ion has a labile inner coordination shell for simple ligands like ammonia and water, but chromium(III) has a very *stable* inner coordination shell. The half-life for the exchange of $Cr(H_2O)_6^{+3}$ with water as followed by the method of isotopic dilution is ca. 30 hours at room temperature.[216] The reaction of cobalt(III) with chromium(II) can be described in terms of the stability of inner coordination shells as in [Eq. (2.124)].

(2.124)   Co(III) *stable* + Cr(II) *labile* → Co(II) *labile* + Cr(III) *stable*

The reaction of chloropentaminocobalt(III) with chromium(II) yields

Table 2.12-1. Atom (or Group) Transfer Reactions

Pontal Atom(s)	1-electron	2-electron
Hydrogen	$R\cdot + R'H \rightarrow RH + R'\cdot$ $RO\cdot + HBr \rightarrow ROH + Br\cdot$ $Cl\cdot + RH \rightarrow R\cdot + HCl$	$R_3C^+ + RH \rightarrow R_3CH + R^+$ $LiAlH_4 + R_2C{=}O \rightarrow R_2CHOH$ $DPNH + RCHO \rightarrow DPN^+ + RCH_2OH$
Oxygen	$(NH_3)_5CoOH_2^{++} + Cr^{++} \rightarrow$ $Co^{++} + CrOH_2^{++}$	$H^+ + I^- + H_2O_2 \rightarrow IOH + HOH$

$$RCH{=}CHR + OsO_4 \rightarrow$$

$$RCH{=}CHR + MnO_4^- \rightarrow$$

Fluorine Fluorines	$CrF^{++} + Cr^{++} \rightarrow$ $CrF_2^+ + Cr^{++} \rightarrow$ but, not through double bridge	
Sulfur		
Chlorine	$CrCl^{++} + Cr^{++} \rightarrow$ $R\cdot + Cl_2 \rightarrow RCl + Cl\cdot$	$CH_2{=}CH_2 + ClOH \rightarrow$
Bromine	$CrBr^{++} + Cr^{++} \rightarrow$ $\phi_3C\cdot + Br_2 \rightarrow \phi_3CBr + Br\cdot$	

$$CH_2{=}CH_2 + Br{-}Br \rightarrow$$

| Iodine | $\phi_3C\cdot + I_2 \rightarrow \phi_3CI + I\cdot$ | $\phi NH_2 + IOH \overset{H^+}{\rightarrow}$ |

hexaaquocobalt(II) and chloropentaquochromium(III) [Eq. (2.125)].

(2.125) $(NH_3)_5CoCl^{++} + Cr_{aq}^{++} + 5H^+ \rightarrow 5NH_4^+ + (H_2O)_6Co^{++} + (H_2O)_5CrCl^{++}$

If radioactive chloride ion is added to the reactants, no radioactive chlorine is found in the chlorochromium ion.[217] It is clear that the chlorine which was originally coordinated to the cobalt becomes coordinated to the chromium in the oxidation-reduction reaction. The reaction is explicable in terms of a bridged transition state, as in (2.126). The

(2.126) $[(NH_3)_5Co \ldots Cl \ldots Cr(H_2O)_5]^{4+}$

rates of the oxidation-reduction reactions are remarkably sensitive to the nature of the pontal group, as shown by the rate constants for some reactions of chromium(III) species with chromium(II) which proceed through a bridged transition state (Table 2.12-2).[217,261,262]

TABLE 2.12-2. RATES OF REACTION OF CHROMIUM(III) IONS WITH CHROMIUM(II)[a,b]

Oxidant	k, l mole^{-1} sec^{-1}	T, °C
CrF^{++}	2.6×10^{-2}	27
$CrCl^{++}$	~8.7	0
$CrBr^{++}$	>60	0
$CrNCS^{++}$ [c]	1.8×10^{-4}	27
CrN_3^{++} [c]	>1.2	27
$(NH_3)_5CrF^{++}$	2.7×10^{-4}	25
$(NH_3)_5CrCl^{++}$	5.1×10^{-2}	25
$(NH_3)_5CrBr^{++}$	3.2×10^{-1}	25
$(NH_3)_5CrI^{++}$	5.5 ± 1.5	25
cis-CrF_2^+	1.0×10^{-2}	25[d]

[a] Ref. 217.
[b] Ref. 261.
[c] The metal ions interact with opposite ends of the pontal group.
[d] Ref. 262.

Although it might have been guessed that two pontal groups would produce a lower-energy transition state than one pontal group, and therefore a greater rate of oxidation-reduction,[263] investigations with *cis*-

[261] D. L. Ball and E. L. King, *J. Am. Chem. Soc.*, **80**, 1091 (1958).
[262] Y.-T. Chia and E. L. King, in ref. 219, p. 109.
[263] A greater rate of oxidation-reduction would be observed only if the stability constant for the complex with a double bridge were comparable to that for a single bridge.

difluorotetraquochromium(III)[262] and *cis*-diaquotetraaminocobalt(III)[264] in reaction with chromium(II) have demonstrated that only one atom or molecule is transferred to the reducing agent.

2.12-3.   The discovery that organic ligands can serve as pontal groups has opened the way to making reasonably small variations in the nature of the pontal group in a given reaction.   Rate constants for the reaction in Eq. (2.127) are tabulated in Table 2.12-3.[217]

TABLE 2.12-3. OXIDATION-REDUCTION RATE CONSTANTS FOR Cr(II) AND
Co(III) WITH ORGANIC PONTAL GROUPS[a]
$$5H^+ + (NH_3)_5Co(III)L + Cr(II) \rightarrow (H_2O)_5Cr(III)L + Co(II) + NH_4^+$$
$$T = 25°C; \quad \mu = 1.00$$

Ligand, L	k, $l\ mole^{-1}\ sec^{-1}$
HOH	0.7
OH⁻	2×10^6
CH₃COO⁻	0.15
CH₃CH₂CH₂COO⁻	0.08
CH₃CH=CHCOO⁻	0.18
HOOCCH₂CH₂COO⁻	0.19
⁻OOCCH₂CH₂COO⁻	~1
CH₃OOCCH₂CH₂COO⁻	0.22
o-HOOCC₆H₄COO⁻	0.057
o-⁻OOCC₆H₄COO⁻	~10
m-HOOCC₆H₄COO⁻	0.10
p-HOOCC₆H₄COO⁻	~40
T = 5°C	
HOOCCOO⁻	>20
cis-HOOCCH=CHCOO⁻	>20
trans-HOOCCH=CHCOO⁻	0.5
trans-⁻OOCCH=CHCOO⁻	2

[a] Ref. 217.

(2.127) $5H^+ + (NH_3)_5Co(III)L + Cr(II) \rightarrow 5NH_4^+ + Co(II) + (H_2O)_5Cr(III)L$

The results in Table 2.12-3 indicate that a carboxylate pontal group produces a somewhat lower rate of oxidation-reduction than a pontal water molecule.   Changes in the carboxylic acid produce comparatively little change in the rate constant for the reaction, unless a second carboxylic acid group is conjugated to the first.   A good example in the table is that of the ligand terephthalic acid monoanion, which causes a reaction to occur about 1000 times faster than the *o*-phthalic acid monoanion. These results are interpreted as meaning that the chromium(II) ion attacks the ligand at the carboxyl group which is *not* coordinated to the cobalt(III), with electron transfer occurring by means of the π-electron

[264] W. Kruse and H. Taube, *J. Am. Chem. Soc.*, **82**, 526 (1960).

system of the conjugated ligand. Such "remote attack" increases the rate of oxidation-reduction because the repulsion between the reactant ions of like charges is reduced.

2.12-4. The proposal that proteins might serve as semiconductors, and thus as electron-transfer agents, has often been put forward. The conductivity and light absorption of proteins are not in agreement with such a role for polypeptides (see Sec. 1.4). Nevertheless, the importance of polypeptide–metal ion complexes in biochemistry (e.g., cytochrome c) justifies an inquiry into the behavior of such systems in oxidation-reduction reactions from a fundamental point of view.[265]

The reduction of a number of polypeptide-cobalt(III) complexes by chromium(II) has been investigated.[268,269] The complexes used were prepared by the reaction of aquopentaminocobalt(III) perchlorate with poly-L-glutamic acid, poly-DL-glutamic acid, and copolymers of DL-alanine and L-glutamic acid. The results may be summarized as follows: Reduction of the cobalt(III) derivative by chromium(II) proceeds from ten to one hundred times as fast for at least part of the total reaction in the case of the polypeptide pentaminocobalt(III) perchlorate as might have been expected from a carboxylatopentaminocobalt(III) perchlorate. A number of difficulties make the interpretation of these results obscure. (Typical results are shown in Table 2.12-4.) The rates for the polypeptide cobalt(III) complexes are inversely proportional to the hydrogen-ion concentration, showing that the reactive species is formed by loss of a hydrogen ion. One source for the hydrogen ion might be a peptide-chromium(II) complex [Eq. (2.128)], but it might then be troublesome to

$$(2.128) \qquad\qquad \overset{|}{\underset{|}{Cr^{++}HN—C}}{=}O \rightleftharpoons H^+ + \overset{\bar{}}{\underset{\diagup}{Cr^{++}N}}—\overset{|}{\underset{|}{C}}{=}O$$

explain why the chromium should supply an electron to an anion. A more likely explanation is that the free carboxylic acid groups are

[265] Although the "stacked" purine and pyrimidine rings of DNA show a reduction in absorption intensity as compared with the individual rings which may be explained as a repulsive interaction of the excited state dipoles with neighboring π-electron systems,[266] no shift of the maximum to longer wavelengths indicative of the presence of a semiconduction band occurs. No shift of the maximum accompanies the reduction of absorption intensity observed for polypeptides which are presumably in the helical form to a considerable extent.[267]

[266] I. Tinoco, Jr., *J. Am. Chem. Soc.*, **82**, 4785 (1960).

[267] I. Tinoco, Jr., A. Halpern, and W. T. Simpson, *Proc. 1st Intern. Symposium on Polyamino Acids*, Madison, Wis., June, 1961.

[268] K. D. Kopple and G. F. Svatos, *J. Am. Chem. Soc.*, **82**, 3227 (1960).

[269] K. D. Kopple, R. R. Miller, and T. C. Muller, *Proc. 1st Intern. Symposium on Polyamino Acids*, Madison, Wis., June, 1961.

involved as anions in complex formation with chromium(II), and that this readily dissociable complex [chromium(II) is labile] can interact with a peptide linkage in an intramolecular reaction to transfer an electron.[270] Although rotation data for the polypeptides which lead to fast reaction indicate some helical structure, the relationship between structure and reactivity is not known since it is not possible to identify the local arrangements of the chain in the region where the oxidation-reduction takes place. A question also exists concerning the "models" for the polypeptide cases, some of which are listed in Table 2.12-4. These molecules, which lack a helical arrangement of peptide bonds, were used to test whether or not chelation by peptide bonds could induce a fast oxidation-reduction reaction. Unfortunately, the ring sizes which would exist if chelates were formed should not lead to stable chelates, and these molecules do not constitute an adequate test of this factor.

TABLE 2.12-4. REDUCTION OF CARBOXYLATOCOBALT(III) BY CHROMIUM(II)[a]
(Compare with Table 2.12-3)

Ligand	T, °C	k, l mole^{-1} sec^{-1}	% of reaction
Glycinate	26	0.06	
Acetylglycinate	26	0.30	
Acetylaminobutyrate	26	0.23	
Copolymer 5.2/1	16.5	>40	44–64
		0.08	20[b]
Copolymer 2.7/1	16.5	>40	50–75
		0.1	50–20[b]
Poly-L-glutamic acid	25	9.6	90

[a] Refs. 268, 269.
[b] Last portion of reaction yielded constants shown.

A reasonable possibility for the mechanism is expressed in Eq. (2.129). If electron transfer through a series of properly organized peptide linkages actually occurs, these experiments do not prove it, but should be regarded instead as an exciting clue pointing toward new possibilities in the acceleration of oxidation-reduction reactions.

[270] Pentamminocobaltic complexes of polyacrylic acid do not show any unusual reactivity. (K. D. Kopple, personal communication.) However, the relative lack of opportunity for carboxylic acid groups directly bonded to the polymer chain to form the appropriate transition states [Eq. (2.129)] in comparison with the carboxylic acid groups of glutamic acid side chains may reduce the usefulness of the model for the purpose intended.

(2.129)

$$\underset{\mathcal{N}}{C}\!-\!O^- + Cr(II) \rightleftharpoons \underset{\mathcal{N}}{\overset{O}{\underset{\parallel}{C}}}\!-\!O^-\cdots Cr(II)$$

$$+$$

$$\overset{H}{\underset{}{-N\!-\!C\!=\!O}}$$

$$\downarrow$$

$$\underset{\mathcal{N}}{\overset{O}{\underset{\parallel}{C}}}\!-\!OCo(III)(NH_3)_5 + \underset{\mathcal{N}}{\overset{O}{\underset{\parallel}{C}}}\!-\!O^{\overline{\cdots}}Cr(III)$$

$$-N\!-\!\overset{\bullet}{C}\!-\!O^-$$
$$\overset{|}{H}\;\;\overset{|}{}$$

$$\underset{\mathcal{N}}{\overset{O}{\underset{\parallel}{C}}}\!-\!O^- + Co(II) + 5NH_3 + \underset{H}{\overset{|}{N}}\!-\!C\!=\!O + \underset{\mathcal{N}}{\overset{O}{\underset{\parallel}{C}}}\!-\!O^{\overline{\cdots}}Cr(III)$$

2.12-5. With appropriate reagents, chemical transformations of the pontal ligands can accompany or prevent the oxidation-reduction reaction. Oxidation of oxalatopentaminocobalt(III) ion with "one-electron" reagents [e.g., cerium(IV), cobalt(III), silver(I) with persulfate] leads to an excellent yield of hexaquocobalt(II) and carbon dioxide[271] [Eq. (2.130)]. The oxidizing agent removes one electron from the ligand

(2.130) $(NH_3)_5CoC_2O_4^+ + Ce(IV) \rightarrow (H_2O)_6Co(II) + Ce(III) + 2CO_2$

and the other electron is removed by the cobalt(III) ion.

"Two-electron" oxidants destroy the oxalato group without affecting the oxidation state of the cobalt(III) ion to which it is coordinated. Reagents used in this reaction are chlorine, hydrogen peroxide, or molybdenum(VI).[271]

The action of one-electron oxidizing reagents on p-aldehydobenzoatopentaminocobalt(III) leads to free terephthalic acid and hexaquocobalt(II), but two-electron reagents form terephthalatopentaminocobalt(III)[272] [Eqs. (2.131) and (2.132)].

(2.131)

$$(NH_3)_5Co(III)O\overset{O}{\underset{\parallel}{C}}\!\!\left\langle\bigcirc\right\rangle\!\!CHO + (H_2O)_6Co(III)$$

$$\downarrow$$

$$5NH_3 + (H_2O)_6Co(II) + HOOC\!\!\left\langle\bigcirc\right\rangle\!\!COOH$$

(2.132)

$$(NH_3)_5Co(III)O\overset{O}{\underset{\parallel}{C}}\!\!\left\langle\bigcirc\right\rangle\!\!CHO + Cl_2 \longrightarrow (NH_3)_5Co(III)O\overset{O}{\underset{\parallel}{C}}\!\!\left\langle\bigcirc\right\rangle\!\!COOH$$

[271] P. Saffir and H. Taube, *J. Am. Chem. Soc.*, **82**, 13 (1960).
[272] R. T. M. Fraser and H. Taube, *J. Am. Chem. Soc.*, **82**, 4152 (1960).

Among the other reactions which accompany or rapidly succeed the electron-transfer step in oxidation-reduction with organic ligands may be mentioned *cis-trans* isomerism (maleato → fumarato),[273] tautomerism (malonato → enol of malonate),[274] and ester hydrolysis. The last-named process possesses a number of chemically provocative features. The reaction of methylmaleatopentaminocobalt(III) with chromium(II) yields hexaquocobalt(II), ammonia, maleatochromium(III) in which the methanol is part of the first coordination shell of the chromium(III) [Eq. (2.133)].[275,276] The oxygen of the methanol was shown to be derived

$$(2.133) \quad (NH_3)_5Co(III)O\overset{\overset{O}{\|}}{C}C\overset{H}{=}\overset{H}{C}C\overset{\overset{O}{\|}}{O}CH_3 + Cr(II) \longrightarrow$$

$$5NH_3 + (H_2O)_6Co(II) + (CH_3OH)(H_2O)_4Cr(III)O\overset{\overset{O}{\|}}{C}C\overset{H}{=}\overset{H}{C}COOH$$

from the water by the use of oxygen-18, proving that the reaction was not merely another example of ester hydrolysis through a tetrahedral intermediate (see Sec. 2.7). Even in the case of the phenyl ester, phenylmaleatopentaminocobalt(III) ion, a substantial portion of the oxygen in the phenol (12%) was derived from the water. Details on the mechanism of the hydrolysis should be of great interest.

Vitamin B_{12} is a complex cobalt(III) compound, and cobamide is a Co(III) derivative. The latter is a coenzyme in a number of interesting transformations which may involve a change in oxidation state for the cobalt.[277] An example of such a reaction is the conversion of 1,2-propanediol to propionaldehyde and ethylene glycol to acetaldehyde.[278]

2.12-6. A number of reactions of hydrogen peroxide probably proceed through transition states in which oxygen serves as a pontal atom between two centers undergoing a change in oxidation state. Bromide ion displaces water from the conjugate acid of hydrogen peroxide [Eq. (2.134)]. A subsequent fast reaction between hypobromous acid and hydrogen peroxide leads to oxygen and hydrogen bromide [Eq. (2.135)].[279]

$$(2.134) \quad Br^- + HOO\overset{+}{H}_2 \rightarrow BrOH + H_2O$$
$$(2.135) \quad HOBr + H_2O_2 \rightarrow O_2 + HBr + H_2O$$

[273] H. Taube, lecture at Enzyme Institute, University of Wisconsin, April 26, 1961.
[274] G. F. Svatos and H. Taube, unpublished results.
[275] R. T. M. Fraser and H. Taube, *J. Am. Chem. Soc.*, **81**, 5000 (1960).
[276] D. K. Sebera and H. Taube, *J. Am. Chem. Soc.*, **83**, 1785 (1961).
[277] Prof. R. H. Abeles, personal communication (see also ref. 466a).
[278] A. M. Brownstein and R. H. Abeles, *J. Biol. Chem.*, **236**, 119 (1961).
[279] W. C. Bray, *Chem. Revs.*, **10**, 161 (1932).

Iodide ion also displaces water from the conjugate acid of hydrogen peroxide but is, in addition, sufficiently nucleophilic to displace hydroxide ion from the hydrogen peroxide molecule [Eqs. (2.136) and (2.137)].[280,281]

(2.136) $\quad I^- + HOO\overset{+}{H}_2 \rightarrow HOI + H_2O \qquad HOI + I^- \rightarrow I_2 + OH^-$

(2.137) $\quad I^- + HOOH \rightarrow HOI + OH^-$

It was concluded from the fact that no exchange could be observed between hydrogen peroxide and hydroxide ion that hydroxide ion could not displace hydroxide ion from hydrogen peroxide, and that the d orbitals of the halide ions were therefore required for stabilization of the transition state for the displacement reaction.[282] Although it may be true that d-orbital stabilization of the transition state contributes to the rate for halide ions, approximate evaluations of nucleophilicities[181] place bromide ion close to hydroxide ion. We might therefore expect that hydroxide ion would displace water from the conjugate acid of hydrogen peroxide, but not hydroxide ion. It would be rather difficult to observe the expected reaction. Thiocyanate ion, which has a nucleophilicity between that of bromide ion and iodide ion, reacts with hydrogen peroxide in both hydrogen-ion-dependent and hydrogen-ion-independent reactions.[283]

2.13. PYRIDINE NUCLEOTIDES

Es war spät abends, als K. ankam. Das Dorf lag in tiefem Schnee. Vom Schlossberg war nichts zu sehen, Nebel und Finsternis umgaben ihn, auch nicht der schwächste Lichtschein deutete das grosse Schloss an. Lange stand K. auf der Holzbrücke, die von der Landstrasse zum Dorf führte, und blickte in die scheinbare Leere empor.

F. Kafka

2.13A. Introduction

2.13A-1. At the beginning of the century, a heat-stable cofactor was found necessary for the fermentation of sugar to alcohol.[284] This cofactor and other factors which exhibited a cooperative behavior with enzymes were called "coenzymes." Eventually, coenzyme I and

[280] H. A. Liebhafsky and A. Mohammad, *J. Am. Chem. Soc.*, **55**, 3977 (1933); *J. Phys. Chem.*, **38**, 857 (1934).

[281] F. Bell et al., *J. Phys. and Colloid Chem.*, **55**, 874 (1951).

[282] M. C. R. Symons, *Chemistry and Industry*, 1480 (1960).

[283] I. R. Wilson and G. M. Harris, *J. Am. Chem. Soc.*, **82**, 4515 (1960).

[284] A. Harden and J. W. Young, *Proc. Chem. Soc.*, **21**, 189 (1905).

coenzyme II were found to be closely related compounds, differing by one phosphate ester group (at 2′-), with the formulas shown in Fig. 2.42.[285] The coenzymes are commonly known as DPN and TPN: diphosphopyridine and triphosphopyridine nucleotides.[286] The respective reduced forms contain one additional hydrogen each (and one less positive charge) and are dihydroforms, or DPNH and TPNH.

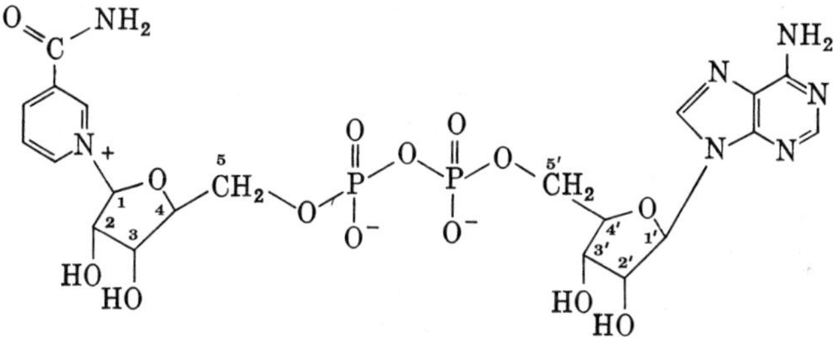

Fig. 2.42. Diphosphopyridine nucleotide (DPN).

The coenzymatic function of DPN is chiefly displayed in oxidation-reduction reactions, and clear chemical evidence exists to show that the chemically significant behavior of the coenzyme with respect to its chief coenzymatic role is an interconversion between a pyridinium ring and a 1,4-dihydropyridine ring (Fig. 2.43).

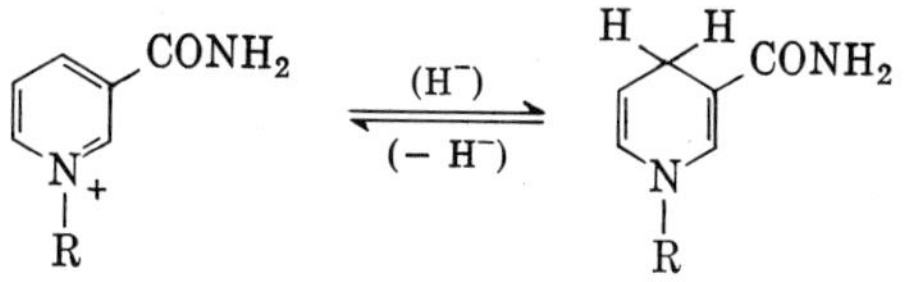

Fig. 2.43. Oxidized and reduced forms of the pyridinium ring.

2.13A-2. Studies in nutrition led to the conclusion that nicotinamide was an essential constituent of the human diet, i.e., a vitamin. It was a matter of scientific delight as well as an important hint in other studies that a place could be found for the nicotinamide on the biochemical and molecular levels.

The most common type of enzymatic conversion in which DPN

[285] An extensive treatment of many aspects of the background and behavior of these coenzymes will be found in N. O. Kaplan, The Pyridine Coenzymes, in "The Enzymes," vol. 3, chap. 12, Academic Press, Inc., New York, 1960.

[286] The unsystematic character of these names has led to the proposal that DPN be termed nicotinamide adenine dinucleotide (NAD). (S. Colowick, personal communication, November, 1960.) Cf. also published proposals on the revision of nomenclature in biochemistry, e.g., Appendix B, *Information Bulletin No. 12*, International Union of Pure and Applied Chemistry.

participates is illustrated by the oxidation of alcohols to aldehydes or ketones (e.g., ethanol, alcohol dehydrogenase, and DPN yield acetaldehyde, alcohol dehydrogenase, and DPNH). The DPNH produced by this reaction can be utilized biochemically for the reduction of carbonyl (or other) compounds. Dehydrogenases which produce free DPN *and* DPNH may be regarded as "hydrogen-transferring." Another enzyme of this class is glucose-6-phosphate dehydrogenase which requires TPNH (or TPN) as cofactor.

A second class of dehydrogenases consists of those in which either DPN *or* DPNH is utilized, but not both. The apparent reason for the reaction with only one oxidation state of the coenzyme is that the "complex" with the transformed substrate and the other state of the coenzyme (and the enzyme) is so stable that no dissociation takes place. An important example of such an enzyme is galactowaldenase which catalyzes the transformation of uridine diphosphogalactose into uridine diphosphoglucose with the aid of the coenzyme DPN.

A third class of enzymes which have a DPN requirement are not dehydrogenases but catalyze entirely different reactions. One example, that of formation of oxalosuccinic acid by carboxylation of α-ketoglutaric acid catalyzed by isocitric dehydrogenase, requires TPNH for enolization (see Sec. 2.3). The product of carboxylation, oxalosuccinic acid, is a substrate for the same enzyme in a reduction by TPNH. More curious is the acetyl phosphatase activity observed for the DPN–glyceraldehyde-3-phosphate dehydrogenase "complex," in which acetyl groups actually become covalently bound to the enzyme, as in the case of ester hydrolysis catalyzed by chymotrypsin.[287] DPN inhibits, however, hydrolysis of p-nitrophenyl acetate catalyzed by the same enzyme.

While the foregoing classification is not rigorous, it might reasonably be expected that some similarities would obtain at the "active site" for the enzymes of the first group.

2.13A-3. It is important to make a somewhat arbitrary distinction between the chemical behavior and the biochemical behavior of DPN. The discussion in this section is directed at the mechanism of oxidation-reduction with the coenzyme, requiring an emphasis on the chemical properties of the pyridinium and dihydropyridine rings. Spectroscopic observations are also very important in indicating a possible mechanism for the DPN oxidation-reduction.

For contrast, other interesting topics which are not germane to an understanding of oxidation-reduction mechanism might be mentioned. The biosynthesis of DPN, the intracellular distribution of DPN, the equilibrium between DPN and TPN, reactions in which DPN (or TPN)

[287] J. H. Park, B. P. Meriwether, P. Clodfelder, and L. W. Cunningham, *J. Biol. Chem.*, **236**, 136 (1961).

functions as coenzyme,[288] and the interesting possibility that differences between the activity of DPN and DPN analogues[285] may be of use in establishing evolutionary patterns on the molecular level[289] are all topics of great concern.

Pyridinium rings add nucleophilic reagents, and, although this process is exemplified by a fair number of cases, detailed knowledge concerning

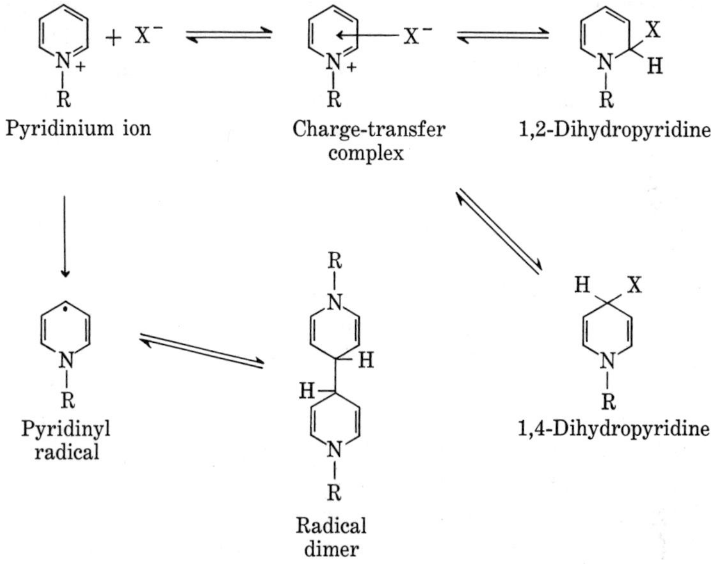

Fig. 2.44. General survey of pyridinium-dihydropyridine reactions.

its operation is lacking. Dihydropyridine rings react with electrophiles in a manner which is understood only to a limited extent.

Other pertinent subjects, which include the charge-transfer spectra of pyridinium complexes, the occurrence and behavior of pyridinyl radicals, and model reactions for DPNH reduction, will be treated briefly along with a postulated mechanism of an enzyme catalyzed DPN reaction.

A general summary of the reactions to be expected for pyridinium-dihydropyridine compounds is shown in Fig. 2.44.

2.13B. The Pyridinium Ring

2.13B-1. The original demonstration that the pyridinium ring was transformed into a dihydropyridine ring in an enzymatic reaction

[288] Cf. E. Racker, *Physiol. Revs.*, **35**, 1 (1955).

[289] N. O. Kaplan, in "The Steric Course of Microbiological Reactions," p. 37, Ciba Foundation Study Group No. 2, J. and A. Churchill, Ltd., London, 1959.

depended upon a study of the properties of model pyridinium compounds.[290,291] There were no indications as to the origin of the extra hydrogen atom; either the solvent or the substrate might have served as the source for the *particular* hydrogen atom acquired by the pyridinium ring to form DPNH.

Oxidation of ethanol-1-d_2 by DPN in the presence of yeast alcohol dehydrogenase yields acetaldehyde-1-d and DPNH which contains *one* atom of deuterium per molecule (and is therefore written DPND).[292] The importance of this experiment cannot be overemphasized. Experiments using reactants with ordinary hydrogen in a deuterium oxide medium suggested strongly that transfer did not occur via the enzyme.[293] The stereochemistry of the reaction with respect to DPN and ethanol is discussed in Sec. 2.13D.

A brief comment on the implications of the experiment just described is in order, since it stands at a turning point in molecular biochemistry. Although the catalytic nature of enzymes was recognized, no clear idea of chemical limitations to their mode of operation existed. As a consequence, proposals that enzymes functioned as "electron conductors"[295] or "proton transmitters"[296] were put forward, including as one of their important tenets that the reactants would not have to be located at the same site on the enzyme. *Direct hydrogen transfer* between substrate and coenzyme demands that a single reaction take place at a single site (although there may be more than one active site per enzyme molecule) and, barring strong evidence to the contrary, suggests a similar initial assumption about all enzyme-catalyzed reactions.

2.13B-2. Transformation of a pyridine to a pyridinium ion causes very little change in the position of the ultraviolet absorption spectrum but does result in a substantial increase in intensity in the 2600 Å region. The advent of DPN analogues (compounds in which the nicotinamide ring of DPN is replaced by another differently substituted pyridinium ring)[285] necessitates some knowledge about the effect of a

[290] P. Karrer, B. H. Ringier, J. Büchi, H. Fritzsche, and U. Solmssen, *Helv. Chim. Acta.*, **20**, 55 (1937).

[291] P. Karrer and O. Warburg, *Biochem. Z.*, **285**, 297 (1936).

[292] H. F. Fisher, E. E. Conn, B. Vennesland, and F. H. Westheimer, *J. Biol. Chem.*, **202**, 687 (1953).

[293] In Sec. 2.3, we pointed out that an enzyme might transfer a proton intramolecularly under certain conditions. While the parallel behavior for a "hydride" ion could be postulated, it is difficult to propose a reasonable pathway[294] and this possibility is therefore not considered in the mechanism proposed in Sec. 2.13G.

[294] B. Vennesland and F. H. Westheimer, in "Mechanism of Enzyme Action," p. 372, Johns Hopkins Press, Baltimore, 1954.

[295] Cf. criticism of this idea in Secs. 2.12 and 1.4.

[296] T. A. Geissman, *Quart Rev. Biol.*, **24**, 309 (1949).

change of substitution upon the position of ultraviolet light absorption. Advances in instrumentation have made the 2000 to 2200 Å region accessible for measurement of spectra; the pattern of change in the spectrum with a change in substitution is different from that in the longer wavelength region and therefore of potential utility. The curves for

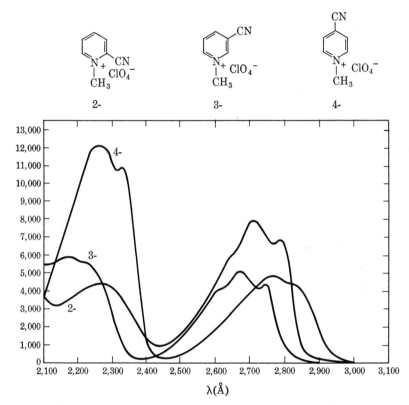

Fig. 2.45. Ultraviolet absorption curves for 1-methyl-2-, -3-, and -4-cyanopyridinium perchlorates in water.

1-methyl-2-, -3-, and -4-cyanopyridinium perchlorates[297] are shown in Fig. 2.45. Ultraviolet spectroscopic data for an illustrative variety of pyridinium ions are presented in Table 2.13-1. In general, only perchlorate salts can provide directly useful information about the 2100 Å region because many anions like iodide and bromide[298] possess strong absorption in this region of the spectrum.

[297] J. W. Patton, Ph.D. Thesis, University of Wisconsin, 1961.
[298] E. M. Kosower, J. Am. Chem. Soc., 80, 3261 (1958).

TABLE 2.13-1. ULTRAVIOLET SPECTROSCOPIC PROPERTIES OF PYRIDINIUM
IONS IN WATER

Substitution	Maxima[a]			Ref.
	λ_{max} (ϵ_{max})	λ_{max} (ϵ_{max})	λ_{max} (ϵ_{max})	
1-Methyl-2-cyano- (ClO_4^-)	2790 (6820)	2710 (7950)	2260 (5460)	297
1-Methyl-3-cyano- (ClO_4^-)	2750 (3350)	2675 (4060)	2180 (5850)	297
1-Methyl-4-cyano- (ClO_4^-)	2775 (4825)		2332 (10900)	297
			2260 (12100)	
1-Methyl-2-carbamido- (ClO_4^-)	2660 (6080)		2100[b]	297
1-Methyl-3-carbamido- (ClO_4^-)	2649 (4480)		2100[b]	299
1-Methyl-4-carbamido- (ClO_4^-)	2660 (4950)		2190 (8100)	297
	2657 (4720)			299
1-Propyl-3-carbamido- (Br^-)	265 (4080)[c]			300
1-Benzyl-3-carbamido- (Br^-)	263 (4250)[c]			300
1-(2-Phenoxyethyl)-3-carbamido- (Br^-)	266 (5360)[c]			300
1-Benzyloxymethyl-3-carbamido- (Br^-)	263 (3970)[c]			300
1-(2,6-Dichlorobenzyl)-3-carbamido- (Br^-)	266 (4420)[c]			300
1-(2,6-Dichlorobenzyl)-3-carboxy- (Br^-)	266 (4130)[c]			300
1-(2,6-Dichlorobenzyl)-3-carbomethoxy- (Br^-)	267 (4180)[c]			300
1-(2,6-Dichlorobenzyl)-3-cyano- (Br^-)	270 (4070)[c]			300
1-*H* (I^-)	2558 (4230)	2509 (4200)		
(ClO_4^-)			2012 (8000)[d]	302
1-Methyl- (I^-)	2558 (4230)	2509 (4200)		301
1,2-Dimethyl- (I^-)	2649 (6150)			301
1,3-Dimethyl- (I^-)	2657 (4690)			301
1,4-Dimethyl- (I^-)	2624 (3270)	2548 (4350)		301
		2497 (4050)		
1,2,4,6-Trimethyl- (I^-)	2732 (7130)	2688 (7360)		301
1,2,3,4,5,6-Hexamethyl- (I^-)	2852 (7300)	2817 (7180)		301
1-*H*-4-methyl- (ClO_4^-)			2170 (8000)[d]	302

[a] The maxima are grouped, when necessary, with the electronic transitions of greatest similarity.

[b] Rising curve with probable maximum somewhat below 2100 Å.

[c] Reported in mμ.

[d] Not specified for individual pyridinium ions, but described in the text of ref. 302 as being about 8000.

[299] E. M. Kosower and S. W. Bauer, *J. Am. Chem. Soc.*, **82**, 2191 (1960).

[300] K. Wallenfels and H. Diekmann, *Ann.*, **621**, 166 (1959).

[301] E. M. Kosower and J. A. Skorcz, *J. Am. Chem. Soc.*, **82**, 2195 (1960).

[302] W. M. Schubert and J. Robins, *J. Am. Chem. Soc.*, **80**, 559 (1958).

2.13B-3.   For many years, a salient feature of DPN chemistry has been the ability of the pyridinium ring to react with nucleophilic reagents to form dihydropyridine derivatives.   Attempts have been made to utilize various results of studies of addition (or supposed addition) reactions in the interpretation of certain aspects of DPN mechanism. Detailed analysis of such equilibria suggests that caution must be exercised in applying the results to the central problem of DPN mechanism in enzyme-catalyzed reactions.   Consider a general addition reaction, as written in Eq. (2.138):

$$(2.138) \qquad RPy^+ + X^- \rightleftharpoons RPyX$$

To a first approximation, the equilibrium constant for the reaction will be determined by the balance between the factors favoring one side or the other of the equation listed in Table 2.13-2.

TABLE 2.13-2. STABILIZING FACTORS FOR REACTANTS IN EQ. (2.138)

$RPy^+ + X^-$	$RPyX$
Solvation energy of RPy^+	Solvation energy of $RPyX$
Solvation energy of X^-	Carbon-X bond energy
Stabilization energy of RPy^+	Stabilization energy of $RPyX$

TABLE 2.13-3. ESTIMATE OF QUANTITIES FOR TABLE 2.13-2, KCAL/MOLE

Solv. en. RPy^+	30–45[a]	Solv. en. RPyI	20[b]
Solv. en. I^-	70[303]	Carbon-iodine bond en.	53[304]
Stab. en. RPy^+	23[305]	Stab. en. RPyI	10[c]
	123–138		83
Solv. en. RPy^+	30–45[a]	Solv. en. RPyCN	20[b]
Solv. en. CN^-	35[d]	C—CN bond en.	103[304]
Stab. en. RPy^+	23[305]	Stab. en. RPyCN	10[c]
	88–103		133

[a] Taken as one-half to one-third of the free energy of solution of sodium ion[303] with the idea that no more than two water molecules are important in solvation of the pyridinium ion as compared with four for sodium.

[b] A generous estimate.

[c] Generous, but based on the stabilization energy of 1,4,4-trimethyl-1,4-dihydropyridine.[306]

[d] Taken as one-half of that of iodide ion.

[303] R. A. Robinson and R. H. Stokes, "Electrolyte Solutions," 2d ed., p. 70, Butterworth & Co. (Publishers) Ltd., London, 1959.

[304] T. L. Cottrell, "The Strengths of Chemical Bonds," 2d ed., Butterworth & Co. (Publishers) Ltd., London, 1958.

[305] G. W. Wheland, "Resonance in Organic Chemistry," p. 99, John Wiley & Sons, Inc., New York, 1955.

[306] T. S. Sorensen, Ph.D. Thesis, University of Wisconsin, 1960.

It is not possible to estimate properly the quantities necessary for the calculation of the equilibrium constant, but some educated guesses may be made for two different anions, iodide and cyanide, as shown in Table 2.13-3, to illustrate trends.

The chief variables affecting the equilibrium of (2.138) are the bond energy of the carbon-X bond and the solvation energy of X^-. A reduction in the solvating power of the solvent causes a shift of the equilibrium to the right, since solvation of the separate ions is much more significant than that for the dihydropyridine derivative. Similarly, if the alkyl group of the pyridinium ring contains many groups capable of hydrogen-bonding, the relative importance of pyridinium ring solvation to the position of the equilibrium is decreased, and addition is favored.[307]

Diphosphopyridine nucleotide reacts with cyanide ion to form a derivative with an absorption spectrum resembling DPNH;[308] there are indications that the reaction is not instantaneous.[309] Since the DPN exchanged only 4-hydrogens in the presence of cyanide ion,[310] in contrast to the reaction of 1-methyl-3-carbamidopyridinium ion with base alone (in which the 2- and, to a small extent, the 6-hydrogens exchanged),[311,312] the 4-position was proposed as the site of addition [Eq. (2.139)]. Confirma-

(2.139)

tion of this assignment is based on the analogy between the absorption spectra of the cyanide adducts from 1-methyl-3-carbamido-[313] and 1-(2,6-dichlorobenzyl)-3-carbamidopyridinium[314] ions to those of 1,4-dihydropyridines[314] (cf. Sec. 2.13D). It should be noted, however, that the deuterium exchange may not uniquely indicate a 4-location for the adduct since there is no proof that it is the adduct itself which undergoes the exchange.[315]

Interest in the cyanide adducts is sufficiently great to warrant a brief

[307] M. R. Lamborg, R. M. Burton, and N. O. Kaplan, *J. Am. Chem. Soc.*, **79**, 6173 (1957).

[308] O. Meyerhof, P. Ohlmeyer, and W. Möhle, *Biochem. Z.*, **297**, 113 (1938).

[309] S. P. Colowick, N. O. Kaplan, and M. M. Ciotti, *J. Biol. Chem.*, **191**, 447 (1951).

[310] A. San Pietro, *J. Biol. Chem.*, **217**, 579 (1955).

[311] A. San Pietro, *J. Biol. Chem.*, **217**, 589 (1955).

[312] H. E. Dubb, M. Saunders, and J. H. Wang, *J. Am. Chem. Soc.*, **80**, 1767 (1958).

[313] M. Marti, M. Viscontini, and P. Karrer, *Helv. Chim. Acta*, **39**, 1451 (1956).

[314] K. Wallenfels and H. Schüly, *Ann.*, **621**, 86 (1959).

[315] E. M. Kosower, in "The Enzymes," vol. 3, chap. 13, Academic Press, Inc., New York, 1960.

list of the equilibrium constants and absorption maxima[316] (Table 2.13-4). An extensive and very carefully measured series of dissociation constants for the sulfite adducts of pyridinium ions has been reported.[317]

TABLE 2.13-4. EQUILIBRIUM CONSTANTS FOR CYANIDE ADDITION[a]
$$RPy^+ + CN \rightleftharpoons RPyCN$$

Substituent on pyridinium ring	K, l mole^{-1}	$\lambda_{max}(RPyCN)$, mμ
1-(2-Phenylethyl)-3-carbamido-	ca. 1	343
1-(2,6-Dichlorobenzyl)-3-carbamido-	ca. 10	339
DPN	ca. 10^2	327
1-Benzyloxymethyl-3-carbamido-	ca. 10^3	326
1-(Tetraacetylglucosyl)-3-carbamido-	ca. 10^4	319
1-(2,6-Dichlorobenzyl)-3,5-dicarbamido-	ca. 10^5	360

[a] Ref. 300.

The relative equilibrium constants observed for the cyanide addition reaction with the 3-acetylpyridine analogue of DPN and DPN are what might have been expected from the equilibrium between the two coenzymes and their reduced forms in the ethanol to acetaldehyde oxidation catalyzed by alcohol dehydrogenase.[318]   This thermodynamic information does not, of course, provide any information about the pathway by which the equilibrium was established.

The rate at which a particular 1,4-dihydropyridine reduces 2,6-dichloro-phenol-indophenol is inversely proportional to the "affinity" of the corresponding pyridine for cyanide ion.[318]   This parallelism was taken as implying that the hydrogen was transferred as a species with anionic character, i.e., as a "hydride" ion.   Relationships between equilibria and kinetics are most useful in very carefully chosen systems;[319] although the conclusion for the oxidation-reduction reaction is a reasonable one, the transition state for the reaction requires further specification by more direct measurements (for example, by isotope effects).

2.13B-4.   Among the variety of nucleophilic reagents known to add to pyridinium rings are hydroxide ion, aniline, dimethylaniline,

---

[316] See ref. 300.   Only orders of magnitude are given because (a) no error limits were established and (b) certain unspecified constants were determined in a medium which contained as much as 33% methanol, a practice [cf. discussion of Eq. (2.138) and ref. 307] which changes the equilibrium constants.

[317] G. Pfleiderer, E. Sann, and A. Stock, *Chem. Ber.*, **93**, 3083 (1960).

[318] K. Wallenfels, in "The Steric Course of Microbiological Reactions," p. 10, Ciba Foundation Study Group No. 2, J. and A. Churchill, Ltd., London, 1959.

[319] Cf. R. W. Taft, Jr., in "Steric Effects in Organic Chemistry," ed. by M. S. Newman, chap. 13, p. 556, John Wiley & Sons, Inc., New York, 1956.

N-methylaniline, sulfoxylate($SO_2^=$), enolate ions, bisulfite ion, hydroxylamine, and mercaptide ions.[285,320,321] The difficulty in establishing the structure of a solid isolated from the reaction of a nucleophile with a pyridinium ring is not always appreciated. For example, 1-benzyl-3-carbamidopyridinium ion reacts with concentrated aqueous potassium iodide to form an oil which crystallizes into bright yellow leaflets.[322] Attempts to examine the solid are fruitless since it is rapidly transformed into a white solid, 1-benzyl-3-carbamidopyridinium iodide. It would be unwarranted to conclude that an addition product has been formed, since

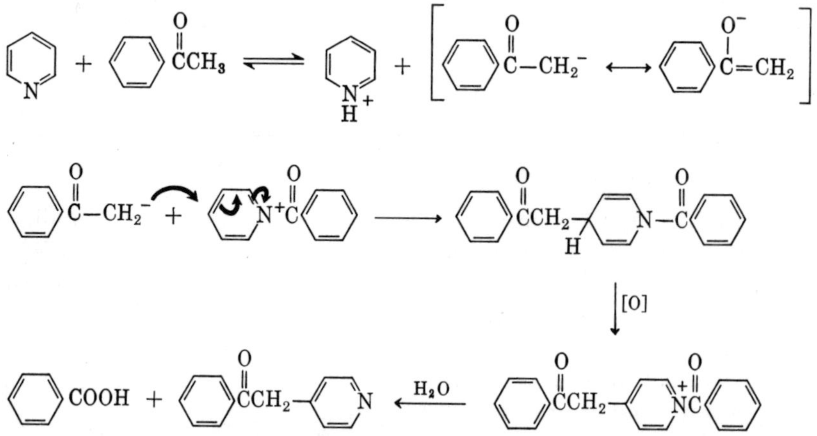

FIG. 2.46. Addition of carbonyl compound to pyridinium rings.

the yellow isomer could be an unstable crystalline form of the pyridinium iodide, in which some charge-transfer light absorption (see Sec. 2-13C) was responsible for the color. The conclusion that 1-(2,6-dichloro-benzyl)-3-carbamidopyridinium ion forms an addition product with iodide ion is unwarranted on the basis of the reported spectroscopic data,[314] for maxima at 292 mμ and 360 mμ are very characteristic for the triiodide ion (I_3^-).[245] The solvent in which these maxima were observed (dioxane) is susceptible to attack by oxygen with formation of hydroperoxides. Hydroperoxides oxidize iodides to triiodide.

In contrast to the case of iodide "addition," the structure of the adduct derived from acetophenone enolate ion and 1-benzoylpyridinium ion was demonstrable in a straightforward way. 1-Benzoyl-4-phenacyl-1,4-dihydropyridine (Fig. 2.46), a pale yellow solid, was oxidized by oxygen

[320] E. M. Kosower, *J. Am. Chem. Soc.*, **78**, 3497 (1956).
[321] J. van Eys and N. O. Kaplan, *J. Biol. Chem.*, **228**, 305 (1957).
[322] E. M. Kosower and P. E. Klinedinst, Jr., *J. Am. Chem. Soc.*, **78**, 3493 (1956).

to the known 4-phenacylpyridine.[323] It is probable that the pyridine nucleotide analogues prepared by the reaction of DPN and carbonyl compounds in basic solution, followed by ferricyanide oxidation, have the new substituent on the 4-position,[324] even though direct chemical proof is lacking.   The most attractive explanation for the formation of very high

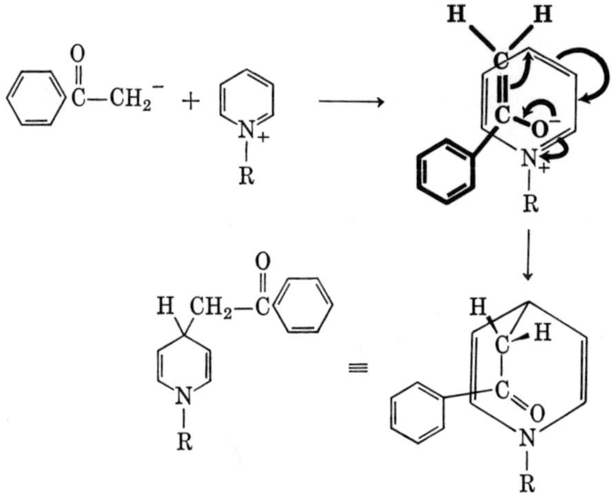

FIG. 2.47. Mechanism of addition of enolate ions to pyridinium rings.

proportions of 4-adduct in certain additions depends upon the inter-mediate formation of a "complex" between the pyridinium ring and the enolate ion (Fig. 2.47).[325]

In contrast to the 4-addition observed for dimethylaniline and 1-ben-zoylpyridinium ion,[328,329] N-methylaniline and aniline must add at the

[323] W. von E. Doering and W. E. McEwen, J. Am. Chem. Soc., **73**, 2104 (1951).

[324] R. M. Burton, A. San Pietro, and N. O. Kaplan, Arch. Biochem. Biophys., **70**, 87 (1957).

[325] The fact that ions of the type $RC{\equiv}C^-$ add at the 2-position of pyridinium rings is not necessarily to be regarded as a serious criticism of the postulate that nucleophiles which complex with the ring tend to add at the 4-position.[326] Implicit in the notion[320] was the requirement of ambident character[327] of the ion (or molecule) acting as addend, so that electrostatic attraction of the positive charge in the pyridin-ium ring and the negative charge in the addend could provide the means for associa-tion, while the juxtaposition of a nucleophilic center in the addend with the 4-position of the ring would lead to addition at the 4-position.   In all cases where the ambidental combination of negative charge and nucleophilicity is present (e.g., enolate ions, sulfoxylate, sulfite[317]), 4-addition appears to be preferred.

[326] T. Agawa and S. I. Miller, J. Am. Chem. Soc., **83**, 449 (1961).

[327] "Ambident" refers to a species with charge localization at a minimum of two centers.

[328] E. Koenigs and E. Ruppelt, Ann., **509**, 142 (1934).

[329] W. E. McEwen, R. H. Terss, and I. W. Elliott, J. Am. Chem. Soc., **74**, 3605 (1952).

2-position with ring opening as the result.   The kinetics of the reaction
between N-methylaniline and 1-(2,4-dinitrophenyl)-pyridinium ion have
been investigated and found to depend upon the first power of hydroxide
ion as well as the first power of each of the principal reactants [Eq.
(2.140)].[330]   The reaction of N-methylaniline (Fig. 2.48) is quite similar

(2.140) $v = k(N\text{-methylaniline})(\text{RPy}^+)(\text{OH}^-)$

to that for many long-known reactions of amines with pyridinium
ions.[331,332]

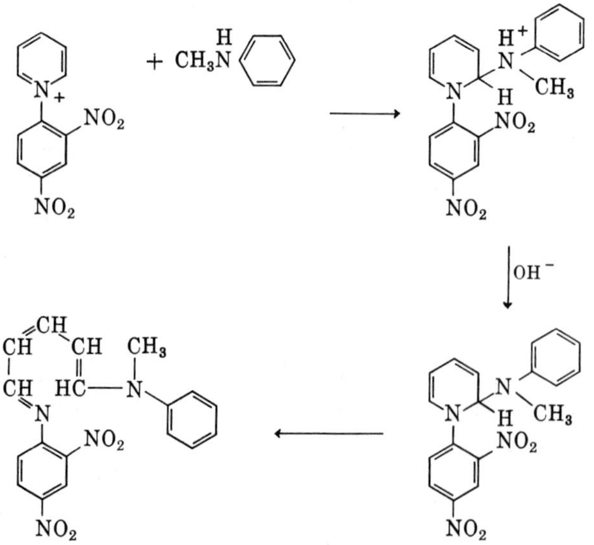

Fig. 2.48. Reaction of N-methylaniline with a pyridinium ion.

2.13B-5.   It has been suggested that the reaction of ethyl mercaptan with DPN in aqueous buffer, pH 11, yields a 4-adduct on the
grounds that the spectrum of the solution in which the adduct is formed
has a resemblance to that for DPNH.[321]   Other criteria[315] were not
applied to the system, the ϵ used in the determination of equilibrium
constants for ethyl and other mercaptans was assumed, and no identifiable
chemical substance was isolated.[321]   The considerable change observed
in the spectrum of 1-(2,6-dichlorobenzyl)-3-carbamidopyridinium ion in
methanol over a hundredfold change in the concentration of benzyl

[330] P. van Laer, Mémoire licencienne, Faculté des Sciences, Université Libre de
Bruxelles, 1957.
[331] W. König, J. prakt. Chem., **69,** 105 (1904).
[332] T. Zincke, Ann., **330,** 361 (1904).

mercaptan[314] is certainly indicative of weak association but does not prove that a 4-adduct is present. The precise nature of the interaction of mercaptides with pyridinium rings is an open question, and one which is in need of further investigation. The spectra observed for the "adducts" of mercaptides to pyridinium rings may be in part due to charge-transfer absorption (see Sec. 2.13C).

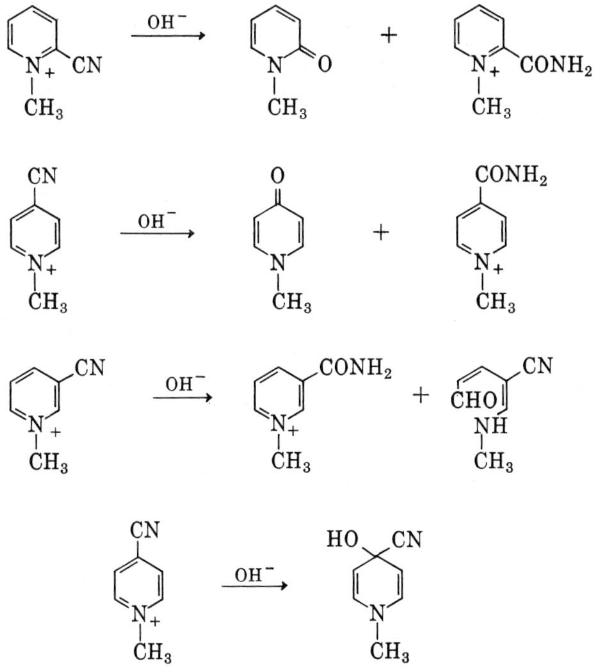

FIG. 2.49. Reactions of cyanopyridinium ions with base.

The proposal that an enzyme mercaptide addition product of DPN is an intermediate in the reactions of glyceraldehyde-3-phosphate dehydrogenase[333] can be criticized on two grounds. First, the maximum (λ_{max}, 360 mμ) is at a wavelength considerably longer than those for a number of mercaptide-DPN "adducts."[334] Combination of the mercaptide-DPN "adducts" with enzyme moves the maximum to *shorter* wavelengths. Second, the low intensity, broad character of the absorption band suggests its interpretation as a charge-transfer absorption band (see Sec. 2.13C).

Addition to pyridinium rings is illustrated in the reaction of cyanopyridinium ions with hydroxide ion[297] (Fig. 2.49). Both 1-methyl-2- and

[333] E. Racker and I. Krimsky, *J. Biol. Chem.*, **198**, 731 (1952).

[334] J. van Eys, N. O. Kaplan, and F. E. Stolzenbach, *Biochim. et Biophys. Acta*, **23**, 221 (1957).

-4-cyanopyridinium ions hydrolyze to a mixture of 1-methyl-2- (or -4-) pyridone and 1-methyl-2- (or -4-) carbamidopyridinium ion, whereas the 3-cyanopyridinium ion yields 1-methyl-3-carbamidopyridinium ion along with ring-opened products resulting from addition of hydroxide ion at the 6-position. The reactions of the cyanopyridinium ions with water (or hydroxide ion) are of some physiological interest since the anti-cholinesterase antidote, 1-methyl-2-aldoximinopyridinium ion (PAM), gives rise to the 1-methyl-2-cyanopyridinium ion upon perfusion through liver.[335] The cyanohydrin is the probable intermediate in the hydrolyses of 2- and 4-cyanopyridinium ions (see last equation, Fig. 2.49), a conclusion derived from a consideration of both kinetic and product studies.[297]

2.13C. Charge-transfer Complexing

The formation of "molecular complexes" is a well-established phenomenon, but the explanation of the *raison d'être* and the properties of such complexes is a relatively recent development.[336] The importance of "molecular complexes" to pyridinium ring chemistry was revealed by detailed study of the "chromoisomer" (colored form)[343] of 1-methyl-pyridinium iodide.[322,344]

2.13C-1. A new species, detected by light absorption in the near ultraviolet, is present in solutions of 1-alkylpyridinium iodides.[345] The variation of "new" absorption with concentration along with the results of a number of other studies[245,346] indicate that the equilibrium should be written as in Eq. (2.141). The species on the right-hand side

---

[335] There are indications that perfusion of the 1-methyl-2-cyanopyridinium ion itself through rat liver leads to 1-methyl-2-methoxypyridinium ion, an unusual result which can be rationalized as arising from the intermediate cyanohydrin through methylation. Another possible source, 1-methyl-2-pyridone, can definitely be excluded by control experiments. (J. L. Way, personal communication.)

[336] The subject of complexing especially as it applies to pyridinium rings is reviewed in ref. 315. The interested reader should examine the papers of Mulliken[337,338] and the slightly earlier, but almost equivalent, proposal of "Complexresonance" by Brackman.[339] Reviews on the subject include those of McGlynn[340] and Briegleb and Czekalla.[341] Some interesting historical aspects can be found in the review by Kröhnke.[342]

[337] R. S. Mulliken, *J. Phys. Chem.*, **56**, 801 (1952).

[338] R. S. Mulliken, *J. Am. Chem. Soc.*, **74**, 811 (1952).

[339] N. Brackman, *Rec. trav. chim.*, **68**, 147 (1949).

[340] S. P. McGlynn, *Chem. Revs.* **58**, 1113 (1958).

[341] G. Briegleb and J. Czekalla, *Angew. Chem.*, **72**, 401 (1960).

[342] F. Kröhnke, *J. prakt. Chem.*, [4]**6**, 235 (1958).

[343] A. Hantzsch, *Ber.*, **44**, 1783 (1911).

[344] E. M. Kosower and J. C. Burbach, *J. Am. Chem. Soc.*, **78**, 5838 (1956).

[345] E. M. Kosower, *J. Am. Chem. Soc.*, **77**, 3883 (1955).

[346] E. M. Kosower, *J. Am. Chem. Soc.*, **80**, 3253 (1958).

(2.141)

of Eq. (2.141) is a charge-transfer complex, and, in this case, should be regarded as an *ion pair with the property of undergoing an observable charge-transfer transition.* A species which absorbs light in a manner best explained by charge-transfer theory can be referred to as a *charge-transfer complex.*[347]

Another type of charge-transfer complex is that formed from benzene and iodine [Eq. (2.142)]. This complex is responsible for the brown color

(2.142)

of solutions of iodine in benzene, with an intense absorption maximum near 3000 Å.[348]

2.13C-2. Charge-transfer complex formation and charge-transfer light absorption are related, but not at all identical, phenomena. This is clear if we consider the case of a generalized donor D and a generalized acceptor A. Donor ability refers to the ease with which a particular molecule, atom, or ion will give up electronic charge and is most easily measured by the ionization potential [Eq. (2.143)]. Acceptor ability depends upon the willingness of a system to accept electronic charge, and is related to the electron affinity of a species [Eq. (2.144)]. The association of the donor D and the acceptor A yields the complex

(2.143) $D \xrightarrow{I_p} D^+ + e^-$ I_p = ionization potential

(2.144) $A + e^- \xrightarrow{E_a} A^-$ E_a = electron affinity

D,A. Light absorption by the complex D,A gives rise to the excited state of the complex D^+,A^- [Eq. (2.145)]. According to charge-transfer theory, some stabilization of the complex D,A formed by association of

(2.145) $D + A \underset{K_{assoc}}{\rightleftharpoons} (D,A) \xrightarrow{h\nu} (D^+,A^-)$

D and A can be attributed to a contribution to the *ground state* by the charge-transferred state, i.e., the *excited state.* In a like manner, some

---

[347] Some confusion has existed on this point (e.g., ref. 285, p. 145). Isolation of a solid does not constitute identification of a product as an "adduct," nor does a color prove that a substance is a "complex." In many cases, properties measured in solution may reflect the presence of species which are not present in the solid. Careful and quantitative studies are necessary to interpret the behavior of a given system, e.g., mercaptide ion and pyridinium ion. This matter is discussed at greater length in ref. 315.

[348] H. A. Benesi and J. H. Hildebrand, *J. Am. Chem. Soc.*, **70**, 2382 (1948).

stabilization of the excited state is achieved through a contribution by the ground state [Eq. (2.146)]. This is essentially a quantum-mechanical formulation of the conclusion that the transfer of an electron from D to A requires less energy in a complex than for the separated species. In addition to the "charge-transfer forces," many other factors can affect both the stability of the ground state (i.e., the association constant) and the required excitation energy (i.e., the position of light absorption). The most important of these additional factors is electrostatic attraction,

$$(2.146) \quad \begin{matrix} \text{Major} \\ \text{form} \end{matrix} \left\{ \begin{matrix} D^+,A^- & \longleftrightarrow & D,A \\ & h\nu & \\ D,A & \longleftrightarrow & D^+,A^- \end{matrix} \right\} \begin{matrix} \text{Minor} \\ \text{form} \end{matrix}$$

arising from the attraction between proximate positive and negative ions [cf. Sec. 2.9, Eq. (2.102)].

The position of charge-transfer light absorption (E_T = transition

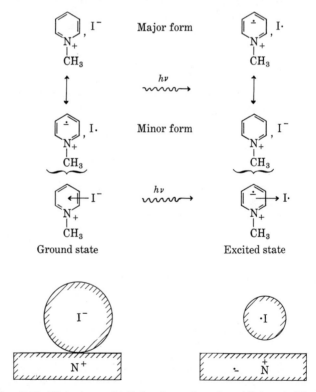

FIG. 2.50. Charge-transfer light absorption of pyridinium iodides.

energy) is empirically known to be a linear function of the ionization potential, Eq. (2.147). (Insufficient data on electron affinities preclude statements about possible linear relationships[341] except for relative affinities measured by the Hammett σ-constant, see below.) The more

$$(2.147) \qquad\qquad E_T = mI_p + b$$

easily a donor gives up an electron (the lower its ionization potential), the longer the wavelength (the lower the transition energy) of the charge-transfer band (light absorption) for a given acceptor.

    2.13C-3. The position of the charge-transfer band of pyridinium iodides is very sensitive to the substitution on the pyridinium ring, and is probably a more reliable measure of the "reducibility" or "one-electron affinity" of the pyridinium ring than reduction potential. The charge-transfer light absorption is expressed in detail in Fig. 2.50, and data for the charge-transfer band of pyridinium iodides are listed in Table 2.13-5.

TABLE 2.13-5. CHARGE-TRANSFER BANDS OF 1-ALKYLPYRIDINIUM IODIDES

Pyridinium ring substituent	λ_{max}, Å	ϵ_{max}	E_T	Solvent	Ref.
1-(4-Methoxybenzyl)-4-carbomethoxy-	4520	960	63.3	A[a]	349
1-Benzyl-4-carbomethoxy	4564	1040	62.7	A	349
1-(4-Chlorobenzyl)-4-carbomethoxy-	4600	1070	62.2	A	349
1-(4-Nitrobenzyl)-4-carbomethoxy-	4693	1180	60.9	A	349
1-(2,6-Dichlorobenzyl)-4-carbomethoxy-	4694	830	60.9	A	349
1-Methyl-3,5-dicarbomethoxy-	4338	2700[b]	65.9	A	349
1-Ethyl-4-carbomethoxy-	4508	970	63.4	A	349
1-Ethyl-4-carbamido-	4075			D[e]	299
1-Methyl-4-cyano-	4905	1000	58.3	B[c]	245
1-Methyl-2-cyano-	4775	1200	59.9	B	245
1-Methyl-2-carboethoxy-	4270	1070	67.0	C[d]	245
1-Ethyl-3-carbamido-	3700			D[e]	299
1-Methyl-3-carbomethoxy-	4070	1850[b]	70.2	C	245
1-Methyl-	3738	1200	76.5	C	350
1,2-Dimethyl-	3640	860	78.5	C	350
1,3-Dimethyl-	3700	1310	77.3	C	350
1,4-Dimethyl-	3590	1230	79.6	C	350
1,2,4,6-Tetramethyl-	3418	480	83.7	C	350
1,2,3,4,5,6-Hexamethyl-	3253	560	87.9	C	350

  [a] *cis*-1,2-Dichloroethylene.
  [b] The spectra of 3- (and 3,5-) substituted pyridinium iodides in nonpolar solvents are unusual and have not been analyzed in detail.
  [c] Methylene chloride.
  [d] Chloroform containing 0.90% ethanol by volume.
  [e] Pyridine.

[349] D. Hofmann, unpublished results.
[350] E. M. Kosower and J. A. Skorcz, *J. Am. Chem. Soc.*, **82**, 2195 (1960).

The first five salts listed in Table 2.13-5 are substituted 1-benzyl-pyridinium iodides. The significant fact about the charge-transfer bands observed for this series is that the transition energies[351] are linear in the Hammett σ-constant, with a ρ_s of -1.70. Data for the other 1-alkyl-4- and -3-monosubstituted pyridinium iodides as transition energies also plot against σ-constant to give a fairly good straight line, with a slope ρ_s of -13.4.[352] These correlations constitute excellent support of the interpretation, since an electron-transfer process should be very sensitive to electron-withdrawal or supply in either the donor or the acceptor. The ρ_s for electron transfer to the pyridinium ring with a variation in substituents located on the ring is among the highest observed for substitution into an aromatic ring. (Charge-transfer to the pyridinium ring can be regarded as "electron substitution.") The measurement of the position of the charge-transfer band offers a sensitive and convenient method for the facile determination of the electron affinity of a pyridinium ring. The electron affinity, in turn, may be useful in evaluating the rates of reactions of the pyridinium ring.

2.13C-4. Complete absorption curves for 1-ethyl-4-carbomethoxypyridinium iodide and perchlorate are shown in Fig. 2.51. The shortest wavelength absorption for the iodide is a combination of iodide ion absorption[245] and pyridinium ring absorption. The band in the neighborhood of 2500 Å is the typical pyridinium ring absorption (see Table 2.13-1), and the next two lower intensity bands of the iodide (completely lacking in the curve for the perchlorate) are the two charge-transfer bands. The long-wavelength charge-transfer band is the most intensively studied,[245,346,350] but the second band is perfectly explicable on the basis of the description of charge-transfer absorption. Briefly, the argument is as follows: If iodide ion undergoes an electronic transition, the process may be formally written as in Eq. (2.148):

(2.148) $I^- \rightarrow I\cdot + e^-$

The iodine atom has two low-lying electronic states resulting from coupling of the spin of the electron, S, with the orbital angular momentum L of the orbital of the electron. Two electronic transitions are to be

[351] $$E_T = h\nu = \frac{2.859 \times 10^5}{\lambda_{max} \text{ (in Å)}} \text{ (kcal./mole)}$$

Thus, the transition energy is the position of the maximum expressed as kcal/mole.

[352] E. M. Kosower and J. A. Skorcz, *Proc. 4th European Molecular Spectroscopy Conf.*, Bologna, Italy, September, 1959, Pergamon Press, London, 1961. Cf. E. M. Kosower, D. Hofmann, and K. Wallenfels, *J. Am. Chem. Soc.*, **84**, (in press), for a definition and discussion of ρ_s.

expected for iodide ion, the separation between the transition energies being equal to the separation between the two low-lying states of the iodine atom, the $^2P_{3/2}$ and $^2P_{1/2}$ states.[245,353]

Now, in the simple theory, the absolute position of the transition would be related to the electron affinity of the environment to which the electron was transferred. In water, for example, the environment would be determined by the dipoles of the water molecules; in proximity to a pyridinium ring, the transition energy would be reduced in accordance

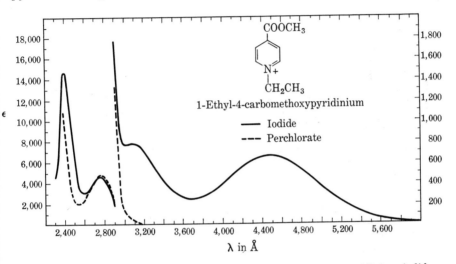

FIG. 2.51. Complete absorption curves for 1-ethyl-4-carbomethoxypyridinium iodide and perchlorate in ethylene dichloride.

with the greater ease with which a pyridinium ring can accept an electron as compared with a collection of solvent dipoles residing in "saturated" bonds. In fact, the theoretically expected separation between two bands is observed for potassium iodide in *water* and for 1-methylpyridinium iodide in *chloroform*, even though the longest wavelength band has changed in position from 2263 to 3738 Å.[245] In contrast, certain other pyridinium iodides exhibit $^2P_{3/2}-^2P_{1/2}$ separations which are either smaller or larger than theoretically expected.[245] It must be concluded that only qualitative conformity to the prediction can be expected.

2.13C-5. The most spectacular property of the charge-transfer light absorption of pyridinium iodides is the remarkable change in the position of the bands with a change in the polarity of the solvent in which the light absorption is measured.[346] The spectrum of 1-ethyl-4-carbo-

[353] J. Franck and G. Scheibe, *Z. physik. Chem.* (*Leipzig*), **139A,** 22 (1928).

methoxypyridinium iodide in a series of solvents is illustrated in Fig. 2.52. The transition energies for this salt in a given solvent are called **Z** values and are used as measures of solvent polarity with some success.[298,346,354–356] The empirical validity of the **Z** values as a measure of solvent polarity was established by a comparison with **Y** values (Fig. 2.53). **Y** values

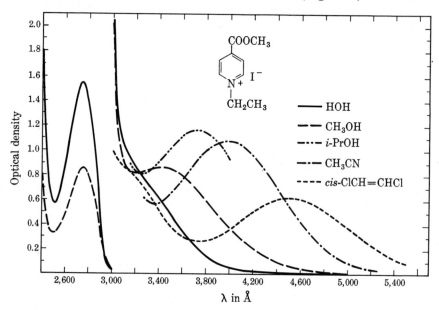

Fig. 2.52. First charge-transfer band of 1-ethyl-4-carbomethoxypyridinium iodide in water, methanol, isopropyl alcohol, acetonitrile, and *cis*-1,2-dichloroethylene.

are defined by Eq. (2.149), in which the rate constants (k and k_0) are those for the reaction of *t*-butyl chloride in a given solvent and in 80% ethanol-water [Eq. (2.150)].[357, 358]

(2.149)
$$\log \frac{k}{k_0} = m\mathbf{Y}$$

(2.150)
$$CH_3\underset{\underset{CH_3}{|}}{\overset{\overset{CH_3}{|}}{C}}{-}Cl \xrightarrow{H_2O} CH_3\underset{\underset{CH_3}{|}}{\overset{\overset{CH_3}{|}}{C}}{}^+ + Cl^-$$

[354] E. M. Kosower and G.-S. Wu, *J. Am. Chem. Soc.*, **83**, 3142 (1961).

[355] E. M. Kosower, G.-S. Wu, and T. S. Sorensen, *J. Am. Chem. Soc.*, **83**, 3147 (1961).

[356] E. M. Kosower, W. D. Closson, H. L. Goering, and J. R. Gross, *J. Am. Chem. Soc.*, **83**, 2013 (1961).

[357] A. H. Fainberg and S. Winstein, *J. Am. Chem. Soc.*, **78**, 2770 (1956), and preceding papers.

[358] S. G. Smith, A. H. Fainberg and S. Winstein, *J. Am. Chem. Soc.*, **83**, 618 (1961).

The explanation for the large solvent effect is quite interesting.   The dipole moment of the pyridinium iodide in the ground state is perpendicular to the plane of the pyridinium ring and parallel to the net dipole of the *cybotactic region*.[346]   The dipole moment of the pyridinium iodide in the excited state is parallel to the plane of the ring, but the

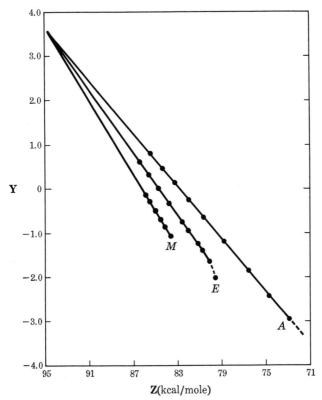

Fig. 2.53. **Z** versus **Y**.   (*Reprinted by permission of the Journal of the American Chemical Society.*)

cybotactic region dipole moment remains perpendicular to the plane of the ring (Franck-Condon principle).[359]   Thus, although the ground state is stabilized through the interaction of the pyridinium iodide ion pair with the solvent, the excited state is *destabilized* because the solvent molecules are organized for a dipole which is not present.   (Interaction between mutually perpendicular dipoles is zero.)   The large solvent effect is due

[359] The dipole moment of the solvent molecule group in the cybotactic region is largely determined by the orientation of the molecular dipoles which are localized in the bonds of the solvent molecules.   The time of an electronic transition is considerably shorter than the time required for a bond to change its position.

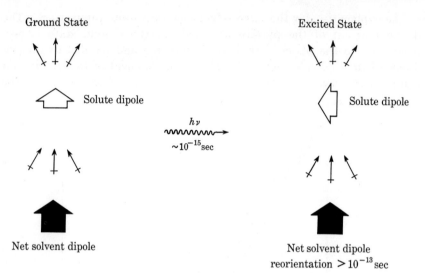

FIG. 2.54. The "dipole flip."

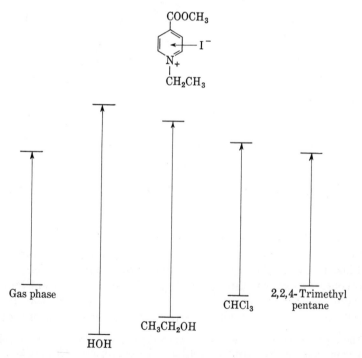

FIG. 2.55. Relative transition energies in various solvents. *(Reprinted by permission of the Journal of the American Chemical Society.)*

to a simultaneous change in the relative positions of the ground and excited states in opposite directions as the solvent is changed from a nonpolar material to a polar one. The "dipole flip" is illustrated in Figs. 2.50 and 2.54, and the relative changes in energy levels are shown in Fig. 2.55.

2.13C-6. The reduction of DPN with sodium dithionite leads to *enzymatically active* DPNH[360] in contrast to the results obtained by other reductive techniques, e.g., electrolysis,[361,362] X rays,[363] and sodium borohydride,[364,365] from which DPNH of low or zero enzymatic activity is

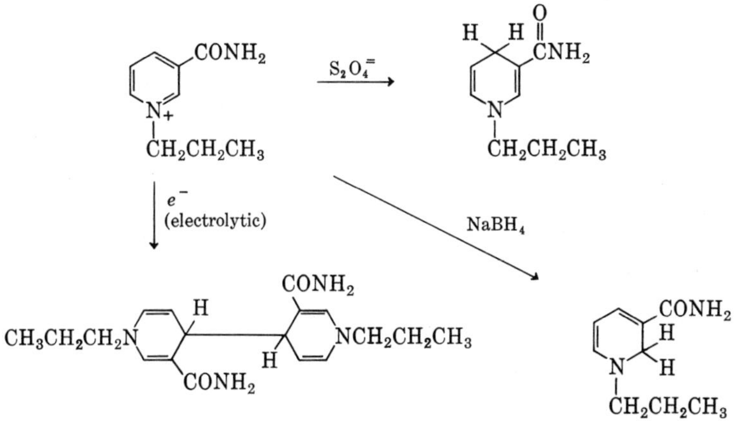

Fig. 2.56. Reduction of 1-propyl-3-carbamidopyridinium iodide.

obtained. Related observations have been made for the model compound 1-propyl-3-carbamidopyridinium iodide.[366] Dithionite reduction forms only the 1,4-dihydropyridine, but sodium borohydride can apparently[367] form either 1,2- or 1,4-dihydropyridine. Electrolytic reduction leads to a dimer formulated as 1,4- on the basis of its ultraviolet spectrum (Fig. 2.56).

Under fairly basic conditions, the reaction of dithionite with DPN (and also with most pyridinium ions) rapidly gives a yellow- or orange-colored

[360] O. Warburg, W. Christian, and A. Griese, *Biochem. Z.*, **282**, 157 (1935).
[361] B. Ke, *Arch. Biochem. Biophys.*, **60**, 505 (1956).
[362] R. F. Powning and C. C. Kratzing, *Arch. Biochem. Biophys.*, **66**, 249 (1957).
[363] A. J. Swallow, *Biochem. J.*, **54**, 253 (1953).
[364] M. B. Matthews, *J. Biol. Chem.*, **176**, 229 (1948).
[365] M. B. Matthews and E. E. Conn, *J. Am. Chem. Soc.*, **75**, 5428 (1953).
[366] Y. Paiss and G. Stein, *J. Chem. Soc.*, 2905 (1958).
[367] Identification of the 1,4-structure in a borohydride reduction of 1-propyl-3-carbamidopyridinium ion rests solely upon an ultraviolet spectrum.

solution,[368,369] which subsequently yields DPNH (or 1,4-dihydropyridines for most pyridinium ions).[370]   The stoichiometry is expressed[370] in Eqs. (2.151) and (2.152).   In one case, that of 1-(2,6-dichlorobenzyl)-3,5-

(2.151) $DPN^+ + S_2O_4^= \rightarrow DPNSO_2^- + SO_2$

(2.152) $DPNSO_2^- + H^+ \rightarrow DPNH + SO_2$

dicarbamidopyridinium bromide, a solid with an elementary composition corresponding to that of the intermediate is isolated from the reaction of the pyridinium ion and sodium dithionite[371] [Eq. (2.153)].   The solid is

(2.153)

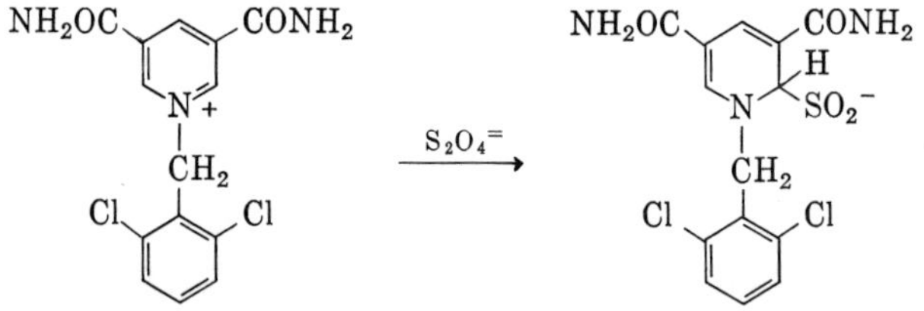

formulated as a 1,2-adduct because of the ultraviolet spectrum.   The 1,4-adduct of sulfoxylate and DPN has been proposed as the intermediate in the formation of DPNH [Eq. (2.154)].[370]

(2.154)

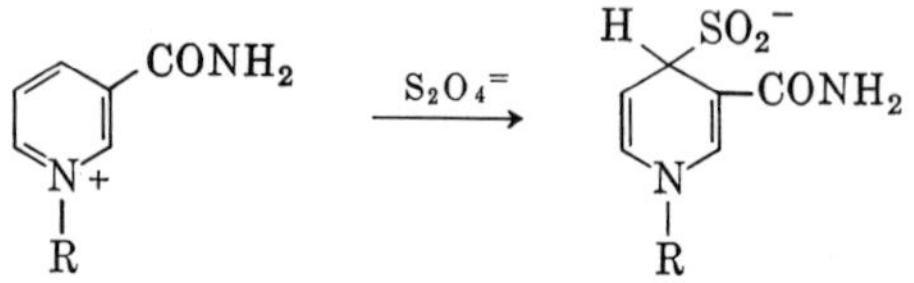

An analysis of the spectrum of the intermediate in the formation of DPNH from dithionite and DPN suggested that the intermediate should be formulated as a charge-transfer complex rather than as an adduct[315] (Fig. 2.57).   The fact that a solid is isolated from a reaction is not direct proof that an adduct is present in solution (*see above*).   Especially significant is that color formation is instantaneous [Eq. (2.153)], followed by a slow crystallization of the solid.[371]   The most reasonable formulation of these observations is that a complex is formed rapidly [Eq. (2.155)], followed by a relatively slow reaction in which a covalent bond is formed [Eq. (2.153)].

(2.155)

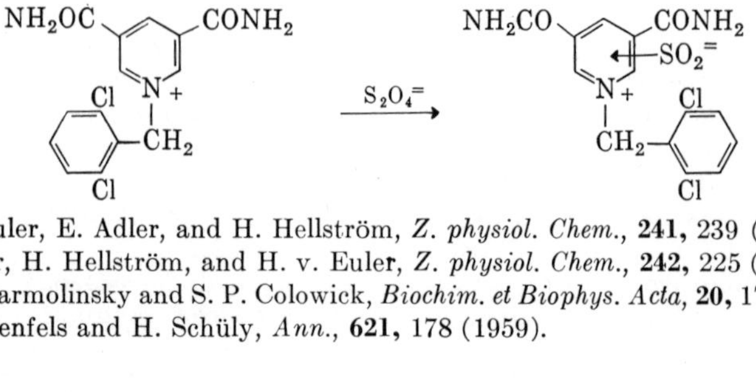

[368] H. v. Euler, E. Adler, and H. Hellström, *Z. physiol. Chem.*, **241**, 239 (1936).

[369] E. Adler, H. Hellström, and H. v. Euler, *Z. physiol. Chem.*, **242**, 225 (1936).

[370] M. B. Yarmolinsky and S. P. Colowick, *Biochim. et Biophys. Acta*, **20**, 177 (1956).

[371] K. Wallenfels and H. Schüly, *Ann.*, **621**, 178 (1959).

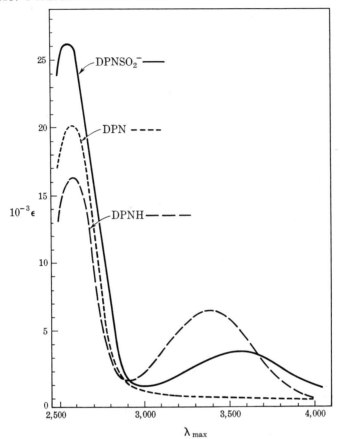

FIG. 2.57. Spectra of DPN, DPNH, DPNSO$_2^-$. (*Reprinted by permission of the Journal of the American Chemical Society.*)

2.13C-7. Evidence that the colored intermediate was in fact a charge-transfer complex was obtained by a comparison of the band positions for the intermediate derived from the reaction of dithionite with 1-ethyl-3- and -4-carbamidopyridinium ions with the band positions for the corresponding charge-transfer complex with iodide ion.[299] The semitheoretical basis for the comparison can be expressed as the rule that, *for a given donor, the difference in transition energies of complexes with a pair of pyridinium ions should be a constant* [Eq. (2.156)].[299] The data are

$$(2.156) \qquad \Delta E_T (D_n) = b_i - b_j$$

listed in Table 2.13-6. Identification of the intermediate as a charge-transfer complex permits an attractive formulation of a transition state

TABLE 2.13-6. SPECTRA OF INTERMEDIATES IN DITHIONITE
REDUCTION OF PYRIDINIUM IONS[d]

Pyridinium ion	λ_{max}	E_T, kcal/mole	ΔE_T, kcal/mole
1-Methyl-3-carbamido-	3730	76.65	
1-Methyl-4-carbamido-	4030	70.94	5.7 ± 0.3
1-Ethyl-3-carbamido-	3720	76.85	
1-Ethyl-4-carbamido-	4025	70.98	5.9 ± 0.3
DPN	3570[a]	80.08	
iso-DPN[b]	3870	73.88	6.2 ± 0.4
Value expected from iodides			6.7 ± 0.3[c]

[a] Ref. 370.

[b] Isonicotinamide (pyridine-4-carboxamide) analogue of DPN (ref. 372).

[c] The difference stated in the table was determined for the 1-ethyl-3- and -4-carbamidopyridinium iodides in pure pyridine[299] (Table 2.13-5). A study of the variation of the band positions with solvent change indicated that the difference (ΔE_T) would be smaller in aqueous solution.

[d] Ref. 299.

which leads to specific formation of a 1,4-dihydropyridine. The specificity is a natural consequence of the geometry predicted for the complex (Fig. 2.58). The fact that a sulfoxylate adduct can be isolated[371] does not preclude the possibility that the reaction mechanism involves a charge-

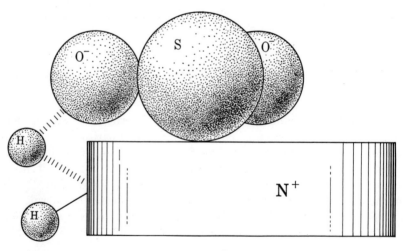

FIG. 2.58. Transition state for specific 1,4-dihydropyridine formation from the colored intermediate. (*Reprinted by permission of the Journal of the American Chemical Society.*)

[372] D. Goldman and S. W. Bauer, unpublished results.

transfer complex as the product-determining intermediate. The structures of the charge-transfer complexes relevant to the comparisons expressed in Table 2.13-6 are shown in Fig. 2.59.[373] In at least one case, the use of sodium dithionite does *not* lead to a 1,4-dihydropyridine ring. The reduction of 1-(2,6-dichlorobenzyl)-2,4-dimethyl-3-carbamidopyridinium ion with sodium dithionite yields in a rather slow

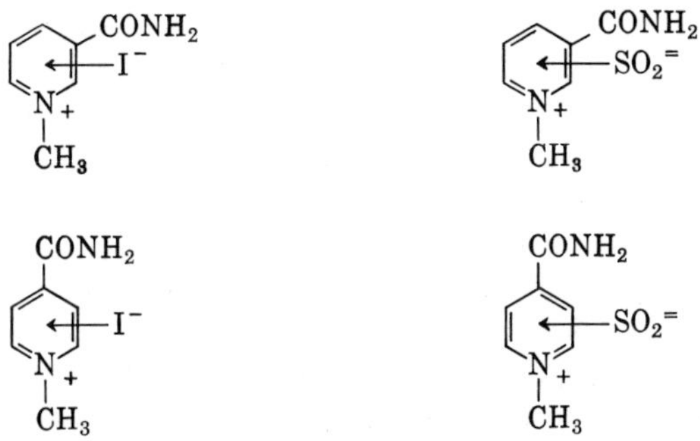

Fig. 2.59. Iodide and sulfoxylate complexes of pyridinium ions.

reaction a dihydropyridine with λ_{max} 3920 Å (ϵ 4690). The use of sodium borohydride[373] rapidly leads to the *same product*. The absorption spectrum and its formation from both reducing agents suggest formulation of the product as a 1,2-dihydropyridine. The low rate of the reaction with sodium dithionite and the anomalous position of reduction are ascribed to steric hindrance by the 4-methyl [Eq. (2.157)].[375] Since

(2.157)

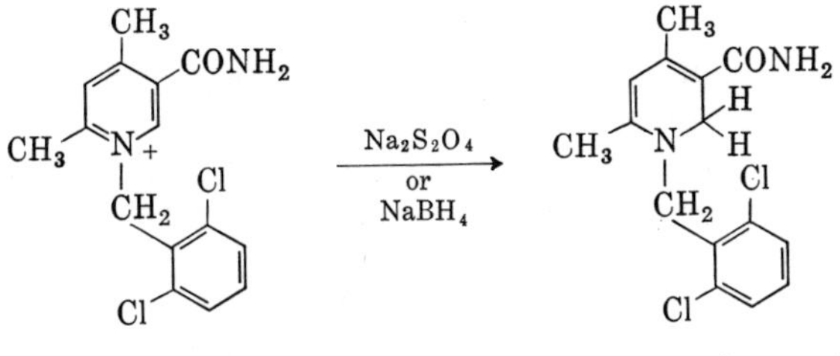

the experimental description[375] implies that complex formation is still rapid (complex formation would be less susceptible to steric hindrance than would a reaction in which a new bond is formed at a hindered center), it is likely that steric hindrance to the transition state for the

---

[373] The deep orange color of the solution during sodium borohydride reduction of pyridinium ions[374,375] *may* be due to charge-transfer light absorption between BH_4^- and RPy^+. Simple addition is excluded on the basis of valence (cf. ref. 374a).

[374] K. Wallenfels and H. Schüly, *Ann.*, **621**, 106 (1959).

[374a] B. M. Graybill and M. F. Hawthorne, *J. Am. Chem. Soc.*, **83**, 2673 (1961).

[375] K. Wallenfels and H. Schüly, *Ann.*, **621**, 215 (1959).

transfer of a hydrogen from the sulfoxylate oxygen to the 4-carbon atom leads to a slow reduction at the 2-position.

2.13C-8. The fact that pyridinium rings serve as acceptors in charge-transfer complexes suggests the possibility that some spectroscopic properties of biological systems containing DPN might be ascribed to charge-transfer transitions. Indeed, indole, tryptophan, serotonin, and other similar molecules give rise to new light absorption when mixed with DPN or model pyridinium salts. The low intensity of the absorptions, their position in the near ultraviolet as broad bands without observable maxima (the maxima are presumably submerged in the pyridinium ring absorption), and the low association constants all support the interpretation of such absorptions as charge-transfer complex absorptions.[376–379,379a] The suggestion that the new absorption maximum observed for the DPN–glyceraldehyde-3-phosphate dehydrogenase complex is due to a charge-transfer transition (p. 378)[320] is made more plausible by the observations with tryptophan.[376,377] The proposal that certain enzyme-DPNH complexes exhibit charge-transfer light absorption[320] is probably erroneous; the effect of the enzyme upon the position of the maximum of DPNH[380] is better understood in the terms described in Sec. 2.13G.

2.13C-9. It is abundantly clear that charge-transfer light absorption may be observed for certain donors in combination with pyridinium rings, and is certainly likely for other suitable donor-acceptor combinations. Except for the spectroscopic results already mentioned, a biological or biochemical role for charge-transfer complexing is still a matter for speculation. The electron-transfer function proposed for β-carotene in photosynthesis depended upon preliminary formation of a charge-transfer complex (Sec. 1.4).[381] The brown color of liver may well be due to the presence of charge-transfer complexes,[382] but it will be a difficult matter to demonstrate experimentally. The small spectroscopic changes which are observed in complexes of flavins and other com-

[376] G. Cilento and P. Giusti, *J. Am. Chem. Soc.*, **81**, 3801 (1959).

[377] G. Cilento and P. Tedeschi, *J. Biol. Chem.*, **236**, 907 (1961).

[378] S. G. A. Alivisatos, G. A. Mourkides, and A. Jibril, *Nature*, **186**, 718 (1960). See later correction of short-wavelength data.

[379] Cf. data on anion-DPN interactions, F. Ungar and S. G. A. Alivisatos, *Biochim. Biophys. Acta*, **46**, 406 (1961).

[379a] S. G. A. Alivisatos, F. Ungar, A. Jibril, and G. A. Mourkides, *Biochim. et Biophys. Acta*, **51**, 361 (1961).

[380] J. van Eys, F. E. Stolzenbach, L. Sherwood, and N. O. Kaplan, *Biochim. et Biophys. Acta*, **27**, 63 (1958).

[381] J. R. Platt, *Science*, **129**, 372 (1959).

[382] A. Szent-Györgyi, "Introduction to a Submolecular Biology," Academic Press, Inc., New York, 1960.

pounds[383] do not resemble the dramatic changes found for many donor-acceptor combinations, and, in particular, lack the strong new "charge-transfer" band.

Small, but significant, increases in rate are observed for the solvolysis of 2,4,7-trinitrofluorenyl p-toluenesulfonate in the presence of aromatic molecules like phenanthrene. The rate increase is related to the association constant for the acceptor (the solvolyzing molecule) and the donor (the aromatic hydrocarbon).[384]

The chemical consequences of charge-transfer complexing may be summarized in the following way: Ground state effects on the properties of a donor or an acceptor with respect to other chemical properties will be fairly small but may be more significant for causing certain transition-state arrangements which lead to particular chemical results. The sulfoxylate complexes in pyridinium ring reduction by dithionite and the proposed complex for one phosphorylation step in oxidative phosphorylation are examples of ground-state effects. Effects due to the excited state will be large, since separation of the associated molecules of the excited state is equivalent to the production of diradicals. Thus, photochemical oxidation-reduction might result from light absorption by a charge-transfer complex, provided that pathways for reaction or energy transfer were favored over return to the ground state through radiationless transition.

2.13D. Dihydropyridines

The model system which contains the chemically significant elements of the DPNH molecule is that of a dihydropyridine. Dihydropyridines having no substituents have been left almost untouched in the chemical literature, even though some interest might have been expected in light of their vinylogous relationship to enamines. Two basic types of dihydropyridines carrying a 1-alkyl group can be written: 1-alkyl-1,2-dihydropyridine (Fig. 2.60A) and 1-alkyl-1,4-dihydropyridine (Fig. 2.60B).

Of greater biological interest are those bearing a 3-carbamido (or other) substituent, for which three isomers can be written, the 1,2- (Fig. 2.60C), the 1,4- (Fig. 2.60D), and the 1,6- (Fig. 2.60E).

2.13D-1. For many years after the discovery that the coenzymatic function of DPN involved interconversion of a pyridinium and dihydropyridine ring, uncertainty existed concerning the precise location of the additional hydrogen in the dihydropyridine ring. Although a 1,2-dihydropyridine was originally favored on rather tenuous grounds,[291]

[383] H. A. Harbury and K. A. Foley, *Proc. Natl. Acad. Sci. U.S.*, **44**, 662 (1958).
[384] A. K. Colter, personal communication; *Am. Chem. Soc. Abstr.* (spring, 1961).

definite resolution of the structural doubt was not possible until the demonstration that hydrogen (deuterium) was transferred directly from the substrate to the pyridinium ring (cf. Sec. 2.13B). It was then possible to prepare a dihydropyridine labeled with deuterium at the position to which the hydrogen had been added. Chemical reoxidation gave a pyridinium ion containing approximately half of the deuterium present in the dihydropyridine. More specifically, reduction of DPN with ethanol-1,1-d_2 in the presence of yeast alcohol dehydrogenase gave DPNH containing one atom of deuterium (DPND). Upon oxidation with neutral potassium ferricyanide, the DPND thus prepared yielded

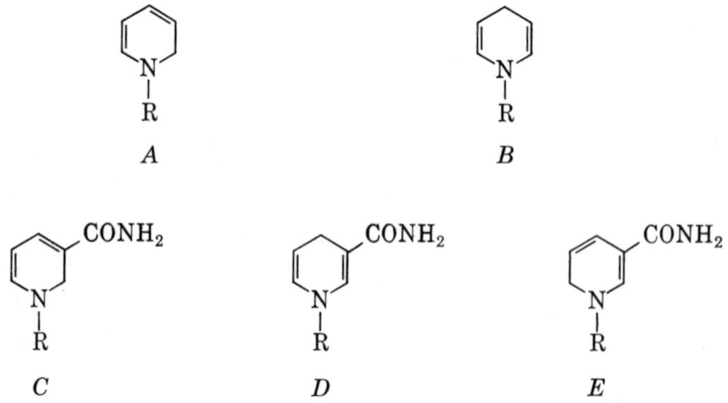

FIG. 2.60. Isomeric dihydropyridines.

DPN containing about one-half of the deuterium present in the DPND. (Alternative methods for obtaining the labeled DPN are also described.)[385] The labeled DPN was cleaved to labeled nicotinamide with *Neurospora* DPNase, and the methiodide of nicotinamide (by reaction with methyl iodide) oxidized to a mixture of 2- and 6-(1-methyl)-pyridones with alkaline ferricyanide. Approximately equal quantities of the two pyridones were formed in the oxidation.[386] Oxidation of the 1-methyl-3-carbamidopyridinium ion did not lead to any loss of deuterium in either the 2- or the 6-pyridone. The deuterium was therefore present at the 4-position (Fig. 2.61).

Isomeric labeled DPNs were prepared by the exchange of appropriately labeled nicotinamides (nicotinamide-2-d, -4-d, or -6-d) with unlabeled DPN catalyzed by DPNase.[387] Only DPN containing nicotinamide

---

[385] M. E. Pullman, A. San Pietro, and S. P. Colowick, *J. Biol. Chem.*, **206**, 129 (1954).

[386] M. E. Pullman and S. P. Colowick, *J. Biol. Chem.*, **206**, 121 (1954).

[387] F. A. Loewus, B. Vennesland, and D. L. Harris, *J. Am. Chem. Soc.*, **77**, 3391 (1955).

labeled in the 4-position was able to transfer deuterium to pyruvate (after reduction by dithionite).

Reduction of 1-methyl-3-carbamidopyridinium ion with sodium dithionite in deuterium oxide, followed by reoxidation with neutral potassium ferricyanide forms a 1-methyl-3-carbamidopyridinium ion which contains deuterium in the 4-position.[388] The course of the reduction of *model* pyridinium compounds thus proceeds in the same fashion

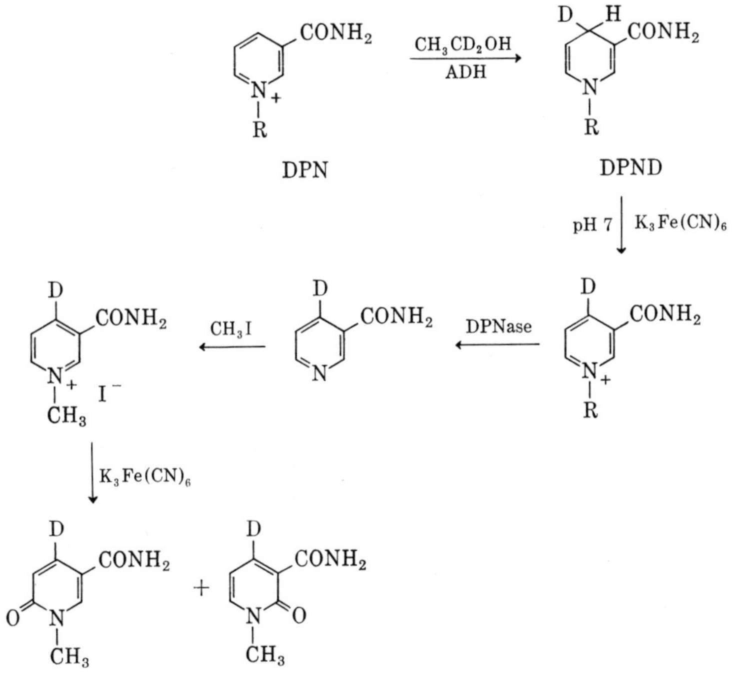

Fig. 2.61. Proof of the 1,4-dihydropyridine structure for DPNH.

with sodium dithionite as the reduction of DPN itself, i.e., a 1,4-dihydropyridine derivative is formed.

Nuclear magnetic resonance spectra of 1-methyl-3-carbamido pyridinium ions, containing, respectively, no deuterium, deuterium introduced by base-catalyzed exchange, and deuterium introduced by sodium dithionite reduction and potassium ferricyanide oxidation in neutral solution, are in accord with the conclusion that sodium dithionite reduction produces, in most cases, a 1,4-dihydropyridine.[389] Sodium carbonate solution in deuterium oxide introduces deuterium rapidly into the

[388] G. W. Rafter and S. P. Colowick, *J. Biol. Chem.*, **209**, 773 (1954).
[389] H. E. Dubb, M. Saunders, and J. H. Wang, *J. Am. Chem. Soc.*, **80**, 1767 (1958).

2-position, and more slowly into the 6-position. The NMR band which is reduced in intensity in the pyridinium ion formed by reoxidation of the sodium dithionite product in deuterium oxide is different from those which disappear on the introduction of deuterium by base-catalyzed exchange.[390]

The three isomeric 1-methyl-3-carbamidopyridinium-2-d, -4-d, and -6-d ions were converted into the dihydropyridines with sodium dithionite, and an examination of their NMR spectra was made.[391] Using either deuterium oxide or acetone-d_6 as solvent, it was shown that only the 4-d ion gave a reduction in intensity of relatively "aliphatic" hydrogen peaks, and that the dihydropyridine produced by sodium dithionite reduction was therefore a 1,4-dihydropyridine.

2.13D-2. The structure of DPNH is that of a 1,4-dihydropyridine (see Fig. 2.60D). Another structural question arises from the observation that oxidation of DPND (prepared by enzymatic reduction of ethanol-1,1-d_2) with acetaldehyde and alcohol dehydrogenase leads to DPN with complete transfer of the deuterium to the acetaldehyde[292] and the formation of only *one* enantiomer of ethanol-1-d.[392] Thus, the enzymatic hydrogen transfer distinguishes with high selectivity between the two chemically equivalent hydrogens located at the 4-position of the dihydropyridine ring. The finding of an enzymatic differentiation between the two 4-hydrogens has led to the idea that a *chemical difference* must be responsible. It was suggested that the 1,4-dihydropyridine ring is not planar, but an equilibrium mixture of two "boatlike" forms.[393] Such forms would indeed have two kinds of 4-hydrogen, an "axial" and an "equatorial." Why these should differ in reactivity is less clear in view of the fact that the transition state for enzymatic oxidation of the 1,4-dihydropyridine ring should resemble to some extent the planar pyridinium ring of DPN.

There are three arguments against a nonplanar structure for the 1,4-dihydropyridine ring, and in this book it is considered that the ring is *planar* wherever it is necessary to specify the geometry. First, the appearance of the model of dihydropyridine (i.e., its planarity) depends upon the choice made for the hybridization around nitrogen. The non-planar model is made with a tetrahedral nitrogen atom (four sp^3 bonds, one containing the lone pair), whereas the planar structure is made using a trigonal nitrogen atom (three sp^2 bonds, one p orbital for the lone pair). The nonplanar formulation implies little overlap between the orbital

---

[390] The conditions described for the base-catalyzed exchange in ref. 389 are close to those which might cause hydrolysis of the amide group (cf. ref. 299).

[391] R. F. Hutton and F. H. Westheimer, *Tetrahedron*, **3**, 73 (1958).

[392] F. A. Loewus, F. H. Westheimer, and B. Vennesland, *J. Am. Chem. Soc.*, **75**, 5018 (1953).

[393] H. R. Levy and B. Vennesland, *J. Biol. Chem.*, **228**, 85 (1957).

containing the nonbonding electrons on nitrogen and the π orbitals of the double bonds. The following arguments both imply that this is not correct, and that, in fact, there is a modest, but real, amount of interaction between these orbitals. Second, the position and intensity of the long-wavelength absorption band in 3-substituted 1,4-dihydropyridines imply a full conjugation of the two double bonds, the nitrogen, and the 3-substituent (cf. Sec. 2.13D-3). Last, measurement of the basicity in acetonitrile solution[394] of the three compounds shown in Fig. 2.62 leads to

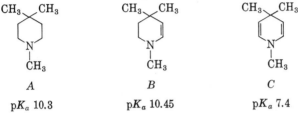

A   B   C

pK_a 10.3 pK_a 10.45 pK_a 7.4

FIG. 2.62. Base strengths of nitrogen bases.

the conclusion that an appreciable amount of stabilization (ca. 4 kcal/mole)[306] is present in 1,4,4-trimethyl-1,4-dihydropyridine (Fig. 2.62C). A brief summary of the factors involved is presented in Fig. 2.63. It should be explicitly noted that the number given is an estimate for the amount by which the base strength of the dihydropyridine (in comparison to an "unstabilized" tetrahydropyridine) is decreased over and above that expected from the fact that the nitrogen is attached to sp^2 orbitals of two double bonds.

Chemical evidence thus favors the *planar* arrangement for the dihydropyridine ring. The biochemical evidence that the two hydrogens at the 4-position are different is interesting but may be adequately explained by postulating that the enzyme can differentiate between the hydrogens by only permitting approach of the acetaldehyde to the dihydropyridine ring on one side (see Sec. 2.13G). It seems highly unlikely that any biochemical function can be ascribed to the fact that some enzymes catalyze reaction of the hydrogen introduced into DPNH by ethanol and alcohol dehydrogenase ("side A"[285]) while others catalyze the removal of the other hydrogen ("side B"). Almost every dehydrogenase (the partial exception is a flavoprotein enzyme[285]) has either one or the other specificity. On the other hand, the twofold "A-B" classification may provide a subtle means for comparison of dehydrogenases derived from different parts of the same organism or from different organisms.

[394] H. K. Hall, Jr., *J. Phys. Chem.*, **60**, 63 (1956).

[395] Decrease in basicity of nitrogen due to its attachment to an sp^2 orbital. The figure used is based on data for the benzoquinuclidines.[396]

[396] P. Schickedantz and H. Schecter, *Chem. Abstr.*, **137**, 23o (1960).

[397] The interaction of a double bond and a nitrogen with a nonbonding pair is taken as equal to 1,3-cyclohexadiene, i.e., 1.8 kcal/mole.[305]

The finding that excitation of DPNH at 2600 Å, the region of adenine absorption, produces fluorescence of the dihydropyridine moiety at 4600 Å, although the same excitation of α-DPNH[398,399] gives no fluorescence, is interesting, but only relevant to possible equilibrium configurations of the DPNH molecule *in solution* and not when associated with an

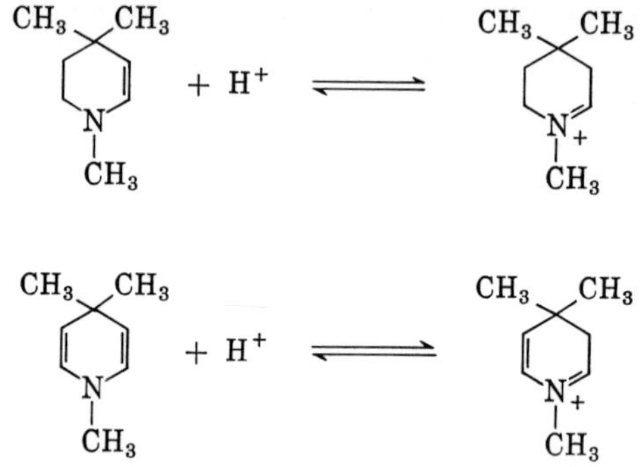

Predicted ΔpK_a = 2.7 (hybridization[395]) - 1.3
                        (tetrahydropyridine
                        stabilization[397]) - 1.3
                        (protonated dihydropyridine
                        stabilization[397]) + $\mathbf{S}$ ("extra"
                        stabilization energy
                        of dihydropyridine)
                 = $0.1 + \mathbf{S}$
Actual $\Delta pK_a = 3.05$
           $\mathbf{S} = 3.05 - 0.1 = 2.95 \equiv$ ca. 4 kcal/mole

FIG. 2.63. Stabilization energy for 1,4,4-trimethyl-1,4-dihydropyridine.

enzyme.   The presumption is that the adenine and dihydronicotinamide ring of DPNH (β-DPNH) must be fairly close in order for the observed energy transfer to occur.

2.13D-3.   The simplest dihydropyridine with an unequivocally known structure is 1,4,4-trimethyl-1,4-dihydropyridine[306] (Fig. 2.62C). It is synthesized by the reaction of methylamine and β,β-dimethylglutaraldehyde[306] [Eq. (2.158)].   The compound is useful for establishing

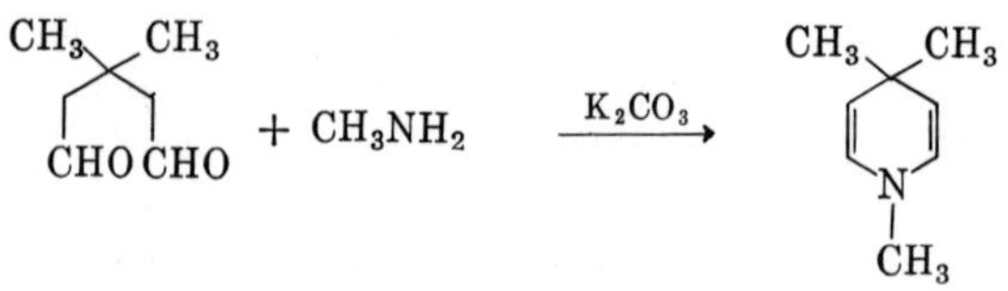

certain fundamental properties of dihydropyridines.

[398] The prefix α refers to the attachment of the nicotinamide ring to the ribose ring of DPN on the side opposite to the 5-CH_2O—group.
[399] S. Shifrin and N. O. Kaplan, *Nature*, **183**, 1529 (1959).

It has been reasonably well established that sodium borohydride reduction of pyridinium ions[364,400] leads in many cases to the 1,6-dihydropyridine structure, in contrast to sodium dithionite, which produces the 1,4-dihydropyridine. A particularly clear example is the reduction of 1-methyl-3-cyanopyridinium ion with both reagents.[401] Sodium borohydride forms 1-methyl-3-cyano-1,6-dihydropyridine (along with some

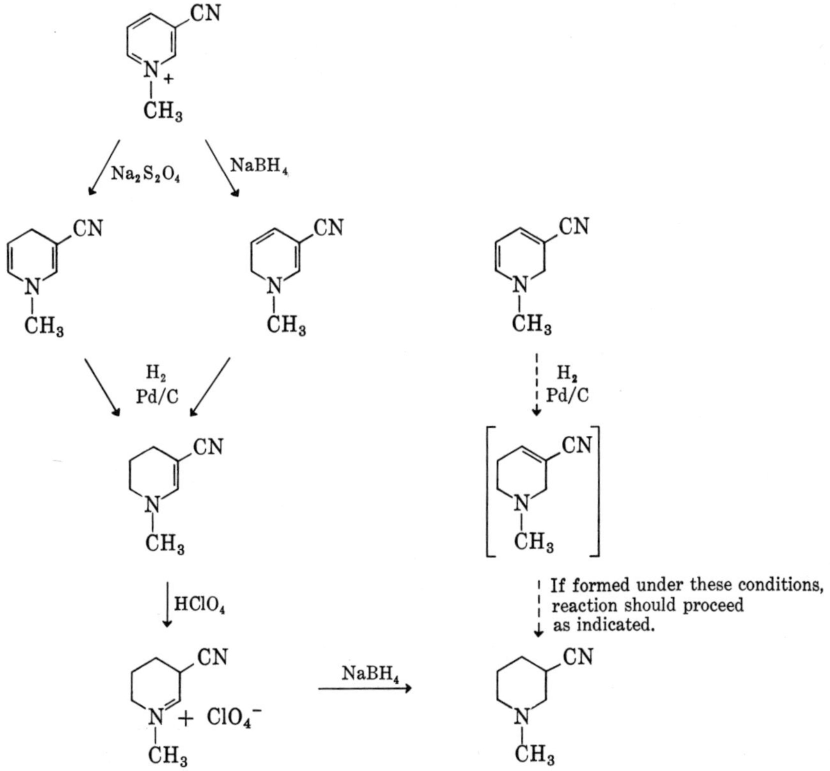

FIG. 2.64. Reduction of 1-methyl-3-cyanopyridinium ion.

tetrahydropyridine), while sodium dithionite yields 1-methyl-3-cyano-1,4-dihydropyridine. Hydrogenation of both isomeric dihydropyridines gives the conjugated 1-methyl-3-cyano-1,4,5,6-tetrahydropyridine, which is reduced only with difficulty to the piperidine. As shown in Fig. 2.64, these results exclude the 1,2-dihydro structure for the sodium borohydride product, although a test of the isomerization of the dihydropyridines in the presence of the catalyst would have made the proof even more convincing.

[400] J. J. Panouse, *Compt. rend.*, **233**, 260 (1951).
[401] K. Schenker and J. Druey, *Helv. Chim. Acta.*, **42**, 1960 (1959).

2.13D-4. The most convenient and characteristic difference between 3-substituted -1,4- and -1,6-dihydropyridines is in the ultraviolet spectroscopic region.[374,402] Typical isomers are listed in Table 2.13-7. The effect of a variation in the 3-substituent is clear from the data.

The electronic transition in 1,4-dihydropyridines with an electron-accepting 3-substituent corresponds to the charge rearrangement shown

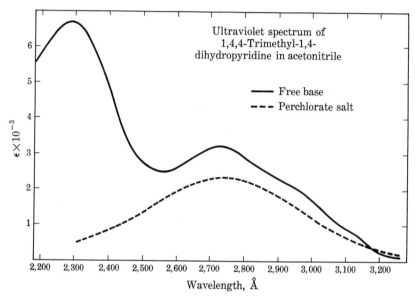

FIG. 2.65. Absorption curve of 1,4,4-trimethyl-1,4-dihydropyridine.

in Eq. (2.159). The transition energy for such a process would be

$$(2.159) \qquad \diagup\kern-0.5em\diagdown C{=}\overset{|}{C}{-}\overset{|}{N}{-}\overset{|}{C}{=}\overset{|}{C}{-}X{=}Y \overset{h\nu}{\rightarrow} \diagup\kern-0.5em\diagdown C{=}\overset{|}{C}{-}\overset{+}{\overset{|}{N}}{=}\overset{|}{C}{-}\overset{|}{C}{=}X{-}Y^-$$

lowered by electron acceptation at 3, or electron supply to the nitrogen, thus resulting in a shift of the absorption maximum to longer wavelengths. Comparison of the 1,4-dihydropyridine compounds 2, 3, and 5 in Table 2.13-7 with cyano, carbamido, and carbomethoxy groups, respectively, shows the expected shift for 3-substituents, while the pairs 1 and 2, 4 and 3, and 10 and 11 demonstrate that increased electron supply

[402] Other dihydropyridines may be of biochemical significance, such as isonicotinic acid derivatives and dipicolinic acid (pyridine-2,6-dicarboxylic acid).[403]

[403] A reduced form of dipicolinic acid may be involved in one of the steps leading to germination of bacterial spores. (H. Halvorsen, personal communication.)

to the nitrogen does lower the transition energy. (Corrections for solvent effects should be applied; see below.)

Table 2.13-7. Spectra of Dihydropyridines

No.	Pyridinium ion·	Solvent[a]	Sodium dithionite reduction product (1,4-dihydropyridine)		Sodium borohydride reduction product (1,6-dihydropyridine)		Ref.
			λ_{max}	ϵ_{max}	λ_{max}	ϵ_{max}	
1	1-Methyl-3-cyano-	P	3400	5600	3490	4950	401
					2400	5400	
2	1-(2,6-Dichlorobenzyl)-3-cyano-	M	3350	6250	3500	6020	374
					2400	6100	
3	1-(2,6-Dichlorobenzyl)-3-carbamido-	M	3500	7510	3550	7450	374
					2650	9840	
4	1-Methyl-3-carbamido-	W	3600	7000			388
		E	3550	6680			391
5	1-(2,6-Dichlorobenzyl)-3-carbomethoxy-	M	3520	7740	3530	7970	374
					2590	7650	
6	1-(2,6-Dichlorobenzyl)-2-methyl-3-carbethoxy-	M	3450	7980	3470	8810	374
					2620	9120	
7	1-(2,6-Dichlorobenzyl)-3,5-dicarbamido-	M	3780	7880	3910	7360	374
					2860	15410	
8	1-(2,6-Dichlorobenzyl)-3,5-dicarbomethoxy-	M	3810	7120	4000	7970	374
					2820	20860	
9	1,2,4,6-Tetramethyl-3,5-dicarbethoxy-	M	3470	8240	3740	6740	374
					2930	10960	
10	1-Benzyl-3-carbamido-	M	3550	7500			404
11	1-Benzyloxymethyl-3-carbamido-	M	3350	6200			404
12	1-(2-Phenoxyethyl)-3-carbamido-	M	3510	7220			374
13	1-(2,6-Dichlorobenzyl)-3-carbodimethylamido-	M	3390	4820	3510	5950	374
					2650	7350	

[a] P = petroleum ether; M = methanol; W = water; E = 95% ethanol.

The effect of the electron-accepting group at 3 can be illustrated in a persuasive way by the data in Table 2.13-8, in which the conjugated system is lengthened by the group of interest. The ultraviolet absorption curve for 1,4,4-trimethyl-1,4-dihydropyridine is given in Fig. 2.65. The shoulders which can be seen in the 3000 Å region are not readily explainable in simple terms. More experimental work on suitable simple compounds as well as a theoretical analysis of the spectra would certainly be desirable for this important ring system.

TABLE 2.13-8. EFFECT OF CONJUGATION ON "ENAMINE" SPECTRA[a]

No.	Structure	Solvent	λ_{max} (ϵ_{max})	Ref.
14	![structure] CH₃ CH₃ ring with N-CH₃	Isoöctane	2708 (3200) 2305 (7500)	306
		Acetonitrile	2732 (3200) 2289 (6700)	306
		Methanol	2703 (3000) 2295 (6700)	306
15	![structure] N-CH₃ with n-C₄H₉	Diethyl ether	2380 (7200)	405
16	![structure] N-CH₃ with CH₂CH₃	Diethyl ether	2310 (5100)	405
17	![structure] piperidine ring CH=CHCH₂CH₃	Diethyl ether	2280 (7500)	405
18	CH_3NH $CH_3C{=}CHCOOC_2H_5$	Cyclohexane	2825 (17,700)	406
19	![structure] CH₃ COOC₂H₅ ring N-H CH₃	Ethanol	2850 (17,800)	407
20	$(C_2H_5)_2NCH{=}CHCCH_2CH_2CH_3$ with O above C	Ethanol	3070 (28,000)	408
21	![structure] COCH₃ ring N-CH₂-phenyl	Ethanol	3710 (10,400)	409
22	![structure] COOCH₃ ring N-CH₂-phenyl	Ethanol	3520 (7250)	409

[a] Ref. 306.

2.13D-5. A subtle spectroscopic effect has been noted with certain 1,4-dihydropyridines.[410] The replacement of a hydrogen at the 4-position with a methyl group leads to an appreciable shift of the absorption maximum to shorter wavelengths (for compounds 23 and 24 in Table 2.13-9, the shift is 200 Å in methanol, equivalent to a transition energy difference of 4.4 kcal/mole). The "methyl effect" is explained as being due to the increased electron density on the oxygen of the carbethoxyl carbonyl in proximity to the methyl group, since models of both ground and excited states indicated that steric hindrance to conjugation could not be responsible. The corresponding cyano derivatives (compounds 25 and 26, Table 2.13-9) for which the increased electron density on the nitrile nitrogen in the excited state must be farther away from the extra methyl group provide evidence for the explanation, showing a transition energy difference of only 1.7 kcal/mole. Comparison of another set of compounds in which the 4-hydrogen has been replaced by a p-nitrophenyl and a p-methoxyphenyl group (compounds 27 and 28, Table 2.13-9), respectively, show a similar (unexpected) response in ultraviolet absorption maximum to the nature of the nonconjugated 4-substituent.[411] The rationalization cited above fits compounds 27 and 28 as well, the p-nitro group removing electrons from the region of increased electron density in the excited state, and the p-methoxy group supplying electrons to that region.

2.13D-6. The charge distribution suggested by Eq. (2.159) for the excited state of dihydronicotinamides predicts a solvent effect upon the position of the absorption maximum, with a lower transition energy (longer-wavelength maximum) expected in more polar solvents. An energy level diagram for a typical system is given in Fig. 2.66. Experimental measurements of the solvent effect[412] (Table 2.13-10) show that a moderate shift to longer wavelengths is found. The direction of the shift indicates that it is not correct to regard dihydronicotinamides as having a ground state with more charge separation than the excited state.[413-415] The dipole moment of 1-benzyl-1,4-dihydronicotinamide is

[404] K. Wallenfels, M. Gellrich, and F. Kubowitz, *Ann.*, **621**, 137 (1959).

[405] N. J. Leonard and D. M. Locke, *J. Am. Chem. Soc.*, **77**, 437 (1955).

[406] S. A. Glickman and A. C. Cope, *J. Am. Chem. Soc.*, **67**, 1017 (1945).

[407] K. Tsuda, Y. Satch, N. Ikekawa, and M. Mishima, *J. Org. Chem.*, **21**, 800 (1956).

[408] K. Bowden, E. Braude, E. R. H. Jones, and B. Weedon, *J. Chem. Soc.*, 45 (1946).

[409] A. C. Anderson, Jr., and G. Berkelhammer, *J. Am. Chem. Soc.*, **80**, 992 (1958).

[410] D. Hofmann, E. M. Kosower, and K. Wallenfels, *J. Am. Chem. Soc.*, **83**, 3314 (1961).

[411] J. A. Berson and E. Brown, *J. Am. Chem. Soc.*, **77**, 444 (1955).

[412] G. Cilento, E. de Carvalho Filho, and A. C. Giora Albanese, *J. Am. Chem. Soc.*, **80**, 4472 (1958).

[413] N. O. Kaplan and M. M. Ciotti, *J. Biol. Chem.*, **221**, 823 (1956).

[414] K. Wallenfels and H. Sund, *Biochem. Z.*, **329**, 59 (1957).

[415] H. R. Mahler and J. Douglas, *J. Am. Chem. Soc.*, **79**, 1159 (1957).

TABLE 2.13-9. "METHYL EFFECT" ON SPECTRA

No.	Compound	Solvent[a]	λ_{max} (ϵ_{max})	$E_T{}^{b}$	Ref.
23		M	3690 (6100)	77.5	410
24		M	3490.(8600)	81.9	410
25		M	3458 (6300)	82.7	410
26		M	3388 (6500)	84.4	410
23[c]		E	3750[c] (3390)[c]		411
27		E	3660[c] (3680)		411
28		E	3570[c] (6360)		411

[a] M = methanol; E = 95% ethanol.
[b] Transition energy in kcal/mole.
[c] There is a moderately large discrepancy between the figures from two different sources for compound 23; it is thought, however, that the trend indicated from 23 to 27 to 28 is correct, i.e., that the error is systematic.

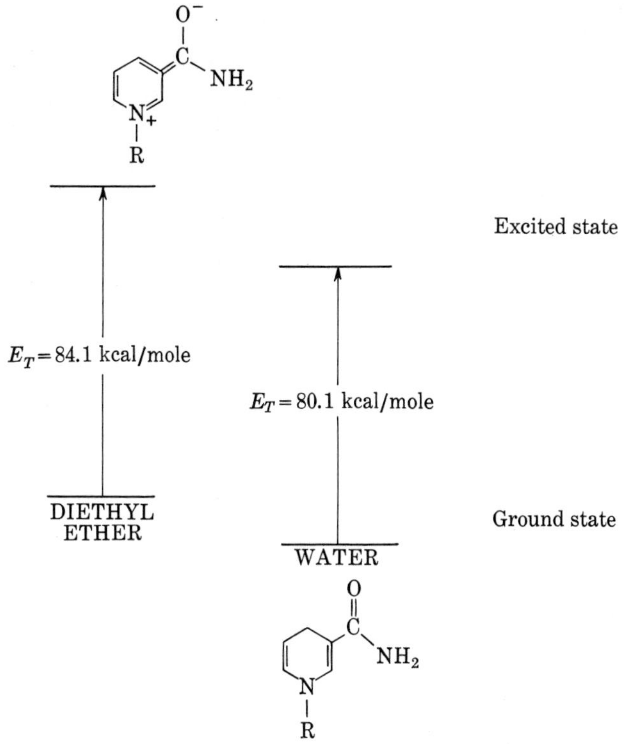

FIG. 2.66. Energy levels for light absorption of dihydronicotinamides. (*Reprinted by permission of Biochimica et Biophysica Acta.*)

3.89 D,[412] much too small for structures with considerable charge separation.

With certain enzymes (liver alcohol dehydrogenase, liver lactic dehydrogenase, and heart lactic dehydrogenase),[380] DPNH forms complexes in which *the ultraviolet maximum has shifted to shorter wavelengths.* Parallel phenomena are found for DPNH analogues, coenzymes in which the dihydronicotinamide ring has been replaced[285] by other dihydro-

TABLE 2.13-10. MAXIMA FOR 1-BENZYL-3-CARBAMIDO-1,4-DIHYDROPYRIDINE[a]

Solvent	λ_{max}, Å	E_T
Diethyl ether	3400	84.1
Cyclohexane	3450	82.8
Ethanol	3540	80.7
Water	3570	80.1

[a] Ref. 412.

pyridine rings, e.g., the 3-acetyl-1,4-dihydropyridine ring (Table 2.13-11). The shape of the absorption curve and probable absorption intensity suggest that the electronic transition observed for the DPNH-enzyme complex is the same as that seen for DPNH. In short, the enzyme has the same effect upon the position of the DPNH long-wavelength absorption maximum as a nonpolar solvent has upon the position of the maximum of 1-benzyl-3-carbamido-1,4-dihydropyridine with respect to the maximum in water. It may be concluded that the zinc ions of liver alcohol dehydrogenase[416] are not located in the neighborhood of the

TABLE 2.13-11. SPECTRA OF DPNH-ENZYME COMPLEXES[e]

Enzyme	DPNH λ_{max}, Å	APDPNH[a] λ_{max}, Å	Py-3-AlDPNH[b] λ_{max}, Å
No enzyme	3400	3650	3550
Liver alcohol dehydrogenase	3250	3500	3400
Beef heart lactic dehydrogenase	3250[c]	3500	3400
Pig heart malic dehydrogenase	No shift[d]	No shift	No shift

[a] 3-Acetyl-1,4-dihydropyridine analogue of DPNH.
[b] 3-Aldehydo-1,4-dihydropyridine analogue of DPNH.
[c] Very poorly defined maximum.
[d] A DPNH-malic dehydrogenase complex has been reported to have a maximum at 3510 Å.[417]
[e] Ref. 380.

amide group of the DPNH in the enzyme-coenzyme complex,[414,415] for this should lead to a lowering of the transition energy required for excitation by light. A positively charged zinc ion close to an oxygen to which charge is transferred by the excitation process should interact to a greater extent with the excited state than with the ground state, displacing the absorption maximum to *longer* wavelengths [cf. Eq. (2.151)].

A second explanation[418] based on the direction in which the spectrum of DPNH changes upon complex formation is that the enzyme provides a nonpolar medium for the DPNH molecule. Although a "nonpolar medium" at the "active site" could explain the spectroscopic result for the position of the DPNH maximum upon combination with the enzyme, other functions of the "active site" would be difficult to explain. The magnitude of the shift (ca. 4 kcal/mole) requires that the light-absorbing

[416] B. L. Vallee, in "The Enzymes," vol. 3, chap. 15, Academic Press, Inc., New York, 1960.
[417] G. Pfleiderer and E. Hohnholz, *Biochem. Z.*, **331**, 245 (1959).
[418] G. Weber, private communication to N. O. Kaplan, quoted in S. Shifrin and N. O. Kaplan, *Advances in Enzymol.*, **22**, 353 (1960).

system behave as if dissolved in diethyl ether (see Table 2.13-10), requiring desolvation of the dihydropyridine portion of the DPNH. In addition, it is unreasonable that a pyridinium ion (DPN) should be generated (in the enzyme-catalyzed reaction) in a nonpolar medium without access to water for solvation. A hypothesis which accounts for the spectroscopic results and which also leads to a reasonable theory of DPN action is presented in Sec. 2.13G.

The spectroscopic differences between 1,4- and 1,6-dihydropyridines[374,401] can offer a useful way of distinguishing between 4- and 6-addition of nucleophiles to the pyridinium ring, provided that absorption intensity measurements can be made so as to exclude the possibility that charge-transfer bands contribute to the observed spectra. The latter are usually broader and less intense than the absorption bands due to dihydropyridines.[315]

2.13D-7. A possible charge-transfer complex of 1,4,4-trimethyl-1,4-dihydropyridine with maleic anhydride has been observed by mixing the two at moderately high concentrations (0.05 M). A new absorption band, λ_{max} ca. 3700 Å, appears immediately and changes only slowly with time [Eq. (2.159a)].[306]

(2.159a)

Protonation of an unsubstituted 1,4-dihydropyridine takes place at the β carbon, rather than the nitrogen. The spectrum of protonated 1,4,4-trimethyl-1,4-dihydropyridine (Fig. 2.65) shows a maximum at 2740 Å (ϵ 2300)[306] much closer to the maximum for 1,3-cyclohexadiene, λ_{max} 2580 Å (ϵ 4800),[419] than that for 1,4-cyclohexadiene, which has only end absorption, ϵ_{2150} ca. 500.[420] The reaction is shown to be completely reversible by the recovery of the original spectrum of 1,4,4-trimethyl-1,4-dihydropyridine upon the addition of a few equivalents of t-butylamine[306] [cf. Eq. (2), Fig. 2.63]. It is important that the protonation experiment be carried out in acetonitrile with the theoretical amount of acid in almost anhydrous medium to avoid further reaction.

The principle of β-protonation in 1,4-dihydropyridines (expected in accordance with the nature of enamine reactivity) implies that further

---

[419] B. V. Erofeev, N. P. Emel'ianov, and S. F. Naumova, *J. Gen. Chem. U.S.S.R.*, **28**, 1342 (1958). The ϵ given is not that of the reference (reported as 10,000) but was obtained from H. Winicov (personal communication).
[420] L. W. Pickett and E. Sheffield, *J. Am. Chem. Soc.*, **68**, 216 (1946).

reaction of the intermediate ion with nucleophilic species will take place at the 6-position. Indeed, it has been shown that the reaction of 1-benzyl-3-carbamido-1,4-dihydropyridine with water in dilute acid solution provides an excellent yield (93%) of a crystalline water addition product with the hydroxyl group at the 6-position[409] [Eq. (2.160)].

(2.160)

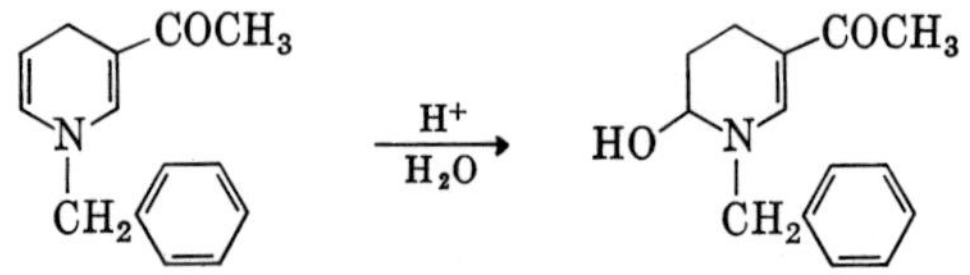

The evidence concerning the product of Eq. (2.160) is so good that other conclusions reached by subsequent investigations should be questioned. For example, it is thought that sulfurous acid and 1-(2,6-dichlorobenzyl)-3-carbamido-1,4-dihydropyridine lead to attachment of the nucleophile at *the 5-position* because both 1,4- and 1,6-dihydropyridines form the same adduct [Eq. (2.161)].[421] This seems unlikely on mechanistic grounds,

(2.161)

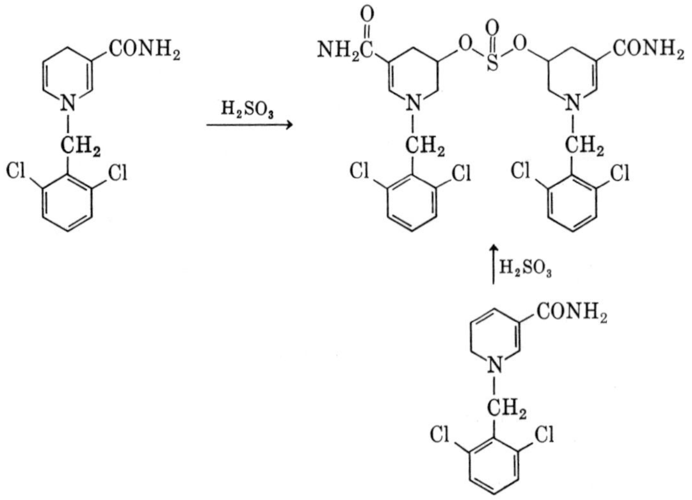

since it is more reasonable to expect that the reaction with sulfurous acid follows a course parallel to that of Eq. (2.160), as indicated in Eq. (2.162).

[421] K. Wallenfels, D. Hofmann, and H. Schüly, *Ann.*, **621**, 188 (1959).   Some doubt now exists about the composition and therefore the structure of the sulfite adduct. In fact, at least four different products are formed from the reaction of sulfurous acid and dihydropyridines.   (Prof. K. Wallenfels, personal communication.)

(2.162)

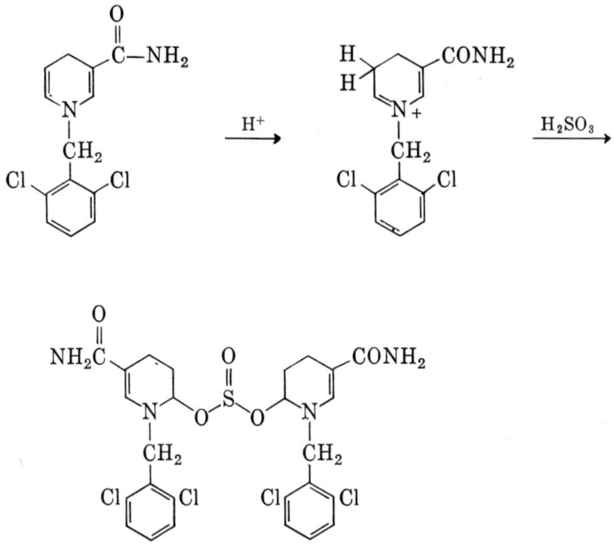

The interpretation of a kinetic study demonstrating that there is a difference in rate of reaction with water and acid of the 1,4- and 1,6-dihydropyridine isomers derived from 1-benzyl-3-carbamidopyridinium ion ignores the possibility that acid-catalyzed rearrangement could occur.[422,423] Such rearrangements can be written but have not yet been demonstrated. Interconversion of the protonated species derived from the benzyldihydropyridines is shown in Eqs. (2.163) and (2.164).

(2.163)

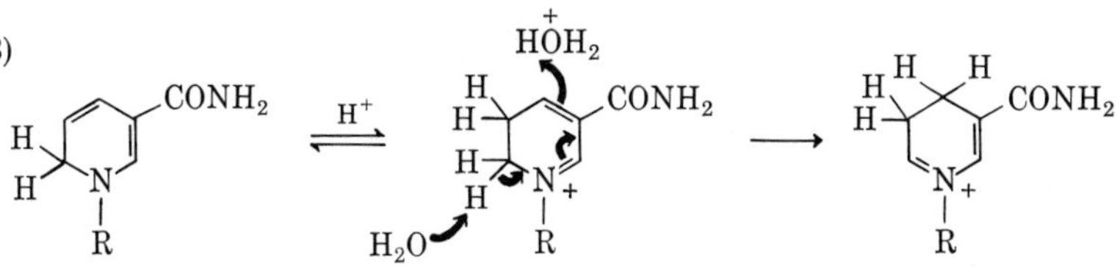

(2.164)

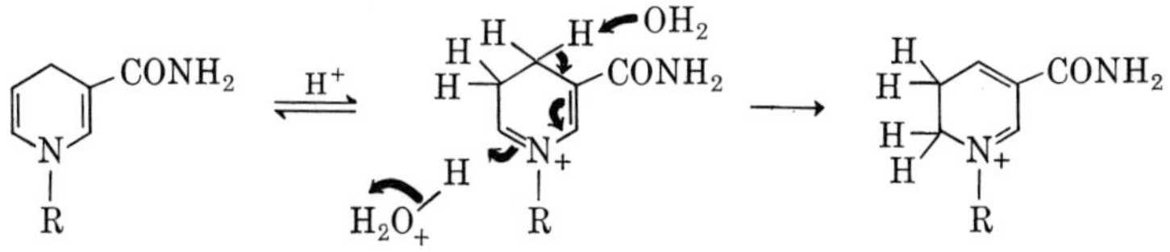

[422] R. Segal and G. Stein, *J. Chem. Soc.*, 5254 (1960). The ratio of absorption intensities for the two absorption bands of the 1,6-dihydropyridine is not that observed for the pure material but indicates contamination by 1,4-dihydropyridine as shown by the increased absorption in the 3500 to 3600 Å region.

[423] It is assumed that such rearrangement does not occur in the reactions of Eq. (2.162).

The addition of nucleophiles to the protonated form of a dihydro-pyridine is accompanied by a marked shift in the absorption maximum to shorter wavelengths, the change for the reaction described in Eq. (2.160) being from 3740 Å to 3070 Å. The latter maximum corresponds quite well to what would be expected for a β-amino-α,β-unsaturated ketone.[409] Further reaction of the adducts is not well understood, although some data are available (cf. ref. 285, pp. 125–127).

Reaction of dihydropyridines with a proton at carbon can be regarded as a instance of enamine nucleophilicity. Attempts to utilize the nucleophilic character of the β carbon in 1,4,4-trimethyl-1,4-dihydropyridine in the displacement of iodide from methyl iodide or in reaction with the acetylium ion probably failed because of the steric hindrance introduced by the presence of the gem-dimethyl groups at the 4-position.[306] A report describing the reaction of DPNH and 1-methyl-3-carbamido-1,4-dihydropyridine with methyl iodide in which it is claimed that loss of the typical dihydropyridine absorption accompanies the formation of a salt containing the elements of methyl iodide is of interest.[424] The formulations given by the authors or as amended slightly by later work[425] are not verified and do not utilize the nucleophilicity of the dihydro-pyridine ring.

2.13E. Pyridinyl Radicals

The addition of one electron to a pyridinium ring or the abstraction of a hydrogen atom from a dihydropyridine yields a *pyridinyl* radical. These radicals are of interest as possible intermediates in certain bio-chemical processes, as possible photochemical products from charge-transfer complexes or other suitable combinations, and as interesting free radicals of simple structure.

2.13E-1. The fact that stable free radicals may be prepared by polarographic reduction of pyridinium ions in acetonitrile has been mentioned in Sec. 2.10. It is rather difficult to measure the reduction potential for most pyridinium ions in aqueous solution because the inhibition of the second reduction step [Eqs. (2.165) and (2.166)] requires a high pH, and many of the compounds of interest have groups (e.g., carbamido, carbethoxy, etc.) which are hydrolyzed under these conditions.

(2.165) $$RPy^+ + e^- \rightarrow RPy\cdot$$
(2.166) $$RPy\cdot + e^- + H^+ \rightarrow RPyH$$

The irreversibility of Eq. (2.166) is responsible for the fact that a reversi-

---

[424] A. N. Ginsburg and L. S. Kleimanova, *Biokhimiya*, **14**, 230 (1949).
[425] C. Sannie and J. J. Panouse, *Bull. soc. chim. biol.*, **36**, 237, 247 (1954).

ble potential cannot be established for the DPN-DPNH system, but can be measured in the presence of an electron "mediator" (a compound which can react in one-electron reactions with either DPN or DPNH). Potentiometric titration of pyridinium ions with chromium(II) at high pH leads to the uptake of one reducing equivalent per pyridinium ion and the formation of colored solutions in the case of 1-alkyl-4-substituted pyridinium ions.[251]   These are thought to be free radicals.

The reduction potentials observed in acetonitrile solution for the pyridinium ions of Eq. (2.167), X = CONH$_2$, COOCH$_3$, and CN,[246] correlate well with the positions of the corresponding charge-transfer bands of the pyridinium iodides in chloroform or methylene chloride.[245] The chemical reactions of the free radicals are described in Sec. 2.10.

(2.167)

2.13F. DPNH Models

The purpose of a model for an enzymatic reaction is to establish, if possible, the characteristics of the transformation.   The model permits the "isolation" of group and medium effects and can, in favorable cases, lead to ideas about transition states.   According to the appropriateness of the model (duplication of reaction, parallelism, or congruency, . . . see Sec. 3.1), useful clues about possible roles for the enzyme in enzymatic reactions may be gained.

2.13F-1.   In spite of numerous attempts to design a model reaction for the reduction of carbonyl compounds by DPNH, no truly successful example has been reported.   Dihydropyridines have been used to reduce malachite green, thiobenzophenones, α-keto acids, benzoquinones, and α,β-unsaturated ketones, acids, and esters.   In the first three instances, as well as in the case of the unsaturated ketone, direct hydrogen transfer has been demonstrated from the dihydropyridine to the reaction partner.

Malachite green is reduced with direct hydrogen transfer from the 4-position by 1-benzyl-1,4-dihydronicotinamide[426] (Fig. 2.67). The transition state is of interest because it involves only charge dispersion rather than charge separation.

Thiobenzophenones are reduced by 1-benzyl-1,4-dihydronicotinamide to the corresponding thiols; DPNH also serves as a reducing agent for

[426] D. Mauzerall and F. H. Westheimer, *J. Am. Chem. Soc.*, **77**, 2261 (1955).

thiobenzophenones.[427,428]   The reactions are first-order in both the dihydropyridine and the thiobenzophenone and, although the reaction is faster in polar solvents than in nonpolar solvents, it is not sensitive to pH.

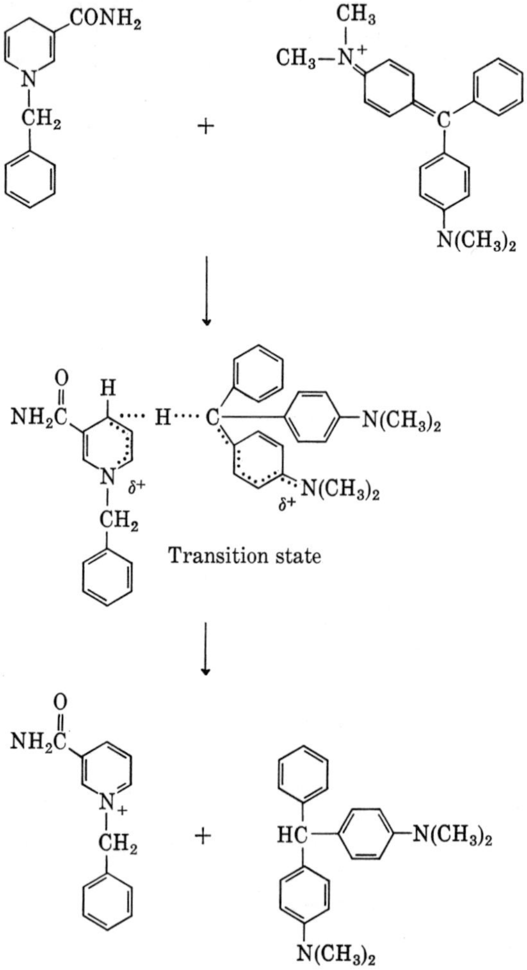

FIG. 2.67. The reduction of malachite green.

The charge separation in the transition state must be compensated internally, possibly by a charge-transfer interaction of the benzhydryl mercaptide and the developing pyridinium ring (Fig. 2.68).   An intra-

[427] R. H. Abeles, R. F. Hutton, and F. H. Westheimer, *J. Am. Chem. Soc.*, **79**, 712 (1957).

[428] The reactivity of thiobenzophenones in comparison with ketones has been discussed by J. C. Powers and F. H. Westheimer, *J. Am. Chem. Soc.*, **82**, 5431 (1960).

molecular proton source, the *o*-hydroxyl group in *o*-hydroxythiobenzo-phenone as substrate, causes a more rapid reaction than found for the unsubstituted thioketone, whereas the corresponding *o*-methoxythio-benzophenone reacts more slowly.

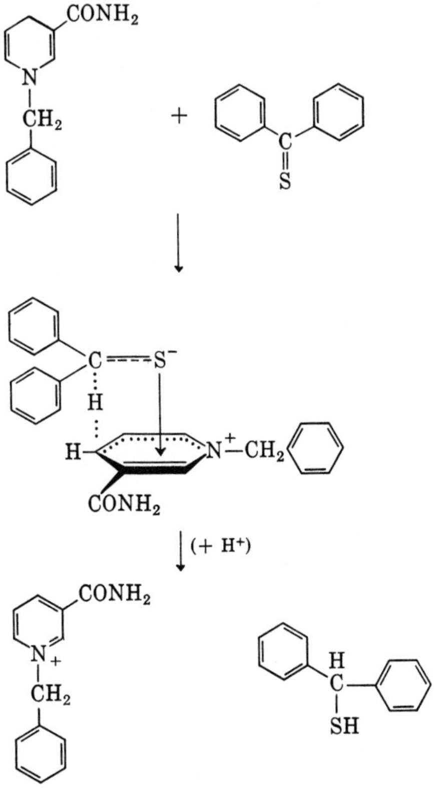

FIG. 2.68. Reduction of thiobenzophenone with a dihydropyridine.

2.13F-2. The "Hantzsch compound," 2,6-dimethyl-3,5-dicarb-ethoxy-1,4-dihydropyridine, transfers hydrogen directly to benzoyl-formic acid. If the reaction is carried out in ethanol-*d*, the mandelic acid isolated contains almost no nonexchangeable deuterium [Eq. (2.168)].

(2.168)

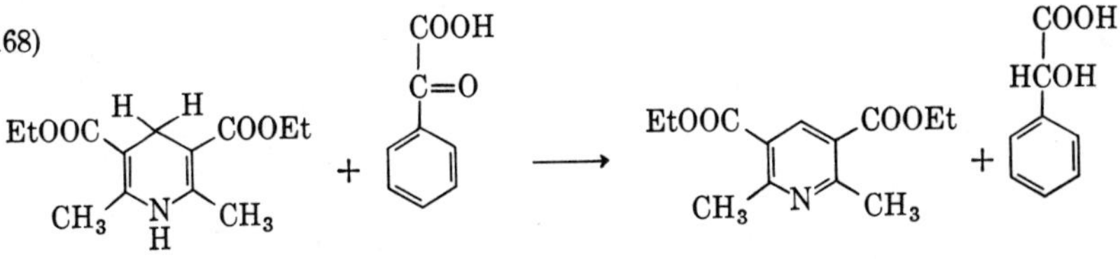

Only a very low yield (ca. 5%) of mandelic acid was obtained, and the yield of lactic acid in a similar reaction with pyruvic acid was equally low.[429] A reduction of pyruvic acid with dihydropyridines under vigorous conditions has been reported.[430]

The "Hantzsch compound" reacts rapidly at room temperature with chloranil (tetrachloro-p-benzoquinone) to form the hydroquinone and pyridine. Much slower reactions at higher temperatures are reported for the "Hantzsch compound" and such α,β-unsaturated carboxylic acids and ketones as maleic acid, maleic anhydride, diethyl fumarate, and benzylideneacetophenone.[431] The course of the reactions was not investigated in detail.

The reduction of the α,β-unsaturated ketone, 1-phenyl-4,4,4-trifluoro-2-butenone, with the dihydropyridine, 1,2,6-trimethyl-3,5-dicarbethoxy-1,4-dihydropyridine, has been demonstrated to occur in reasonable yield in refluxing methanol containing pyridinium perchlorate as buffer. Direct hydrogen transfer was proved with the 4,4-dideuterodihydropyridine [Eq. (2.168a)].[431a]

(2.168a)

2.13G. A Mechanism for DPNH Action

One of the important aims of studies of enzyme mechanisms is the description of the transition state (or states) involved in a given transformation. The usual technique for constructing such descriptions is to combine information on the nature of the groups present at the "active site" with principles derived from model systems.

2.13G-1. Several imaginative schemes have been proposed for the reaction of DPN with ethanol, including a mechanism dependent upon the participation of two DPN molecules,[289] a pathway which some-

[429] R. H. Abeles and F. H. Westheimer, *J. Am. Chem. Soc.*, **80**, 5459 (1958).

[430] K. Wallenfels and D. Hofmann, *Tetrahedron Letters No. 15*, 10 (1959).

[431] E. A. Braude, J. Hannah, and R. Linstead, *J. Chem. Soc.*, 3257 (1960).

[431a] B. E. Norcross, P. E. Klinedinst, Jr., and F. H. Westheimer, *Am. Chem. Soc. Abstr.*, **140**, 74Q (1961); *J. Am. Chem. Soc.*, **84**, 797 (1962).

how utilized an addition product of an enzyme sulfhydryl group and DPN,[333] and a couple of varieties of Meerwein-Ponndorf-Oppenauer equilibrium between alcohols and carbonyl compounds catalyzed by alkoxides.[414,415] The latter two depend upon the zinc atom to form the required alkoxide.

The first two schemes are *ad hoc* and without adequate analogy in organic chemistry, while the last two are excluded on the basis of the shift in the spectrum of DPNH upon combination with certain dehydrogenases. If the zinc atom were in the region of the amide group as required in these mechanisms, the DPNH-ADH (alcohol dehydrogenase) complex, for example, would exhibit a shift of maximum to longer wavelengths, since the zinc ion would favor the charge distribution of the excited state. The observed shift is to shorter wavelengths.[432] In any event, there is evidence from experiments with ADH and complexing agents[416] and competition with cadmium[433] that zinc ion is connected with the binding of DPN to the enzyme rather than the oxidation-reduction step itself. Thus, it is unlikely that the stereospecificity of the acetaldehyde reduction is associated with the zinc ion.[434]

2.13G-2. The maximum of DPNH at 3400 Å shifts to 3250 Å in the ADH complex[432] (see also Table 2.13-11). The inadequacy of a nonpolar "active site"[418] as the source of the spectroscopic shift has been mentioned. A possible explanation for the shift is suggested by data and calculations on an α,β-unsaturated ketone system which has a positive charge at a quaternary nitrogen near the β carbon of the system [Eq. (2.169)].[435] The compound with the positive charge absorbs at shorter

(2.169)

wavelengths than the analogue which has a methylene in place of the nitrogen. Calculations[298] demonstrated that the spectroscopic shift to shorter wavelengths was due to a repulsion between the positive charge on the nitrogen and the increased positive charge present at the β carbon in the excited state.

It is postulated that the shift observed in the DPNH spectrum when complexed is due to the proximity of a positive charge to the nitrogen of the dihydropyridine ring. It is proposed that the positive charge resides

[432] H. Theorell and R. K. Bonnichsen, *Acta Chem. Scand.*, **5**, 1105 (1951).

[433] A. Witter, *Acta Chem. Scand.*, **14**, 1717 (1960).

[434] D. D. Ulmer and B. L. Vallee, *J. Biol. Chem.*, **236**, 730 (1961).

[435] E. M. Kosower and D. C. Remy, *Tetrahedron*, **5**, 281 (1959).

on the nitrogen of an alkylammonium ion, e.g., the ε-amino group of a lysine residue.

2.13G-3.   A location for the alkylammonium group can be chosen on *independent* grounds.   One hydrogen bond can be made to the nonbonding (sp^3) electrons of the oxygen in the ribose ring to which the dihydronicotinamide is attached.   Another hydrogen bond is proposed to the nonbonding electrons (sp^2) of the oxygen of the carbonyl group of an acetaldehyde molecule, placed so that the carbon of the carbonyl group is directly above the 4-carbon of the dihydropyridine ring.   The second hydrogen bond is based on the assumption that the arrangement in the DPNH-ADH complex is close to that in the DPNH-ADH-CH$_3$CHO transition-state complex.   From models and scale drawings, an alkyl-ammonium ion hydrogen bonded to two groups as described would be located ca. 3.0 Å from the nitrogen of the dihydropyridine ring.

It can be estimated that a positively charged nitrogen located 3.0 Å from the nitrogen of the dihydropyridine ring would increase the observed transition energy for light absorption by the dihydropyridine by ca. 5.2 kcal/mole.[436,437]

2.13G-4.   The observed shift in the maximum of DPNH on complex formation with ADH is equivalent to a transition energy change of 3.9 kcal/mole.   Comparison with the calculated value of 5.2 kcal/mole for the positively charged nitrogen 3.0 Å from the nitrogen of the dihydro-pyridine ring suggests that the hypothesis is a reasonable one.   If hydrogen bonding is a necessity for binding of acetaldehyde, it would be expected that only one side (either the "A" or the "B" side) of the DPNH ring would be able to provide a hydrogen in the transition state for reduction.

The stereospecificity of the reduction with respect to acetaldehyde, leading to the formation of only one enantiomer of ethanol-1-*d* when a deuterium is transferred, is explicable in terms of a "hydrophobic region" at the "active site" which can distinguish the small alkyl group (hydrogen) from the large alkyl group (methyl).   Good evidence for a "hydrophobic region" at the "active site" exists in the discovery that long-chain fatty acid amides complex with DPNH and ADH.[438]

All these facts and reasonable suppositions may be combined into a picture for the transition-state complex for the reduction of acetaldehyde by DPNH-ADH (Fig. 2.69).

[436] E. M. Kosower, *Biochim. et Biophys. Acta.*, **56,** 474 (1962).

[437] The figure 5.2 kcal/mole is derived for a location of the positive charge on the side of the ring opposite to the 3-carbamido group; ca. 4.2 kcal/mole is obtained for the transition energy increase induced by a positive charge on the same side as the 3-carbamido group.

[438] A. D. Winer and H. Theorell, *Acta Chem. Scand.*, **14,** 1729 (1960).

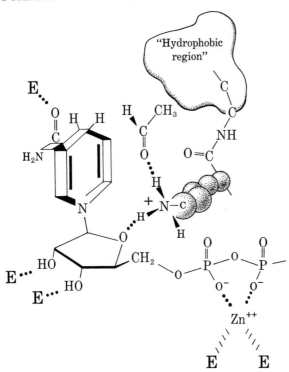

Fig. 2.69. Transition state complex for the reduction of acetaldehyde by DPNH and ADH. (*Reprinted by permission of Biochimica et Biophysica Acta.*)

Observations which indicate that altered DPN molecules have reduced enzymatic activities are not in disagreement with the proposed mechanism. Such molecules are DPN lacking the 2'-hydroxyl group[439] and the α-isomer of DPN.[440]

[439] H. B. Klenow and B. Andersen, *Biochim. et Biophys. Acta*, **23**, 92 (1957).
[440] N. O. Kaplan, S. P. Colowick, and A. Nason, *J. Biol. Chem.*, **191**, 473 (1951).

2.14. FLAVINS

La cinquième planète était très curieuse. C'était la plus petite de toutes. Il y avait là juste assez de place pour loger un réverbère et un allumeur de réverbères. Le petit prince ne parvenait pas à s'éxpliquer à quoi pouvaient servir, quelque part dans le ciel, sur une planète sans maison, ni population, un réverbère et un allumeur de réverbères.

A. de Saint-Exupéry*

Riboflavin, vitamin B_2, was identified as an essential portion of several coenzymes shortly before the discovery that nicotinamide functioned as a vitamin by serving a key role in a coenzyme.[441]   The coenzymes incorporating riboflavin have been much less available for research than

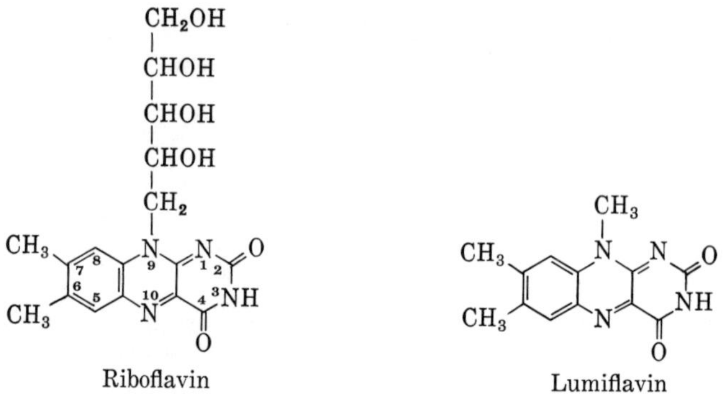

FIG. 2.70. Riboflavin and lumiflavin.

riboflavin itself, and much of the knowledge about flavins has come from work on riboflavin.[441]   The coenzymes are FMN, flavin mononucleotide (the name is a misnomer, but is always used), a 5'-phosphate ester of riboflavin, and FAD, flavin adenine dinucleotide, a mixed anhydride (pyrophosphate) of FMN and adenylic acid.

The formula for riboflavin (and its numbering system) is shown in Fig. 2.70 along with that for lumiflavin. Tightly bound flavin-protein combinations exist which do not apparently contain either FMN or FAD.[441]

The principal substrates for flavoprotein enzymes in oxidation reactions

---

* From A. de Saint-Exupéry, "Le Petit Prince," p. 49, Librairie Gallimard, Paris, all rights reserved.

[441] Many aspects of flavin chemistry and behavior may be found in the excellent and critical review by H. Beinert, in "The Enzymes," vol. 2, chap. 10, Academic Press, Inc., New York, 1960.

are the reduced pyridine nucleotides (DPNH and TPNH), α-amino and α-hydroxy acids, aldehydes, purines, and certain saturated carbon compounds from which hydrogen is removed to form a double bond.   These are all very important reactions in metabolic schemes, but the mechanisms are obscure.

2.14A. Spectroscopic and Photochemical Behavior

2.14A-1.   Riboflavin absorbs light in two main regions between 2400 and 5000 Å with three clearly defined maxima.   In spite of the importance of the spectra to an understanding of the photochemical

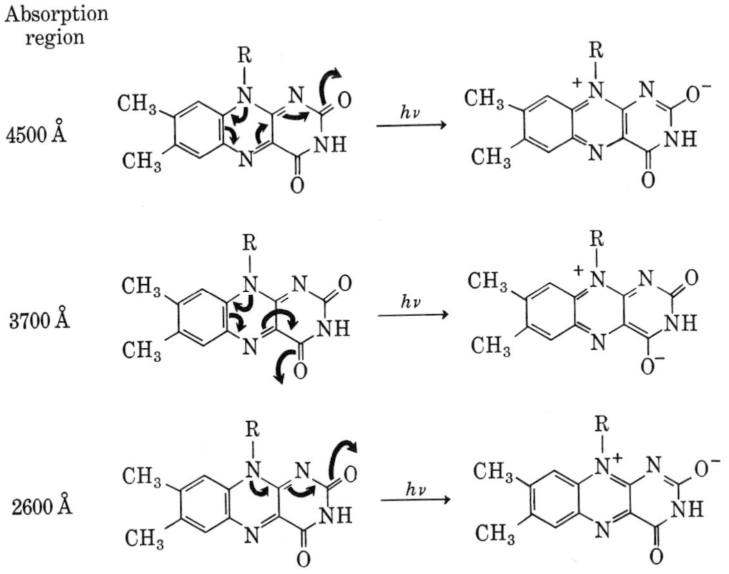

FIG. 2.71. Charge rearrangements postulated for light absorption by riboflavin.

reactions of riboflavin and to any attempt to interpret spectroscopic data for flavoproteins, few theoretical or experimental studies of the spectra have been made.   The maxima for riboflavin and several derivatives[442] are listed in Table 2.14-1, and expressions for the possible charge rearrangements which take place on light absorption in the various spectral regions are given in Fig. 2.71.   The fact that substituents affect the long-wavelength maxima and not the short-wavelength maximum is in agreement with the assignments shown, but they should not be regarded as anything but crude approximations to the actual excited state, useful in discussing properties of the molecule after light absorption has occurred.

[442] R. Kuhn, H. Vetter, and H. W. Rzeppa, *Ber.*, **70**, 1302 (1937).

Examination of the spectrum for the 5,7-dimethylisoalloxazine isomer of riboflavin[443] reveals a complex set of electronic transitions for the long-wavelength absorption band.   The effect of solvent on the spectrum of 3-methyl lumiflavin indicates that the visible absorption bands are only slightly sensitive to solvent but that the "3700 Å band" is moderately sensitive.   [λ_{max} 335 mμ (CCl$_4$) → λ_{max} 369 mμ (H$_2$O).][444]

Flavins have a useful fluorescence with a maximum in the neighborhood of 5400 Å, while the reduced flavins do not fluoresce at all.   Although an absolute quantum yield for the fluorescence of riboflavin at pH 7 in water is reported as 0.26 with excitation by the mercury line at 3660 Å,[445] the susceptibility of the excited state to "quenching"[446] and the nature of the photochemical reactions observed for riboflavin (see below) require that great caution be used in interpretation of results.

TABLE 2.14-1. ABSORPTION MAXIMA OF RIBOFLAVIN AND CONGENERS

Isoalloxazine

Substance	$\lambda_{1,max}$, Å (ϵ)	$\lambda_{2,max}$, Å (ϵ)	$\lambda_{3,max}$, Å (ϵ)	Ref.
Riboflavin	4450 (12,500)	3730 (10,600)	2660 (32,500)	447
FMN (Riboflavin-5'-phosphate)	4450 (12,500)	3730 (10,400)	2660 (31,800)	447
FAD (see text)	4500 (11,300)	3750 (9,300)	2630 (38,000)	447
Isoalloxazine	4400	3350	2680	442
6,7-Tetramethylene-	4400	3570	2670	442
5,7-Dimethyl-	4400	3600 3920	2660	442, 443
6-Methyl-	4400	3560	2670	442
6,7-Dimethyl-	4450	(3650)	2700	442
6,7-Tetramethylene-	4500	3630	2660	442
6,8-Dimethyl-	4500	3720	2700	442

[443] R. Kuhn, P. Desnuelle, and F. Weygand, *Ber.*, **70**, 1293 (1937).   The nature of the sugar on the 9-position has no influence on the spectrum.

[444] H. A. Harbury, K. F. LaNove, P. A. Loach, and R. M. Amick, *Proc. Natl. Acad. Sci. U.S.*, **45**, 1708 (1959).

[445] G. Weber and F. W. J. Teale, *Trans. Faraday Soc.*, **53**, 646 (1957).

[446] The ability of a material to decrease the intensity of observed fluorescence is described in terms of "quenching," whatever the detailed mechanism might be.

[447] L. G. Whitby, *Biochem. J.*, **54**, 437 (1953).

2.14A-2. Many years ago, the light sensitivity of riboflavin was noted[448] and later, a crystalline product of photolysis was found to be lumiflavin (Fig. 2.70).[449] Photolysis of a model compound, 9-(2'-hydroxyethyl)-isoalloxazine, in neutral or acid solution, formed acetaldehyde and alloxazine [Eq. (2.170)] along with quantities of formaldehyde. The relative amounts of formaldehyde and acetaldehyde varied in a striking way with a variation in the initial concentration of the isoalloxazine. It was shown that both acid and base "catalyzed" the reaction, and that replacement of the hydroxyl hydrogen with an acetyl group reduced the photolysis rate by a factor of twenty-five.[450] More recent studies suggest that these results cannot be interpreted in a simple fashion, for irradiation of riboflavin in oxygen-free aqueous solution produces dihydroriboflavin and hydrogen peroxide.[451] Reoxidation of the reduced riboflavin with oxygen leads to an additional quantity of hydrogen peroxide. The photochemical reduction of riboflavin by water [Eq. (2.171)] is "accelerated"[451] by "activators." Investigation of the photolysis of riboflavin

(2.170)

$+ CH_3CHO$

(2.171)

$+ H_2O_2$

in the presence of methionine in oxygen-free water demonstrates that the "activator" participates in an early stage of the over-all reaction, because dihydroriboflavin and methionine sulfoxide are produced, even though hydrogen peroxide (or oxygen) cannot convert methionine into the sulfoxide[451] [Eq. (2.172)]. It is suggested that complex formation

$$(2.172) \qquad Rbf + CH_3SCH_2CH_2\underset{\overset{|}{NH_2}}{C}HCOOH \xrightarrow[H_2O]{h\nu} RbfH_2 + CH_3\overset{\overset{O}{\|}}{S}CH_2CH_2\underset{\overset{|}{NH_2}}{C}HCOOH$$

between methionine and riboflavin is an important factor and that con-

[448] O. Warburg and W. Christian, *Biochem. Z.*, **254**, 438 (1932).

[449] R. Kuhn and T. Wagner-Jauregg, *Ber.*, **66**, 1577 (1933).

[450] M. Halwer, *J. Am. Chem. Soc.*, **73**, 4870 (1951).

[451] W. J. Nickerson and G. Strauss, *J. Am. Chem. Soc.*, **82**, 5007 (1960). Cf. also G. Strauss and W. J. Nickerson, *J. Am. Chem. Soc.*, **83**, 3187 (1961).

ductivity data are in support of such complexation.[451] Lumiflavin undergoes the same type of photochemical reactions as riboflavin, ruling out the necessity of the ribityl side chain for such reaction. [The reaction products in many photolyses of flavins include fragments from the side chain, Eq. (2.170); the route for their formation *must* be complex.]

It has been claimed that DPNH (and TPNH and NMNH[452]) react with flavins in a nonenzymatic "model reaction" to give dihydroflavins ("leucoflavins") on the basis of a study in which the dihydropyridine (e.g., DPNH), a flavin (riboflavin, FAD, etc.), and ferricytochrome c were reacted and found to form a pyridine, the original flavin, and ferrocytochrome c.[453] The authenticity of the reaction is called into serious doubt by the finding that DPNH and riboflavin (and other flavins, FMN, lumiflavin, etc.) *do not react in the dark*.[454,455,456a] Model reactions of flavins would indeed represent a fruitful area of study in molecular biochemistry. It should be remembered that flavoproteins are much less susceptible to photolytic reactions,[457] that most flavoproteins (whether dissociable or not) are not fluorescent,[446] and that most of the biochemical reactions catalyzed by flavoproteins do not appear to involve free flavins.

2.14B. Flavin "Semiquinones"

2.14B-1. One-equivalent reduction of p-benzoquinone forms a free radical called a "semiquinone"; the latter is reasonably stable in alkaline solution, partially because of the symmetry of the radical anion [Eq. (2.173)]. The neutral radical has a considerable tendency to

$$(2.173)$$

[452] The dihydro derivative of nicotinamide mononucleotide.

[453] T. P. Singer and E. B. Kearney, *J. Biol. Chem.*, **183**, 409 (1950).

[454] K. Uehara, I. Muramatsu, and M. Makita, *Vitamins* (*Kyoto*), **13**, 261 (1957); *Chem. Zentr.*, **129**, 9520 (1958).

[455] A report of a reaction between DPNH and FMN (*presumably* in the dark) has appeared,[456] but the experiments were not described in great enough detail to accept as having precedence over the negative result mentioned in the text.

[456] B. Commoner and B. B. Lippincott, *Proc. Natl. Acad. Sci. U.S.*, **44**, 1110 (1958).

[456a] Confirmation of the work reported in ref. 454 is made by W. R. Frisell and C. G. Mackenzie, *Proc. Natl. Acad. Sci. U.S.*, **45**, 1568 (1959).

[457] H. Theorell, *Biochem. Z.*, **279**, 186 (1935).

(2.174)

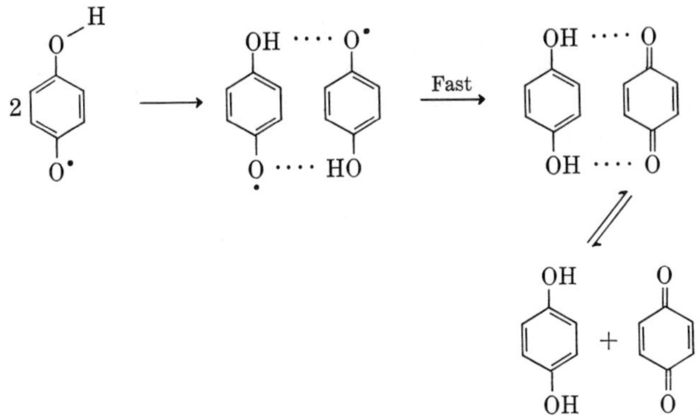

dimerize, the dimer quinhydrone being in equilibrium with the hydro-quinone and quinone [Eq. (2.174)].

It is now thoroughly established that flavins can be reduced by the addition of one electron to a free radical, almost always referred to as a semiquinone[441,458] [Eq. (2.175)]. Polarography of riboflavin at acid pH

(2.175)

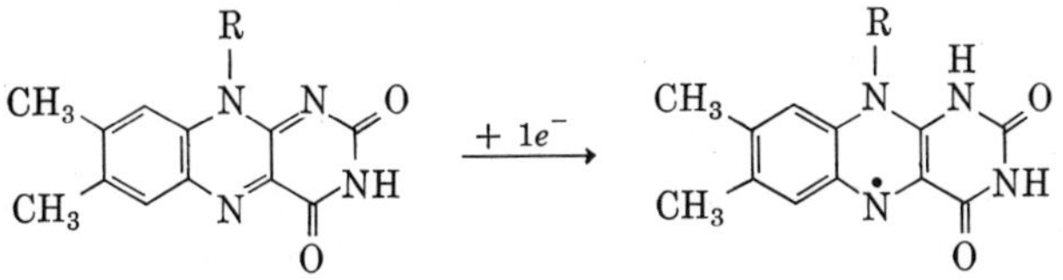

gives two waves, corresponding to two one-electron reduction steps.[459] The change of the potential with the proportion of riboflavin reduced in neutral solution is higher than expected for a reversible two-electron reduction, indicating some reversible one-electron reduction.[441] This is the method of the "index potential." Solids obtained from reduction of a flavin are sufficiently paramagnetic to exhibit magnetic susceptibility, but they do not have a close enough relationship to the free radicals formed in solution to warrant consideration here.[441] The most elegant and recent demonstration of the occurrence of flavin free radicals is accomplished by the detection of microwave absorption by the free radical in a strong magnetic field. (The technique is called ESR, electron spin resonance.)[460,461]

Rapid absorption spectrophotometry has also been utilized to great advantage in connection with chemical reduction of flavins to show that an intermediate is formed after one reducing equivalent has been added

[458] Cf., however, O. Hemmerich, *Experientia*, **16**, 534 (1960).
[459] J. R. Merkel and W. J. Nickerson, *Biochim. et Biophys. Acta*, **14**, 303 (1954).
[460] H. Beinert, *J. Am. Chem. Soc.*, **78**, 5323 (1956).
[461] A. Ehrenberg, *Acta Chem. Scand.*, **11**, 205 (1957).

and that this intermediate is neither the oxidized form nor the reduced flavin (i.e., flavin plus two electrons). The "semiquinone" from FMN has an absorption band of relatively low intensity (ϵ at least 1000 to 1500) between 5000 and 5500 Å, and a dimer band which varies in position with pH between 7700 and 10,100 Å in the range pH 0 to 12.0.[460]

2.14B-2. It is probable that flavin free radicals play some part in the enzyme reactions catalyzed by flavoproteins, but there is as yet no proof for this possibility.[441] "It should also be kept in mind that optical as well as EPR (i.e., *ESR*) data thus far available show only that semiquinones are formed during chemical oxidation-reduction and flavoprotein catalysis in vitro but give no information on the actual sequence of events. It is not clear whether semiquinone formation observed under anaerobic conditions is the consequence of actual one-electron transfer from substrate or of secondary oxidoreduction between completely reduced flavin and flavin which is still in the oxidized form."[462] The two possibilities may be described by Eqs. (2.176) and (2.177) and

(2.176) $\quad\quad\quad SH_2 + F \rightarrow \dot{S}H + \dot{F}H \dashrightarrow$ etc.

(2.177) $\quad\quad\quad SH_2 + F \rightarrow FH_2 + S$

$\quad\quad\quad\quad\quad\quad FH_2 + F \rightarrow 2\dot{F}H$

have obvious bearing upon the location of the "crossover point" for metabolic oxidation. This "point" is the place where two-electron steps become one-electron steps.

Another complication present in flavoproteins is the presence of metal ions such as iron and molybdenum. Both have been shown to undergo valence change during reaction,[463-465] but there is as yet no indication as to the role which these metal ions play or their relation to the flavin. It is interesting but not necessarily of biochemical relevance that molybdenum(VI) complexes with FMN[466] since the protein may also be important in the binding. An interpretation of some aspects of the role of Mo(VI) in xanthine oxidase has been offered to rationalize the fact that an ESR signal assigned to Mo(V) has the same kinetics of appearance as the signal assigned to the riboflavin radical.[466a,466b] Flavin "semiquinone" complexes readily with metal ions.[458]

[462] Ref. 441, p. 415.

[463] H. Beinert and R. H. Sands, *Biochem. Biophys. Research Comm.*, **1**, 171 (1959).

[464] H. Beinert, personal communication.

[465] R. C. Bray, B. G. Malmström, and T. Värngard, *Biochem. J.*, **73**, 193 (1959).

[466] J. T. Spence and J. Tocatlian, *J. Am. Chem. Soc.*, **83**, 816 (1961).

[466a] R. J. P. Williams, in "Advances in the Chemistry of the Coordination Compounds," pp. 74–75, The Macmillan Company, New York, 1961.

[466b] Cf. R. C. Bray, T. Värngard, and A. Ehrenberg, to be published.

The light absorption of FMN complexed with old yellow enzyme has a maximum at 4650 Å, displaced 200 Å (ca. 3.0 kcal/mole) from the position of free FMN.[467] The formation or considerable strengthening of a hydrogen bond to the 2-oxygen in the excited state might account for such a shift and serves to define one part of the interaction between the flavin and the protein.

The interesting suggestion has been made that a charge-transfer complex of DPNH and a flavin present in the terminal oxidation chain directly participate in the formation of a "high-energy phosphate," e.g., ATP; see Fig. 1.14.[468–470] Although the calculations are encouraging, no experimental support for the hypotheses advanced has been reported.

While it is possible to write a number of speculative mechanisms concerning the mode of flavin participation in biochemical reactions, it is wiser to point out that flavin research should represent both an exciting and a fertile field of molecular biochemistry. The stereochemistry of the dehydrogenation reaction catalyzed by succinic dehydrogenase is *trans*,[471] a suggestion that an ionic rather than a free-radical mechanism is involved.

2.15. PHOSPHATES

כבוד אלהים הסתר דבר.

וכבוד מלכים חקור דבר"

Proverbs 25:2

2.15A. Introduction

2.15A-1. Phosphate derivatives play an unusually important role in biological systems, ranging from their structural function in the hereditary material, deoxyribonucleic acid (DNA), to their capability as intermediates in biochemical synthesis, adenosine triphosphate (ATP) being one excellent example. Biologically important phosphates are grouped into a small number of chemical classes in Table 2.15-1.

The chief distinction conferred upon a molecule containing a phosphate derivative as a structural element is the negative charge carried by the oxygen attached to the phosphorus. In simple molecules, the negative

[467] H. Theorell, *Biochem. Z.*, **278**, 263 (1935).
[468] B. Grabe, *Arkiv Fysik*, **17**, 97 (1960).
[469] B. Grabe, *Arkiv Kemi*, **15**, 323 (1960).
[470] B. Grabe, Inaugural Dissertation, University, Stockholm, 1960.
[471] T. T. Tchen and H. van Milligan, *J. Am. Chem. Soc.*, **82**, 4115 (1960).

charge might serve as a binding site to an enzyme (e.g., DPN; cf. Sec. 2.13G) or participate in the stabilization of a lipid–polar nonlipid interface (as may be the case with α-lecithin). In polymeric phosphates (DNA, RNA), the negative charges must be concerned with the shape of the molecule; the behavior of polyelectrolytes is not well understood.

TABLE 2.15-1. BIOLOGICALLY IMPORTANT PHOSPHATE DERIVATIVES

General formula	General types	Specific examples
PO_4H_3	Orthophosphoric acid	
$ROPO_3H_2$	Hydroxyalkyl phosphates	α-D-Glucose-1-phosphate
		D-Glucose-6-phosphate
		D-Fructose-1,6-diphosphate
		D-Glyceraldehyde-3-phosphate
		2-Phospho-D-glyceric acid
		Adenosine monophosphate (AMP)
	Alkyl phosphate	Pyridoxal-5-phosphate
	Enol phosphate	Phosphoenolpyruvic acid
	Acyl phosphate	Acetyl phosphate
		3-Phospho-D-glyceryl phosphate
$RNHPO_3H_2$	Phosphoramidate	Creatine phosphate
		Arginine phosphate
$(RO)_2PO_2H$	Dialkyl phosphate	α-Lecithin
		Adenosine-2',3'-cyclic phosphate
		RNA, DNA
$(RO)_3PO$	Trialkyl or triaryl phosphate	Tri-o-cresyl phosphate[a]
$ROPO_2HX$	Acyl adenylate	Acetyl adenylate
		Adenyl sulfate
$(RO)_2POX^c$	Dialkyl phosphoro-fluoridate	Diisopropyl fluorophosphate[b] (DFP)
$RO(R)POX^c$	Alkyl alkylphos-phonofluoridate	Isopropyl methylphosphono-fluoridate (Sarin)
$ROPOPO_3H_2$ with $\overset{O}{\overset{\|}{}}$ above and OH below	Alkyl pyrophosphate	Adenosine diphosphate (ADP)
$ROPOPOR'$ with $\overset{O\ O}{\overset{\|\ \|}{}}$ above and $\underset{H\ H}{\underset{\|\ \|}{O\ O}}$ below	P_1P_2-dialkyl pyrophosphate	DPN, coenzyme A
$\begin{matrix} H \\ \| \\ O \\ \| \\ HO-P-O-PO_3H_2 \\ \| \\ O \end{matrix}$	Pyrophosphoric acid	

TABLE 2.15-1. BIOLOGICALLY IMPORTANT PHOSPHATE DERIVATIVES (*Continued*)

General formula	General types	Specific examples
$ROPOPOPO_3H_2$ (with O, O double bonds and O, O, H, H groups)	Alkyl triphosphate	Adenosine triphosphate (ATP)
$(RO)_2POP(OR)_2{}^c$ (with O, O double bonds)	Tetraalkyl pyrophosphate	Tetrabenzyl pyrophosphate

a Poisonous compound ingested occasionally by humans.

b Anticholinesterase.

c Many other compounds which are derivatives of phosphorus have considerable biological activity, usually of the anticholinesterase type.[472]

2.15A-2.   On the basis of the fact that certain phosphate derivatives have "considerable" free energies of hydrolysis and participate readily in certain synthetic reactions, while other derivatives have "low" free energies of hydrolysis, two categories of phosphate derivatives were formulated.[473]   It was at one time thought that the first-named group had "energy-rich" oxygen-phosphorus or nitrogen-phosphorus bonds.[473]   Such a formulation is not comprehensible in terms of modern theories of the nature of chemical bonding, and the idea has been severely criticized.[474]   The original two groups have been expanded to three: "low," "intermediate," and "high," the designations referring to the free energies of the aqueous hydrolysis reaction,[475] rather than supposed properties of particular bonds.   However, since this classification implies that the free energies of hydrolysis arise from the free energies of formation,[476,476a] it is not really satisfactory.   In aqueous solution, the solvation

[472] R. D. O'Brien, "Toxic Phosphorus Esters," Academic Press, Inc., New York, 1960.

[473] F. Lipmann, *Advances in Enzymol.*, **1**, 99 (1941).

[474] R. J. Gillespie, G. A. Maw, and C. A. Vernon, *Nature*, **171**, 1147 (1953).

[475] E.g., J. B. Neilands and P. K. Stumpf, "Outlines of Enzyme Chemistry," pp. 143–156, John Wiley & Sons, Inc., New York, 1958.

[476] A treatment of the free energies of hydrolysis in terms of internal characteristics of phosphate derivatives utilized intramolecular electrostatic repulsion, "opposed resonance," etc., and ignored the far larger factor of solvation energies.[477]   The conclusions are quoted by others (ref. 475, p. 155).   A quantum-mechanical calculation of the electron distribution in acyl phosphates, ADP and ATP led to the conclusion that the "bridge" oxygens were positively charged, and therefore susceptible to ready displacement.[478]

[476a] Cf. also R. J. Rutman and P. George, *Proc. Natl. Acad. Sci. U.S.*, **47**, 1094 (1961).

[477] T. L. Hill and M. F. Morales, *J. Am. Chem. Soc.*, **73**, 1656 (1951).

[478] B. Grabe, *Arkiv. Fysik*, **15**, 207 (1959).

of polyions represents an energy factor of considerable magnitude, and the variation in the solvation energy alone from reactants to products might be sufficient to account for the net free energy of hydrolysis [Eq. (2.178)]. In addition, the heat of ionization, the entropy change in the

$$\text{(2.178)} \qquad \underset{\underset{-O}{|}}{\overset{\overset{O}{\|}}{R}}OP-\underset{\underset{O^-}{|}}{\overset{\overset{O}{\|}}{O}}P-O^- + 2H_2O \longrightarrow ROPO_3^= + HPO_4^= + H_3O^+$$

hydrolysis, and the difference in *net* bond energies between the reactants and products all contribute to the observed free energy of hydrolysis.[474]

The most serious drawback to the classification by free energies of hydrolysis is its obscuration of the chemical problems of the biological utilization of phosphates.[478a] We should like to know, for example, how an enzyme catalyzes the reaction of phosphoenolpyruvic acid with adenosine diphosphate to yield pyruvic acid and adenosine triphosphate. The real chemical problem is to identify the nature of the transition states utilized by the enzyme-catalyzed reaction, and then, if possible, to compare these to model reactions which proceed through similar transition states. Such a comparison might involve the free energies of activation for the reactions in question, and therefore a study of the rates. The thermodynamic relationship of adenosine triphosphate to its hydrolysis products in water is irrelevant to such questions, although it is certainly a matter of concern when considering the over-all problem of biological utilization of the energy available from reduced carbon compounds. Inasmuch as the classification of phosphates on the basis of their free energies of hydrolysis has not produced an empirical generalization of great value, to say nothing of the unsound character of its misapplication on physical chemical grounds, it will not be further considered in this book.

2.15B. Properties of Phosphates

2.15B-1. All biologically important phosphates possess at least one dissociable hydrogen. Phosphoric acid is a moderately strong acid, and it is not surprising that most phosphates are markedly dissociated at physiological pH. The pK_a values for a number of phosphates are listed in Table 2.15-2.

[478a] Caution should also be exercised in the interpretation of results for 2-acyl-thiazolium ions. Cf. C. P. Nash, C. W. Olsen, F. G. White, and L. L. Ingraham, *J. Am. Chem. Soc.*, **83**, 4106 (1961).

TABLE 2.15-2. DISSOCIATION CONSTANTS FOR PHOSPHORIC ACIDS

Compound (T, °C)	pK_1	pK_2	pK_3	pK_4	Ref.
H_3PO_4 (25°)	2.13	7.21	13.0	......	479
$H_4P_2O_7$ (18°)	0.85	1.96	6.68	9.39	479
$H_5P_3O_{10}$ (25°)	....[d]	1.06[b]	2.30[c]	6.26[a,c]	480
$CH_3OPO_3H_2$ (22°)	1.52	6.58	......	......	481
$(CH_3O)_2PO_2H$ (25°)	0.76	.....	......	......	482
$CH_3COPO_3H_2$	....	4.8	......	......	483
CH₂—O O 　\\　　// 　　P 　/　\\ CH₂—O'　'OH	0.7	.....	......	......	484

[a] $pK_5 = 9.90.$[c]
[b] At $\mu = 1.0.$
[c] At $\mu = 0.$
[d] Completely dissociated in 0.01 M HCl.

2.15B-2. Any understanding of the biochemical behavior of phosphates on the molecular level must be preceded by an inquiry into the mechanisms by which phosphates may react. Considerable progress has been made through a combination of kinetic investigations and isotope distributions in products. The earliest studies on the kinetics of hydrolysis of monophosphate monoesters revealed that a plot of rate against pH (the "pH-rate profile") had a maximum at pH 4,[485,486] attributable to the higher reactivity of the monoanion. A similar study confirmed that a maximum existed in the pH-rate profile for the hydrolysis of 2-methoxy-1-methylethyl phosphate, and that the shape of the pH-rate profile could be predicted from a knowledge of the first and second dissociation constants of the phosphate.[487] The pH-rate profile for methyl phosphate is shown in Fig. 2.72, along with a curve calculated on the basis that the maximum rate at pH 4 is the reaction rate for pure monoanion.[481] The comparison of the experimental curve with the calculated shows that the dianion hydrolyzes at a much lower rate than

[479] K. S. Pitzer, *J. Am. Chem. Soc.*, **59**, 2365 (1937).
[480] J. I. Watters, E. D. Loughran, and S. M. Lambert, *J. Am. Chem. Soc.*, **78**, 4855 (1956).
[481] C. A. Bunton, D. R. Llewellyn, K. G. Oldham, and C. A. Vernon, *J. Chem. Soc.*, 3574 (1958).
[482] C. A. Bunton, M. M. Mhala, K. G. Oldham, and C. A. Vernon, *J. Chem. Soc.*, 3293 (1960).
[483] F. Lipmann and L. C. Tuttle, *Arch. Biochem.*, **13**, 373 (1947).
[484] P. C. Haake, Ph.D. Thesis, Harvard University, 1960.
[485] M. C. Bailly, *Bull. soc. chim. France*, **9**, 421 (1942).
[486] A. Desjobert, *Bull. soc. chim. France*, **14**, 809 (1947).
[487] W. W. Butcher and F. H. Westheimer, *J. Am. Chem. Soc.*, **77**, 2420 (1955).

the monoanion in the solutions used for the study, that neutral methyl phosphate reacts at an appreciably lower rate than the monoanion, and that a moderately rapid reaction occurs with the conjugate acid. A further complication in the interpretation of the results is the fact that

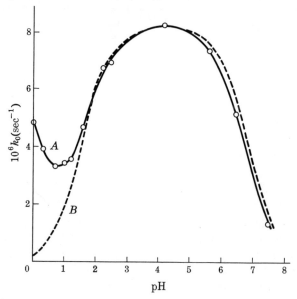

FIG. 2.72. pH-rate profile for the hydrolysis of methyl phosphate at 100°: *A*, experimental; *B*, calculated. (*Reprinted by permission of the Journal of the Chemical Society.*)

the mode of bond cleavage is not always the same. The monoanion reacts exclusively by P—O bond breakage, the neutral species apparently only by C—O fission, and the conjugate acid by both processes.[481] It is important to compare rates for the same bond-breaking process when considering the reactivities of different compounds. The rates are listed in Table 2.15-3. The reactions are summarized in Eqs. (2.179) to (2.181).

(2.179)
$$CH_3OP \overset{O}{\underset{OH}{\overset{\displaystyle \|}{\diagdown}}} {}^{O^-} + H_2O^{18} \longrightarrow CH_3OH + H_2PO_4^{18\ -}$$

(2.180)
$$CH_3OP \overset{O}{\underset{OH}{\overset{\displaystyle \|}{\diagdown}}} {}^{OH} + H_2O^{18} \longrightarrow CH_3O^{18}H + H_2PO_4^{-}$$

(2.181)
$$CH_3-O-\overset{+OH}{\overset{\displaystyle \|}{P}}(OH)_2 + H_2O^{18} \longrightarrow CH_3O^{18}H + H_3PO_4^{18}$$

2.15B-3.   The pH-rate profile for benzyl phosphate does not have a maximum at pH 4 because the acid catalyzed reaction is faster than the corresponding reaction for methyl phosphate, presumably as a result of the greater ease with which a displacement reaction may be effected upon a benzyl derivative.[488]   The biologically important α-D-glucose-1-phosphate hydrolyzes rapidly in acid solution.[489]   The pH-rate profile at 82°C has a shoulder (Fig. 2.73) at pH 5, the maximum

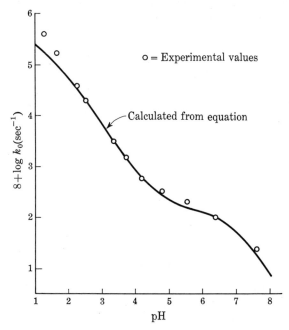

FIG. 2.73. pH-rate profile for α-D-glucose-1-phosphate.   (*Reprinted by permission of the Journal of the Chemical Society.*)

expected at pH 4 for the monoester monoanion being obscured by the very fast reaction of the neutral species.[490]   The monoanion hydrolyzes with P—O cleavage, but the neutral compound undergoes only C—O cleavage. The latter reaction is about 10^3 times faster than the neutral species hydrolysis of methyl phosphate, and therefore must represent a different mechanism (e.g., ionization).

The reaction of 2,3,4,6-tetra-O-methyl-α-D-glucopyranosyl chloride with methanol is first-order in the halide and unaffected by the addition

[488] J. Kumamoto and F. H. Westheimer, *J. Am. Chem. Soc.*, **77,** 2515 (1955).

[489] A. Desjobert, *Bull. soc. chim. biol.*, **33,** 42 (1951).

[490] C. A. Bunton, D. R. Llewellyn, K. G. Oldham, and C. A. Vernon, *J. Chem. Soc.*, 3588 (1958).

of methoxide ion.[491]   The reaction is best interpreted as an ionization to the glucopyranosyl ion, then subsequent reaction with methanol to form the methyl glucoside.   The product is 94% β-glucoside, so that the reaction proceeds with almost complete *inversion*.   The observation that chloride ion affects the extent of inversion, but not the order of the reaction, suggests that the reactive intermediate is an ion pair.[491]   Such intermediates in the reaction of sugar phosphates in enzyme-catalyzed reactions could well serve to maintain stereochemical specificity.[112]   The reaction of the glucopyranosyl chloride with methanol is depicted in Fig.

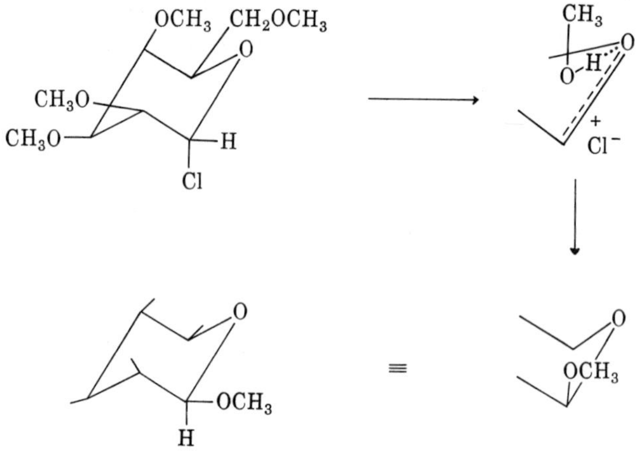

FIG. 2.74. Methanolysis of 2,3,4,6-tetra-*O*-methyl-α-D-glucopyranosyl chloride.

2.74.   A true displacement reaction, first-order in the glucosyl chloride and first-order in thiophenoxide ion, is found in *n*-propyl alcohol.[491] The stability of the glucopyranosyl carbonium ion is found to be lower than that of the *t*-butyl carbonium ion, insofar as these stabilities are reflected in the transition states for the hydrolysis of *t*-butyl β-D-glucopyranoside, which yields *t*-butyl carbonium ion and glucose.[492]   However, the difference is not great, since the rate constant for acid-catalyzed hydrolysis of the *t*-butyl β-D-glucopyranoside is only about 10^3 times greater than that for methyl β-D-glucopyranoside, and the latter reacts by way of a pyranosyl carbonium ion.[492,492a]   These facts are worth keeping in mind when considering the mechanism of enzyme-catalyzed reactions

[491] A. J. Rhind-Tutt and C. A. Vernon, *J. Chem. Soc.*, 4637 (1960).

[492] C. Armour, C. A. Bunton, S. Patai, L. H. Selman, and C. A. Vernon, *J. Chem. Soc.*, 412 (1961).

[492a] Excellent support for the proposal that a cyclic pyranosyl carbonium ion is an intermediate in acid-catalyzed reactions of pyranosides is found in the oxygen isotope effect observed for methyl α-D-glucopyranoside hydrolysis and the lack of reactivity of a thioglucopyranoside in attempted acid-catalyzed reaction.[492b]

[492b] B. E. C. Banks, Y. Meinwald, A. J. Rhind-Tutt, I. Sheft, and C. A. Vernon, *J. Chem. Soc.*, 3240 (1961).

of sugar phosphates, especially the sugar-1-phosphates (when the sugar is an aldose).

2.15B-4. The hydrolysis of the neutral methyl phosphate as well as the conjugate acid through C—O cleavage probably proceeds through displacement of dihydrogen phosphate or phosphoric acid by water. The alternative, requiring formation of a methyl carbonium ion, seems highly unlikely. The P—O cleavage found for the conjugate acid is somewhat complicated by the occurrence of "extra" oxygen exchange, implying that P—O cleavage can take place with departure of a water molecule or a methanol molecule. It is probable from studies on ethylene phosphate that the transition state for both processes is pentacovalent, and it is not inconceivable that an unstable pentacovalent intermediate is formed. Pentacovalent esters or other derivatives of phosphorus have been noted in a couple of instances.[493–495,495a,495b] The transition states are presumably analogous to those shown for the reactions of ethylene phosphate.

2.15B-5. The most curious aspect of the hydrolysis of mono-alkyl phosphates is the reactivity of the monoanion. The dialkyl phosphate monoanion, dimethyl phosphate monoanion, is far less reactive than the monoester monoanion, implying that the presence of both an OH and an O^- are required for "special" reactivity.[482,487] An alternative formulation, the reaction of hydroxide ion with the neutral methyl phosphate, cannot be kinetically distinguished from a reaction of the monoanion, but would require a second-order rate constant of ca. 10^7 l mole^{-1} sec^{-1}. The second-order constant for the reaction of hydroxide ion with *tri*methyl phosphate is only 3.3×10^{-2} l mole^{-1} sec^{-1} at 100°C, and no reason for such a large rate difference can readily be seen.[496] A possible explanation is that the monoanion decomposes to form meta-phosphate ion, which subsequently reacts with water to form orthophosphate anion.[487] A proposed transition state[487] is shown in Eq. (2.182).

$$(2.182) \qquad \begin{array}{c} O_{\cdots} \underset{P}{\overset{\parallel}{\diagup}} O \\ RO \diagdown O \\ \vdots \qquad \mid \\ H \diagdown_{O} \cdots H \\ \mid \\ H \end{array} \longrightarrow RO + \begin{array}{c} O \diagdown \underset{P}{\diagup} O \\ \mid \\ O^- \end{array} + H_2O$$

$$\downarrow H_2O$$

$$H_2PO_4^-$$

[493] F. Ramirez and N. B. Desai, *J. Am. Chem. Soc.*, **82**, 2652 (1960).

[494] F. R. Atherton, *Chem. Soc. (London), Spec. Publ. No. 8*, 77, 1957 (cf. ref. 495).

[495] J. R. van Wazer, "Phosphorus and Its Compounds," vol. 1, pp. 70–75, Interscience Publishers, Inc., New York, 1958.

[495a] Cf. ref. 517a.

[495b] F. Ramirez, N. B. Desai, N. Ramanthan, and R. B. Mitra, *Am. Chem. Soc. Abstr.*, **140**, 106Q (1961).

[496] Unpublished results by P. Barnard, quoted in ref. 481.

Although numerous compounds called monomeric and dimeric metaphosphates have been reported, no representative of these classes has a proved existence. A succinct review of these reports predicts that dimetaphosphates might be made with care, but that such ions would rapidly hydrolyze in water to pyrophosphate.[497] The behavior of monomeric metaphosphate cannot yet be defined (i.e., as a transient intermediate), but support for the pathway shown in Eq. (2.182) [or the alternative in (2.183)] can be derived from several sources. First, the relative rates for the hydrolysis of a series of monoaryl phosphate monoanions are in rough accord for the cleavage of the P—O bond with formation of the phenol (the rate factors are too small for what one might expect for formation of phenoxide ions) (Table 2.15-4). Second, the hydrolysis of such substances as N,N,N'-trimethylphosphorodiamidic fluoride in base[498] seems best explained[499] by the formation of nitrogen analogues of the metaphosphate ion [Eq. (2.184)]. Similarly, a positively charged species analogous to metaphosphate has been postulated for the aqueous hydrolysis of N,N,N',N'-tetramethylphosphorodiamidic chloride [Eq. (2.185)].[500] Third, oxidation of certain

(2.183)

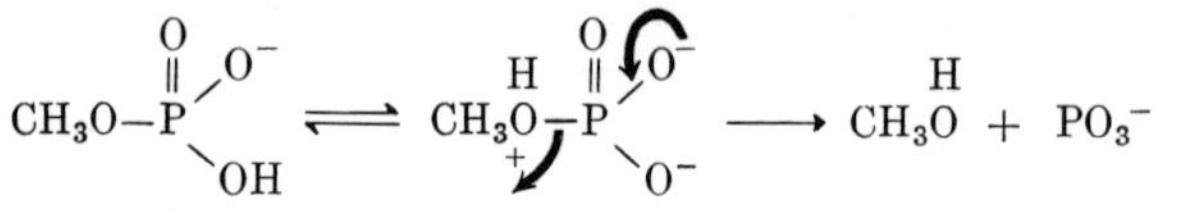

(2.184)

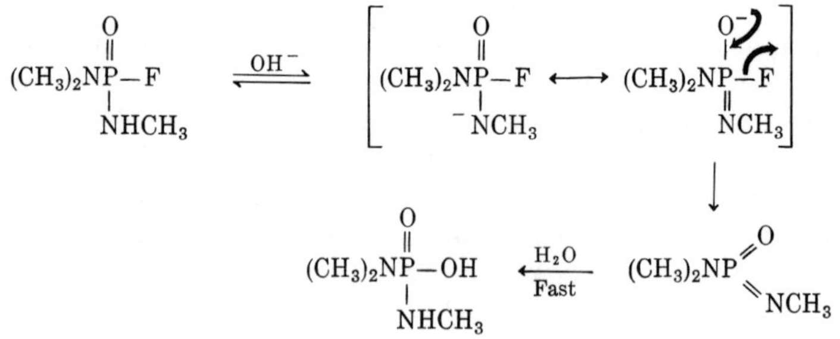

(2.185)

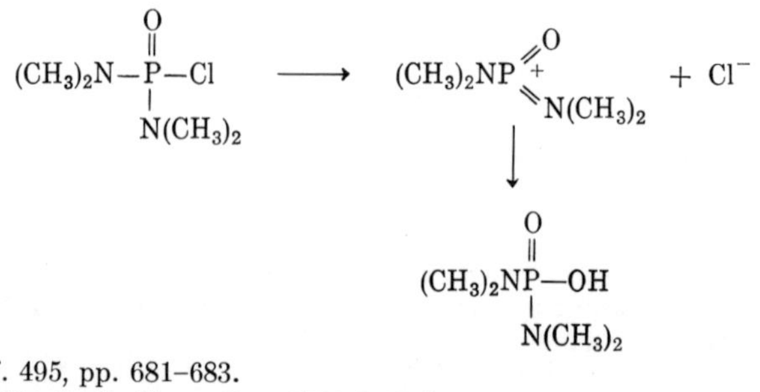

[497] Ref. 495, pp. 681–683.
[498] D. Heath, *J. Chem. Soc.*, 3796 (1956).
[499] F. H. Westheimer, *Chem. Soc. (London), Spec. Publ. No. 8*, p. 181, 1957.
[500] H. K. Hall, Jr., *J. Org. Chem.*, **21**, 248 (1956).

quinol phosphates gives rise to quinones, phosphate ion, *pyrophosphate* ion, and *trimetaphosphate* ion.[501]   The analogy between Eq. (2.183) and a probable transition state for the important step in the quinol phosphate oxidation is very striking, and it would be difficult to explain the presence of the polyphosphate ions in any other way.   The oxidation reaction is of interest as a model for oxidative phosphorylation (Fig. 2.75).

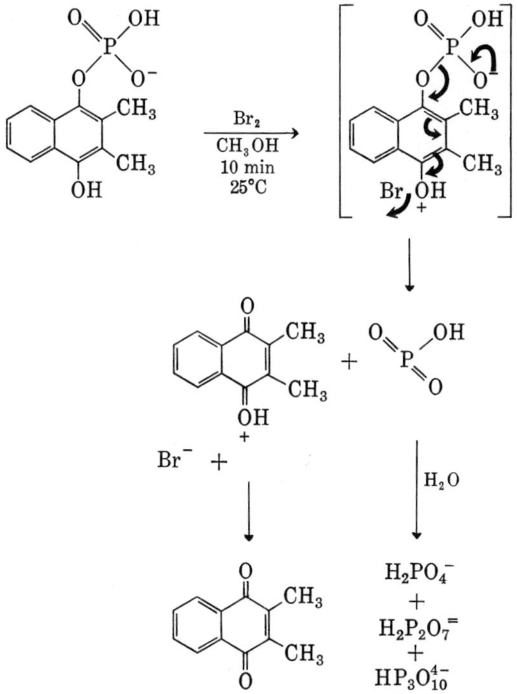

FIG. 2.75. Oxidation of quinol phosphates.[501]

2.15B-6.   Dialkyl phosphates exhibit a reactivity pattern different from that of the monoalkyl phosphates.   No maximum is evident in the pH-rate profile for the hydrolysis of dimethyl phosphate;[482] in fact, the slope for the plot of k_0 versus pH in the pH range 2.51 to 4.17 is almost exactly 1, suggesting that the monoanion of the dimethyl phosphate is quite unreactive.   From a comparison of the observed rate for the solvolysis of the neutral dimethyl phosphate and that for the monoanion of methyl phosphate, it is estimated that the monoanion of the dialkyl phosphate could be no more than one ten-thousandth as reactive as the monoanion of the monoalkyl phosphate.[482]

[501] V. M. Clark, D. W. Hutchinson, G. W. Kirby, and A. Todd, *J. Chem. Soc.*, 715 (1961).

The neutral dimethyl phosphate and its conjugate acid do not differ greatly in reactivity, and even in 5 M perchloric acid, some 33% of the total hydrolysis reaction proceeds through the neutral ester.[482]   Some discrepancy exists between determinations of the extent of C—O and P—O cleavage for the neutral species and the conjugate acid.[482,502]   One set of data indicates that the conjugate acid reacts completely by C—O

TABLE 2.15-3. RATES OF HYDROLYSIS OF PHOSPHATES IN WATER

Compound	Species (Cleavage)	T, °C	k	Conditions	Ref.
$(CH_3O)PO_3H_2$	Dianion	100	Very slow	....	481
	Monoanion (P—O)	100	8.23×10^{-6} sec^{-1}	$\mu = 0$	481
	Neutral (C—O)	100	0.50×10^{-6} sec^{-1}	$\mu = 0$	481
	Conjugate acid (C—O)	100	2.00×10^{-6} 1 mole^{-1} sec^{-1}	$\mu = 0$	481
	Conjugate acid (P—O)	100	1.08×10^{-6} 1 mole^{-1} sec^{-1}	$\mu = 0$	481
	Monoanion and OH$^-$ (P—O)	125	ca. 0.6×10^{-6} 1 mole^{-1} sec^{-1}	....	503
	Monoanion and OH$^-$ (C—O)	125	ca. 5.4×10^{-6} 1 mole^{-1} sec^{-1}	....	503
$(CH_3O)_2PO_2H$	Monoanion (C—O)	100	Very slow	....	482
	Monoanion (P—O)	100	ca. 1×10^{-9} sec^{-1}	$\mu = 0$	482
	Neutral (C—O)	100	3.3×10^{-6} sec^{-1}	$\mu = 0$	482^a
	Neutral (P—O)	100	0.9×10^{-6} sec^{-1}	$\mu = 0$	482^a
	Conjugate acid (C—O)	100	0.91×10^{-6} 1 mole^{-1} sec^{-1}	$\mu = 0$	482^a
	Conjugate acid (P—O)	100	0.11×10^{-6} 1 mole^{-1} sec^{-1}	$\mu = 0$	482^a
$(CH_3O)_3PO$	Neutral (P—O)	35	3.3×10^{-4} 1 mole^{-1} sec^{-1}	....	504
α-D-glucose-1-phosphate	Monoanion (P—O)	82	1.45×10^{-6} sec^{-1}	....	490
	Neutral (C—O)	82	4.00×10^{-3} sec^{-1}	....	490
CH₂—O O	Monoanion and OH$^-$ (P—O)	25	4.7×10^{-4} 1 mole^{-1} sec^{-1}	KOH, $\mu = 0.66$	503
$\quad\searrow\nearrow$		25	39.2×10^{-4} 1 mole^{-1} sec^{-1}	$0.17\ M$ Ba^{++}, KOH	503
P	Conjugate acid	30	2.06×10^{-3} sec^{-1}	....	505
CH₂—O OH			6.18×10^{-2} 1 mole^{-1} sec^{-1}	....	484^b
		0	1.2×10^{-4} sec^{-1}	....	505
			3.54×10^{-3} 1 mole^{-1} sec^{-1}	....	484^b

^{a} Some uncertainty exists about the division of total rate between C—O and P—O modes of cleavage; see text and ref. 502.

^{b} Rate = k_2(H$^+$)(EHP).   Calculated by P. C. Haake (ref. 484) using pK_a(EHP) = 0.7 estimated from variation in rate with acidity found by Cox (ref. 503).

502 P. C. Haake and F. H. Westheimer, *J. Am. Chem. Soc.*, **83,** 1102 (1961).

503 J. R. Cox, Jr., PhD. Thesis, Harvard University, as quoted in ref. 484.

504 P. Barnard, C. A. Bunton, D. R. Llewellyn, K. G. Oldham, B. Silver, and C. A. Vernon, *Chem. & Ind. (London)*, 760 (1955).

505 J. Kumamoto, J. R. Cox, Jr., and F. H. Westheimer, *J. Am. Chem. Soc.*, **78,** 4858 (1956).

cleavage[502] and the other set[482] implies that a small fraction (11%) of the conjugate acid reacts by P—O cleavage. Ordinarily, a small difference of this sort would not be critical, but the rate constant for P—O cleavage of the conjugate acid is relevant to a consideration of the acid-catalyzed reaction of ethylene phosphate. The neutral dimethyl phosphate reacts almost completely (see above) with P—O cleavage [Eqs. (2.186) and

$$(2.186) \qquad H_2O^{18} \longrightarrow CH_3 OP \overset{\overset{+H}{\underset{}{\parallel}} \overset{O}{\underset{}{\diagup}} OCH_3}{\underset{OH}{\diagdown}} \longrightarrow HO^{18} CH_3 + CH_3OPO_3H_2$$

$$(2.187) \qquad H_2O^{18} + P \overset{\overset{O}{\underset{}{\parallel}} OCH_3}{\underset{\underset{OH}{\mid}}{\diagdown} OCH_3} \longrightarrow HO^{18} P \overset{O}{\underset{\underset{OH}{\mid}}{\diagup}} OCH_3 + CH_3O^-$$

(2.187)]. It may be noted in Table 2.15-3 that neutral dimethyl phosphate is almost ten times as reactive as neutral methyl phosphate.

Table 2.15-4. Hydrolysis Data on Monoanions of Monophosphates[a,e]

Compound	Relative rate	E_a, kcal/mole
Methyl phosphate	1.00[b]	30.6
Phosphoric acid	ca. 0.11, ca. 0.5[d]	
Phenyl phosphate	32.0	28.3
p-Tolyl phosphate	26.6	
p-Nitrophenylphosphate	66.8	29.7
α-D-Glucose-1-phosphate	1.85	30.0
Glycerol-1-phosphate	1.66	29.9
Glycerol-2-phosphate	3.34	30.3
2-Methoxy-1-methylethyl phosphate	8.90	c
Ethanolamine phosphate	3.72	29.6
Ethyl phosphate	0.74	
Benzyl phosphate	1.61	c

[a] Where P—O cleavage has not been demonstrated, it is assumed.
[b] From Table 2.15-3.
[c] Assumed $E = 30.0$ kcal/mole.
[d] A detailed study yielded higher rates than those previously estimated.[507]
[e] Ref. 506.

2.15B-7. Dialkyl phosphate groups are the structural units in deoxyribonucleic acids (DNA) and ribonucleic acids (RNA). The

[506] C. A. Vernon, *Chem. Soc.* (*London*), *Spec. Publ. No. 8*, 22 (1957).
[507] C. A. Bunton, D. R. Llewellyn, C. A. Vernon, and V. A. Welch, *J. Chem. Soc.*, 1636 (1961).

hydrolysis of the latter materials under alkaline conditions proceeds through an intermediate formulated as a five-membered ring cyclic phosphate.[508] The cyclization involves the "neighboring" hydroxyl group on the 2'-position of the ribose ring and results in the cleavage of the phosphorus-oxygen bond attached to the 5'-carbon of the ribose of the next nucleotide moiety [Eq. (2.188)]. Subsequent reaction of the cyclic ester with water produces a mixture of 2'- and 3'-phosphates. The cyclic esters were quite reactive, in contrast to dialkyl phosphates,

(2.188)

and it was therefore instructive to synthesize the simplest cyclic phosphate, ethylene phosphate.[505,509]

Ethylene phosphate proved to be extremely reactive, under both acid[505] and alkaline conditions.[503] Dimethyl phosphate was chosen as the reference compound for an evaluation of the reactivity of the ethylene phosphate. Two factors make comparison of the two compounds difficult. Dimethyl phosphate hydrolyzes so slowly in comparison to the cyclic phosphate that extrapolating its reaction rate to a lower temperature is inaccurate (ranges of almost 90° for the alkaline reaction and 70° for the acid reaction are involved). The second factor is the unknown

[508] D. M. Brown and A. R. Todd, *J. Chem. Soc.*, 52 (1952).
[509] J. Lecocq, *Compt. rend.*, **242**, 1902 (1956).

extent of P—O cleavage which occurs in the acid-catalyzed reaction (see above). Even with these limitations, the comparison between dimethyl phosphate and ethylene phosphate shows conclusively that the cyclic phosphate is far more reactive than the reference compound, and that the rate factor in favor of the cyclic phosphate for P—O cleavage may be as high as 10^8. The reaction of ethylene phosphate with labeled water is shown in Eq. (2.189).

$$(2.189) \quad \begin{array}{c} CH_2-O \\ | \\ CH_2-O \end{array} \!\!\! \begin{array}{c} O \\ \diagup\!\!\diagup \\ P \\ \diagdown \\ OH \end{array} \;+\; H_2O^{18} \;+\; H^+ \quad \longrightarrow \quad \begin{array}{c} CH_2OH \\ | \\ CH_2OP-OH \\ \diagdown \\ OH \end{array} \!\!\! \begin{array}{c} \\ O^{18} \\ \diagup\!\!\diagup \end{array}$$

2.15B-8. The high reactivity of the cyclic phosphates as compared with the noncyclic phosphates has been attributed to strain in the ring.[510] Only the five-membered cyclic phosphate is strained, apparently, for cyclic phosphates with larger rings are comparable or lower in reactivity than dimethyl phosphate. The anion of trimethylene phosphate reacts with hydroxide ion less than ten times as fast as dimethyl phosphate at 100°C.[511] A direct demonstration of the thermodynamic

TABLE 2.15-5. THERMODYNAMIC DATA ON PHOSPHATE HYDROLYSIS[b]

Compound	Total heat evolved, kcal/mole	Heat of solution, kcal/mole	Net heat of saponification, kcal/mole
Methyl ethylene phosphate	29.5 ± 0.6	0.0 ± 0.2	29.5
Dimethyl-2-hydroxyethyl phosphate	24.6 ± 0.3	2.7 ± 0.1	21.9
Trimethyl phosphate[a]	ca. 22	2.5 ± 0.1	ca. 20

[a] Slow reaction under accessible conditions, leading to inaccurate results.
[b] Ref. 512.

instability of the ethylene phosphate *vis-à-vis* its hydrolysis product is possible by measurement of the heat of hydrolysis combined with the heat of solution (Table 2.15-5).[512] The compounds utilized are methyl ethylene phosphate, dimethyl-2-hydroxyethyl phosphate, and trimethyl phosphate. Their hydrolyses are given in Eqs. (2.190) to (2.192).

[510] F. H. Westheimer, *Chem. Soc. (London), Spec. Publ. No. 8*, 1, 1957.
[511] H. G. Khorana, G. M. Tener, R. S. Wright, and J. G. Moffat, *J. Am. Chem. Soc.*, **79**, 430 (1957).
[512] J. R. Cox, Jr., R. E. Wall, F. H. Westheimer, *Chem. & Ind. (London)*, 929 (1959).

(2.190)

$$\underset{CH_2-O}{\overset{CH_2-O}{\Big|}}\underset{\diagdown}{\overset{\diagup}{P}}\underset{OCH_3}{\overset{O}{\diagdown}} \quad \xrightarrow[\substack{k_2 \sim 30 \text{ l. mole}^{-1} \\ \text{sec}^{-1}\ (0.40)}]{\text{OH}^-} \quad \underset{CH_2OP}{\overset{CH_2-OH}{\Big|}}\underset{\diagdown O^-}{\overset{O}{\diagdown}}OCH_3$$

Overnight
CH$_3$OH ↓

(2.191)

$$\underset{CH_2OP-OCH_3}{\overset{CH_2OH}{\Big|}}\underset{\diagdown OCH_3}{\overset{O}{\diagup}} \quad \xrightarrow{\text{OH}^-} \quad \underset{CH_2OP-OCH_3}{\overset{CH_2OH}{\Big|}}\underset{\diagdown O^-}{\overset{O}{\diagup}}$$

(2.192) $(CH_3O)_3PO \xrightarrow{\text{OH}^-} CH_3OH + (CH_3O)_2P \overset{\diagup O}{\underset{\diagdown O^-}{}}$

The nature of the strain has not been established. Crude estimates of the angular strain (the normal O—P—O angle is possibly somewhat smaller than tetrahedral, about 104° in dibenzyl phosphate)[513] suggest that only ca. 3 kcal/mole arises from angle strain.[510] Other variables which may provide a clue are dihedral angle between the C—O—P bonds, the P—O bond length, and the role of the oxygen nonbonding electrons.[502,510] The high rates observed for both alkaline and acid hydrolysis of ethylene phosphate correspond to free energies of activation which are ca. 9 kcal/mole lower than those for dimethyl phosphate. If the entropy of activation does not differ very much for the two types of phosphate ester, the implication is clear that a considerable proportion of the strain measured thermochemically (7–9 kcal/mole) is relieved in the transition state. In this manner, the strain provides the "driving force" for the rapid reaction of ethylene phosphate.[513a]

2.15B-9. An extremely interesting aspect of phosphate chemistry was revealed when it was discovered that oxygen exchange between H_2O^{18} and ethylene phosphate occurred during hydrolysis.[502] Three possible transition states for the oxygen exchange and the hydrolysis reactions are outlined in Fig. 2.76. The transition states labeled I and II are geometries patterned directly after that of the bimolecular displacement reaction on carbon. In I, the O—P—O angle of the ring has been expanded to 120° from 98°,[510] and in II, the angle of the ring has decreased to 90°. Since it is unlikely (though not altogether impossible) that strain could be relieved by both increasing and decreasing the O—P—O angle, and since strain must be relieved in both the exchange and hydrolysis reactions to account for the high rates found, I and II

[513] J. D. Dunitz and J. S. Rollett, *Acta Cryst.*, **9**, 327 (1956).

[513a] Investigation of the rates of hydrolysis of a series of cyclic sulfites with hydroxide ion has led to the tentative conclusion that high reactivity is associated with the presence of a rigid, strained system within the molecule.[513b]

[513b] P. B. D. de la Mare, J. G. Tillett, and H. F. van Woerden, *Chem. & Ind.* (*London*), 1533 (1961).

are rejected as probable transition states for the reactions of ethylene phosphate.[502]   The transition states III and IV would probably lead to inversion of stereochemical configuration at phosphorus, but V and VI

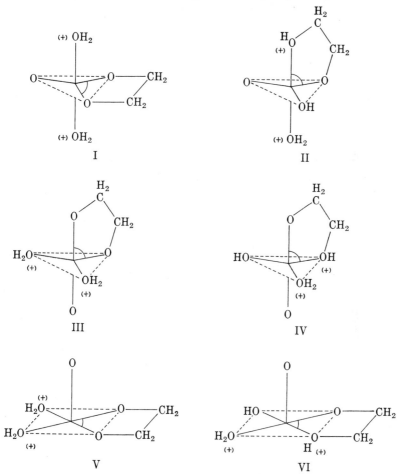

FIG. 2.76. Transition states for ethylene phosphate hydrolysis.   (*Reprinted by permission of the Journal of the American Chemical Society.*)

would give retention.   Insofar as the stereochemistry of hydrolysis of phosphonates, $(RO)_2RPO$, (or thio derivatives) is relevant[514,515] [Eq.

[514] M. Green and R. F. Hudson, *Proc. Chem. Soc.*, 227 (1959).

[515] J. Michalski and A. Ratajczak, *Chem. & Ind. (London)*, 1241 (1960).[516]

[516] This work derives from the resolutions carried out by H. S. Aaron, T. M. Shryne, and J. T. Miller, *J. Am. Chem. Soc.*, **80**, 107 (1958).   Cf. also H. S. Aaron, J. Braun, T. M. Shryne, H. F. Frack, G. E. Smith, R. T. Uyeda, and J. I. Miller, *J. Am. Chem. Soc.*, **82**, 596 (1960).

(2.193)], inversion is the expected result, and III and IV the probable

$$(2.193)^{514} \qquad CH_3-\underset{\underset{O}{\overset{\parallel}{P}}}{\overset{O}{\parallel}}-OCH_3 \xrightarrow{Na^+ i\text{-}OPr^-} \qquad CH_3-\underset{\underset{O\ i\text{-}Pr}{\overset{\parallel}{P}}}{\overset{O}{\parallel}}-OCH_3$$

$$\alpha_D^{20} +44° \qquad\qquad\qquad \alpha_D^{20} -11°$$

transition states.[502] Optically active phosphonium compounds also undergo reaction with hydroxide ion and inversion, but the mechanism may be complex.[517,517a] That angle contraction (and presumably, relief of strain) can give rise to substantial rate effects is shown by the facts that 1-silabicyclo[2.2.1]heptane and 1-methyl-1-silacyclobutane are 10^4 to 10^5 times more reactive toward hydroxide ion than triethylsilane.[518] Retention of stereochemical configuration is the only possible result for the bicyclic compound, and retention has been demonstrated for the deuteride replacement of hydride at an assymmetric silicon atom.[519] Since both silicon and phosphorus react through pentacovalent transition states (in many instances), the opposite stereochemical results for the two atoms suggest caution in choosing a preferred transition state for the hydrolysis of phosphates without further investigation.

2.15B-10. The hydrolysis reactions described in the foregoing sections have, for the cases of P—O cleavage, involved nucleophilic attack of water on phosphorus except for the monoanions of monoesters for which it is probable that water reacted with an intermediate, the metaphosphate ion. The groups which were expelled from the phosphorus were alcohols (alkoxides) or water (in exchange). A more general survey of nucleophilic reactivity toward the phosphorus in phosphates would be in order. Although only a limited amount of space can be

[517] A. Bladé-Font, C. A. Vander Werf, and W. E. McEwen, *J. Am. Chem. Soc.*, 82, 2396 (1960).

[517a] C. A. Vander Werf, W. E. McEwen, A. Bladé-Font, K. Kumli, G. Axelrad, and M. Zanger, *Am. Chem. Soc. Abstr.*, 140, 93Q (1961), have found that the kinetics of reaction of phenyl methyl ethyl benzylphosphonium ion with hydroxide ion are *first-order* in the former and *second-order* in the latter. The hydroxide-ion reaction is stereospecific and leads to a stereochemical configuration for the phosphine oxide opposite to that obtained through a Wittig reaction (very strong base plus a ketone). Since the Wittig reaction is the more likely to proceed with retention, the hydroxide-ion reaction must go with *inversion*. A pentacovalent phosphorus intermediate is quite consistent with these results.

[518] L. H. Sommer, O. F. Bennett, P. G. Campbell, and D. R. Weyenberg, *J. Am. Chem. Soc.*, 79, 3295 (1957).

[519] L. H. Sommer and C. L. Frye, *J. Am. Chem. Soc.*, 81, 1013 (1959).

devoted to this interesting subject in the present discussion, it is worth noting that the area has broad scientific and industrial importance. A number of widely used insecticidal compounds (as well as the so-called "nerve gases") are phosphorus compounds which react with the "active site" of the enzyme cholinesterase to form phosphorylated enzyme which is only slowly hydrolyzed and is completely inactive biologically. The enzyme can be reactivated by certain compounds which display, among other requirements, nucleophilic reactivity toward phosphorus.[472,520] The reactions to be described are not, strictly speaking, displacements if an intermediate pentacovalent phosphorus compound forms. For convenience, we shall refer to these nucleophilic replacements as displacements.

A general equation for the problem might be formulated as in Eq. (2.194), in which G_1 and G_2 are alkyl, alkoxyl, alkylthio, aryl, etc., Y is sulfur or oxygen, X is alkoxyl, aroxyl, halide, etc., and N is a nucleophilic atom, molecule, or group. The product of the displacement

$$(2.194) \qquad N + G_1G_2PYX \rightarrow NG_1G_2PY + X$$

reaction need not be stable.

The reaction of Sarin, isopropyl methylphosphonofluoridate, with hydroperoxide ion is very rapid.[521] The product is unstable and forms oxygen in the presence of hydrogen peroxide with a pH-rate profile that suggests the decomposition of the peroxy acid[522] [Eqs. (2.195) and (2.196)]. It will be noted that the methyl hydroperoxide ion was extremely reactive toward the carbonyl group of p-nitrophenyl acetate (Table 2.7-2).

$$(2.195) \qquad \underset{(CH_3)_2CHO}{\overset{CH_3}{>}}\!\!P\!\!\underset{F}{\overset{O}{<}} + OOH^- \longrightarrow \underset{(CH_3)_2CHO}{\overset{CH_3}{>}}\!\!P\!\!\underset{OO^-}{\overset{O}{<}} + HF$$

$$(2.196) \qquad \underset{(CH_3)_2CHO}{\overset{CH_3}{>}}\!\!P\!\!\underset{OO^-}{\overset{O}{<}} + H_2O_2 \longrightarrow \underset{(CH_3)_2CHO}{\overset{CH_3}{>}}\!\!P\!\!\underset{O^-}{\overset{O}{<}} + O_2 + H_2O$$

If the nucleophilic group is available within the molecule (i.e., a neighboring group), intramolecular reaction can occur. A maximum in the pH-rate profile is found for the hydrolysis of salicyl phosphate at

[520] I. B. Wilson, *Federation Proc.*, **18**, 752 (1959).
[521] L. Larsson, *Acta Chem. Scand.*, **12**, 723 (1958).
[522] G. Aksnes, *Acta Chem. Scand.*, **14**, 2075 (1960).

pH 5.3.[523] From dissociation constants for phosphoenolpyruvic acid,[524] pK_2 3.4 and pK_3 6.35, one may conclude that at pH 5, two hydrogens are dissociated. A similar conclusion holds for salicyl phosphate. The reaction has been written as in Eq. (2.197).

(2.197)

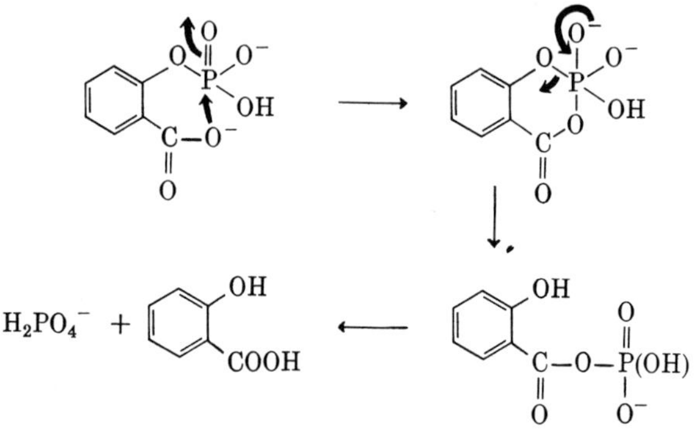

Hydroxylamine and hydroxamic acids react with diisopropylphosphorofluoridate (DFP) to give unstable intermediates which hydrolyze in water [Eq. (2.198)].[525] One of the best-known compounds capable

(2.198)

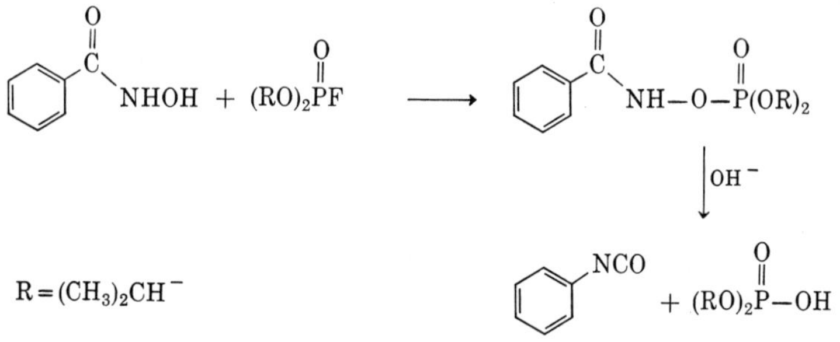

$R = (CH_3)_2CH^-$

of reaction with anticholinesterases is 1-methyl-2-aldoximinopyridinium iodide, or 2-PAM.[520] Its fame derives from the fact that it is one of the most potent reactivators of inhibited (i.e., phosphorylated) cholinesterase.[520] However, both *syn*- and *anti*-4-formyl-1-methylpyridinium iodide oximes reactivate Sarin-inhibited eel acetylcholinesterase at similar rates. The naïve molecular complementarity theory advanced previously[520] to account for the reactivation must therefore be modified.[525a]

[523] J. D. Chanley, E. M. Gindler, and H. Sobotka, *J. Am. Chem. Soc.*, **74**, 4347 (1952).

[524] F. Wold and C. E. Ballou, *J. Biol. Chem.*, **227**, 301 (1957).

[525] B. E. Hackley, Jr., R. Plapinger, M. Stolberg, and T. Wagner-Jauregg, *J. Am. Chem. Soc.*, **77**, 3651 (1955).

[525a] E. J. Poziomek, D. N. Kramer, W. A. Mosher, and H. O. Michel, *J. Am. Chem. Soc.*, **83**, 3916 (1961).

2.15B-11. The ready removal of phosphate from casein in reaction with alkali is probably due to a 1,2 elimination reaction[526] [Eq. (2.199)]. The conclusion was based on the finding that no oxygen-18

$$(2.199) \quad \overset{H}{\underset{N}{\diagdown}} \overset{O}{\underset{C}{\parallel}} \quad \xrightarrow[\substack{0.3N \\ 37° \\ 15 \text{ hours}}]{OH^-} \quad \overset{H}{\underset{N}{\diagdown}} \overset{O}{\underset{C}{\parallel}} \quad + \ HPO_4^=$$

was incorporated into the phosphate derived from the casein, thus excluding the possibility of attack on phosphorus. Other phosphates which carry a similar electron-withdrawing group on the β carbon appear to eliminate phosphate readily. Examples are 2-cyanoethyl phosphate[527-529] and 2-carbamidoethyl phosphate.[529] Deoxyribose-3-phosphate is far less stable than the 5-phosphate in attempted chromatography at pH 10, and there is a strong presumption that elimination of the phosphate group beta to the carbonyl occurred.[530] Adequate rate measurements are not available for other cases in which it is suspected that elimination has occurred, e.g., erythrose-4-phosphate[531] and ribose-3-phosphate.[532]

An elimination reaction of a different type is probably responsible for the formation of cyanate ion and phosphate ion from carbamyl phosphate[533] [Eq. (2.200)].

$$(2.200) \quad \underset{\underset{B}{\overset{\uparrow}{}}}{\overset{O}{\underset{H}{HN-C-OPO_3^=}}} \quad \longrightarrow \quad \overset{+}{BH} + HNCO + PO_4^{3-} \quad \longrightarrow \quad \overset{+}{BH} + NCO^- + HPO_4^=$$

A decarboxylative elimination of phosphate leads to isopentenyl pyrophosphate (see Sec. 1.8).

2.15B-12. Monoacyl phosphates (acetyl phosphate and carbamyl phosphate) and acyl alkyl phosphates (the acyl adenylates) occur in biological systems. The proton dissociation equilibria for acetyl

[526] L. Anderson and J. J. Kelley, *J. Am. Chem. Soc.*, **81**, 2276 (1959).

[527] E. Cherbuliez and J. Rabinowitz, *Helv. Chim. Acta*, **39**, 1461 (1956).

[528] G. M. Tener, *J. Am. Chem. Soc.*, **83**, 159 (1961).

[529] E. Cherbuliez, *Chimia* (*Switz.*), **15**, 327 (1961).

[530] H. G. Khorana, personal communication.

[531] C. E. Ballou, H. O. L. Fischer, and D. L. MacDonald, *J. Am. Chem. Soc.*, **77**, 5967 (1955).

[532] J. X. Khym, D. G. Doherty, and W. E. Cohn, *J. Am. Chem. Soc.*, **76**, 5523 (1954).

[533] M. E. Jones and F. Lipmann, *Proc. Natl. Acad. Sci. U.S.*, **46**, 1194 (1960).

phosphate are shown in Eq. (2.200a). The pK_2 for acetyl phosphate has been measured as c̀a. 4.8.[483] The pH-rate profile for the hydrolysis of acetyl phosphate has been measured at 39° in water.[534] The general

$$(2.200a) \quad CH_3\overset{\overset{O}{\|}}{C}-O-\underset{\underset{OH}{|}}{\overset{\overset{O}{\|}}{P}}-OH \underset{}{\overset{K_1}{\rightleftharpoons}} CH_3\overset{\overset{O}{\|}}{C}-O-\underset{\underset{OH}{|}}{\overset{\overset{O}{\|}}{P}}-O^- \underset{}{\overset{K_2}{\rightleftharpoons}} CH_3\overset{\overset{O}{\|}}{C}-O-\underset{\underset{O^-}{|}}{\overset{\overset{O}{\|}}{P}}-O^-$$

pattern of the plot bears a similarity to the pH-rate profile for benzyl phosphate[488] in that the range best interpreted as hydrolysis of the monoanion merges into a considerably faster reaction ascribable to the neutral acetyl phosphate at lower pH. The rate constant for the monoanion is ca. 1.3×10^{-4} sec^{-1} at 39°C; a rough guess for the minimum rate constant at 100°C is 8.3×10^{-3} sec^{-1}, or a relative rate of 1000 with respect to the monoanion of methyl phosphate (see Table 2.15-5). The predominance of P—O cleavage for acetyl phosphate in the pH range 4 to 6[535] permits the mechanism for the hydrolysis of the mono-

$$(2.201) \quad CH_3\overset{\overset{O}{\|}}{C}-O-P \qquad \longrightarrow \quad CH_3COH + PO_3^-$$

anion to be expressed [in Eq. (2.201)] in analogy with Eq. (2.183). In contrast to the unreactive dianions of monoalkyl phosphates, the dianion of acetyl phosphate hydrolyzes at about one-third the rate for the monoanion. The most straightforward explanation of the dianion reactivity is that ready formation of acetate ion overcomes the normally unfavorable process shown in Eq. (2.202), leading to the formulation given in Eq. (2.203).[535a] At extreme pH values, acetyl

$$(2.202) \quad RO\overset{\overset{O}{\|}}{P}\overset{O^-}{\underset{O^-}{}} \quad \longrightarrow \quad RO^- + PO_3^-$$

$$(2.203) \quad \cdot CH_3\overset{\overset{O}{\|}}{C}-O-\overset{\overset{O}{\|}}{P}\overset{O^-}{\underset{O^-}{}} \quad \longrightarrow \quad CH_3\overset{\overset{O}{\|}}{C}-O^- + PO_3^-$$

[534] D. E. Koshland, Jr., *J. Am. Chem. Soc.*, **74**, 2286 (1952).

[535] R. Bentley, *J. Am. Chem. Soc.*, **71**, 2765 (1949).

[535a] Evidence consistent with this hypothesis has been obtained by G. di Sabato and W. P. Jencks (to be published). The entropies of activation, $\Delta S^{\pm}$, for the hydrolysis of acetyl phosphate monoanion and dianion are -3.6 and 3.7 e.u., respectively. In comparison, hydrolyses which presumably utilize a solvent molecule in the transition state have $\Delta S^{\pm}$ values from -20 to -50 e.u. in those cases which involve only charge dispersal in the transition state. The volume changes of activation, $\Delta V^{\pm}$, are also small for the hydrolyses of both acetyl phosphate anions.

phosphate reacts readily with C—O cleavage [Eq. (2.204)]. Another aspect of acetyl phosphate reactivity will be mentioned under metal-ion catalysis in Sec. 2.15D. Glyceraldehyde-3-phosphate dehydrogenase

$$(2.204) \quad \underset{CH_3COPO_3^=}{\overset{O}{\underset{\|}{}}} + OH^- \longrightarrow \underset{\underset{OH}{|}}{\overset{O^-}{\underset{|}{CH_3C-OPO_3^=}}} \longrightarrow \overset{O}{\overset{\|}{CH_3C-O^-}} + HOPO_3^=$$

hydrolyzes acetyl phosphate with C—O cleavage, probably through intermediate formation of an acetyl-enzyme compound.[536]

The reactions of aminoacyl adenylates are probably analogous to acetyl phosphate monoanion.[537,537a]

A complete study of the solvolysis of carbamyl phosphate over the pH range 0 to 12 has been carried out. Ionization to the carbamyl acylium ion, NH_2CO^+, which can be trapped as the azide, occurs in certain pH ranges[537b] [cf. Eq. (2.185)].

2.15B-13. Only a single phosphatase, an enzyme which hydrolyzes monoester phosphates, has been obtained in reasonably pure form, and that is the nonspecific alkaline phosphatase of *Escherichia coli*.[538,539] It follows that relatively little can be said about the mechanism or mechanisms through which the phosphomonoesterases operate. Nevertheless, it has been established that P—O cleavage is the usual result for the hydrolysis of a number of phosphates by a number of phosphatases.[540-542] A phosphatase has been used to ensure P—O bond cleavage in 2-hydroxyethyl phosphate, the product of hydrolysis of ethylene phosphate, in order that the oxygen-18 content of the phosphate moiety might be examined.[502] Some phosphatases catalyze a slow exchange of oxygen-18 into phosphate,[541] but this is not always true.[542]

2.15B-14. A few of the enzymes known as phosphorylases have been studied in considerable detail and have been isolated in crystalline

[536] J. H. Park and D. E. Koshland, Jr., *J. Biol. Chem.*, **233**, 986 (1958).

[537] J. Baddiley and J. G. Buchanan, *Quart. Revs.*, **12**, 168 (1958).

[537a] The finding[535a] that solvolysis of acetyl phenyl phosphate in 90% methanol proceeds with C—O cleavage suggests caution in discussions of secondary acyl phosphates. However, an aminoacyl moiety may not behave in the same way as an acetyl group. Furthermore, an enzymatic reaction might favor energetically similar but somewhat less favorable modes of cleavage.

[537b] D. Samuel, Weizmann Institute, personal communication.

[538] A Garen and C. Levinthal, *Biochim. et Biophys. Acta*, **38**, 470 (1960).

[539] G. Schmidt and M. Laskowski, in "The Enzymes," vol. 5, chap. 1, Academic Press, Inc., New York, 1961.

[540] M. Cohn, *J. Biol. Chem.*, **180**, 771 (1949).

[541] S. S. Stein and D. E. Koshland, Jr., *Arch. Biochem. Biophys.*, **39**, 229 (1952).

[542] C. A. Bunton, B. L. Silver, and C. A. Vernon, *Proc. Chem. Soc.*, 348 (1957).

form.[543]   A typical reaction catalyzed by one of the crystalline enzymes, polysaccharide phosphorylase, is given in Eq. (2.205).   The reaction proceeds with retention of configuration at the carbon atom undergoing

(2.205)   [Glucose]$_n$ + H$_3$PO$_4$ $\rightleftharpoons$ glucose-1-phosphate + [glucose]$_{n-1}$
            1,4(α-D-Glucopyranosyl) α-D-Glucopyranose-1-phosphate
                    units
                  Glycogen

substitution.   The enzyme does not catalyze the exchange of inorganic phosphate with glucose-1-phosphate.   The reaction has been interpreted as a "double displacement" reaction[113] largely on the grounds that retention of configuration was observed.   The interpretation includes the postulate of an enzyme-substrate compound, and the failure to observe the exchange with radioactive phosphate and glucose-1-phosphate which one might expect for such an intermediate is explicable if the $(n - 1)$ glucose polymer is a coenzyme for the reaction [Eqs. (2.206) and (2.207)].

(2.206)   X ... GOG$_{n-1}$ $\rightarrow$ X—G + HOG$_{n-1}$
                              H
                              Y   Y

(2.207)   X—G + H$_2$PO$_4^-$ $\rightarrow$ X + GOPO$_3^=$

"Front-side displacement" was put forward as a conceivable alternative to "double displacement" with the same stereochemical result.   Its plausibility was based on analogy with the $S_N i$ reaction of thionyl chloride with 1-phenylethanols; such reactions are now considered carbonium ion reactions involving formation and collapse of an "intimate" ion pair.[109,110]

Aside from the difficulty in determining how many displacements at a given center actually occur so that the *net result* is even or odd, a note of caution should be introduced on the basis of the fact that it is relatively difficult to perform bimolecular displacements on carbons which are part of a six-membered ring, and in particular, 1-glucosyl derivatives show no propensity for this variety of substitution mechanism (see page 234).   An alternative proposal which postulates the intermediate formation of a glucopyranosyl carbonium ion—enzyme anion "intimate" ion pair[112] is shown in Fig. 2.77.   If the proximity of the anion (shown here as carboxylate for illustration) is brought about by the combination of the $(n - 1)$ glycogen chain with the enzyme protein, it is not surprising that the glucose-1-phosphate–phosphate exchange reaction is not

[543] M. Cohn, in "The Enzymes," vol. 5, chap. 12, Academic Press, Inc., 1961.

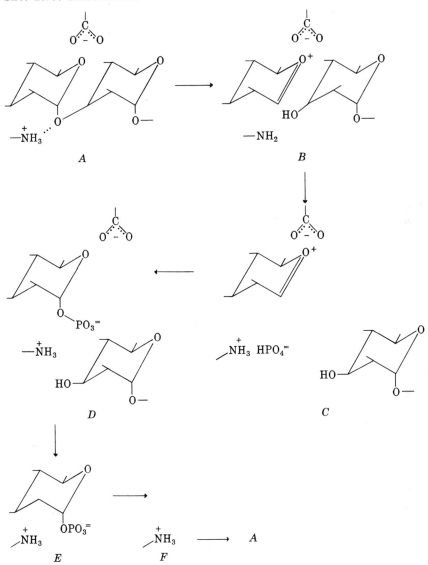

FIG. 2.77. Mechanism of polysaccharide phosphorylase action ($-NH_3^+$ represents any appropriate proton donor; $-C\!\!\begin{smallmatrix} O \\ \\ O \end{smallmatrix}-$ represents any appropriate anion).

observed under the most carefully controlled conditions.[544,545]   Electrostatic interaction between a carboxylate negative charge and an oxygen bearing, for example, one-quarter of a positive charge at a distance of 3 Å (i.e., *no covalent bond!*) might be, depending upon the dielectric constant chosen for the space separating the charged partners, as much as 8 to 9 kcal/mole.   (For simplicity, the additional attraction due to the positive charge on the 1-carbon and the repulsion due to the negative charge accumulating on the phosphate leaving group in the transition state are ignored.)   If such attraction were effective in lowering the activation free energy for the transition state, a rate factor of ca. 10^6 over the case where anionic stabilization was not available might result. Thus, the fact that a chain ("primer") of at least three glucose units is required for the conversion of glucose-1-phosphate into glycogen [the reverse of Eq. (2.207)] is explicable in terms of the mechanism proposed, and in agreement with the previous explanation for the lack of exchange, namely, that a polyglucose is a coenzyme for the reaction.[546]   In the absence of "primer" the rate of polymer formation is reduced by at least a factor of 2000.[547]

2.15B-15.   Ribonuclease is the only enzyme for which the complete amino acid sequence has been elucidated.[548]   The enzyme effects the hydrolysis of the 3',5'-phosphodiester linkage which occurs in ribonucleic acids, via intermediate formation of 2',3'-cyclic phosphate.   The first step (ring closure) is apparently much more rapid than the second, which leads to a 3'-phosphate [cf. Eq. (2.188)].   (RNase replaces OH^- and only 3'-phosphate is formed in place of a mixture of 2'- and 3'-phosphates.[549])   The ribonuclease sequence along with some assorted information on the effects of various treatments upon enzymatic activity is shown in Fig. 2.78.[548]   An attempt to account for the enzymatic activity of ribonuclease in terms of the groups present and some assumptions about the amount of helical structure present has been reported,[550] but it is difficult to write adequate mechanisms on the molecular level when

[544] M. Cohn and G. T. Cori, *J. Biol. Chem.*, **175**, 89 (1948).

[545] B. Illingworth, H. S. Jansz, D. H. Brown, and C. F. Cori, *Proc. Natl. Acad. Sci. U.S.*, **44**, 1180 (1958).

[546] D. H. Brown and C. F. Cori, in "The Enzymes," vol. 5, chap. 13, Academic Press, Inc., New York, 1961.

[547] D. H. Brown, B. Illingworth, and C. F. Cori, *Proc. Natl. Acad. Sci. U.S.*, **47**, 479 (1961).

[548] C. B. Anfinsen and F. H. White, Jr., in "The Enzymes," vol. 5, chap. 7, Academic Press, Inc., New York, 1961.

[549] H. G. Khorana, in "The Enzymes," vol. 5, chap. 6, Academic Press, Inc., New York, 1961.

[550] J. M. Parks, Protein Structure and Function, *Brookhaven Symposia in Biol.*, No. 13, BNL 608 (C-30), p. 132, 1960.

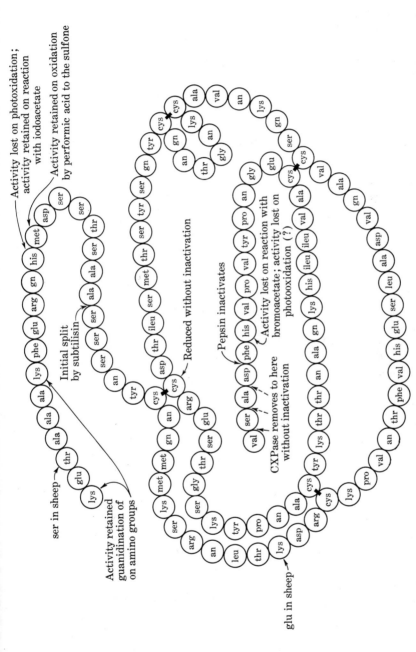

FIG. 2.78. Schematic diagram of bovine pancreatic ribonuclease. The sequence shown here is revised according to Anfinsen, Potts, Berger, and Cooke (personal communication to B. Witkop); Smyth, Moore, and Stein (personal communication to B. Witkop); and Gross and Witkop (1961) (personal communication from B. Witkop). (*By permission of Academic Press, Inc.*)

the secondary and tertiary structures of the enzyme in the "active complex" remain undefined.[550a]

Enzymes which hydrolyze the phosphodiester bond in deoxyribonucleic acid are called deoxyribonucleases.[551] Comparatively little information is available on these enzymes with regard to their mode of action on the molecular level.

The foregoing has been a necessarily sketchy discussion of enzymes which hydrolyze monoalkyl phosphates with P—O cleavage, catalyze the reaction of monoalkyl phosphates with C—O cleavage, hydrolyze dialkyl phosphates with formation of a cyclic phosphate to a neighboring hydroxyl group, and hydrolyze dialkyl phosphates. In each case, too little is known about the "active sites" to make any concrete comparisons of the enzymatic reactions with the chemistry of the model reactions.

2.15C. Polyphosphates

2.15C-1. The ubiquitous occurrence and biological activity of compounds containing the P—O—P or P—O—P—O—P groupings demands, at the very least, a scrutiny as detailed as that given to the simple phosphates. Unfortunately, the complications noted in the discussion of phosphates are multiplied for the polyphosphates to an almost bizarre degree, and even the determination of relatively simple parameters like acid dissociation constants requires a fairly sophisticated investigation. Controversy and experimental difficulties surround attempts to evaluate the nature of the polyphosphate species present in particular solutions, primarily caused by the association of the polyanions with cations, as an able and critical review of the field has pointed out.[552]

Although admirable progress has been made in the synthesis of complex naturally occurring polyphosphates like DPN[553] and coenzyme A,[554] comparatively little has been attempted in the way of mechanistic studies on polyphosphates. Even such apparently simple derivatives as tetraalkyl pyrophosphates exhibit complex behavior,[510] and compounds like tetraethyl pyrophosphate are subject to "reorganization" into complex mixtures of phosphate esters.[555] Thus, it would be of particular importance in this area to ensure that the reaction under study was that of the species of interest and not some "reorganization" product. The

[550a] A concise discussion of the problem of ribonuclease mechanism has been given by F. H. Westheimer, "Enzymes and Enzyme Models," paper presented to Symposium IV, Fifth International Congress of Biochemistry, Moscow, August 10–16, 1961.

[551] M. Laskowski, Sr., in "The Enzymes," vol. 5, chap. 8, Academic Press, Inc., New York, 1961.

[552] R. M. Bock, in "The Enzymes," vol. 2, chap. 1, Academic Press, Inc., New York, 1960.

[553] N. A. Hughes, G. W. Kenner, and A. Todd, *J. Chem. Soc.*, 3733 (1957).

[554] J. G. Moffatt and H. G. Khorana, *J. Am. Chem. Soc.*, **83**, 663 (1961).

[555] E. Schwarzmann and J. R. Van Wazer, *J. Am. Chem. Soc.*, **83**, 365 (1961).

mechanisms suggested in this discussion are thus, of necessity, quite tentative and simple.

2.15C-2. Pyrophosphate ion is produced in many biochemical reactions and is relatively stable at neutral pH and 37°C. Triphosphate ion has not been positively identified as an important biochemically active species, but the enzymatic synthesis of inorganic polyphosphates[556,578a] and the importance of the monoalkyl triphosphates in

TABLE 2.15-6. HYDROLYSIS RATES OF POLYPHOSPHATES

Reactant[a]	T, °C	k, sec^{-1}	E, kcal/mole	Ref.
$H_5P_2O_7^+$	70	ca. 7×10^{-4} [b,c]	. . . .	557
$H_4P_2O_7$	70	6.6×10^{-4} [b]	21.9 (328°)	557
$H_3P_2O_7^-$	70	9.6×10^{-4} [b]	28.1 (328°)	557
$H_2P_2O_7^-$	70	9.25×10^{-6}	. . . .	557
$HP_2O_7^{3-}$	70	1.23×10^{-6}	. . . .	557
$P_2O_7^{4-}$	70	. . . .[d]	. . . .	557
$(H_4P_2O_7 + H_3P_2O_7^-)$[e]	60	1.12×10^{-5}	. . . .	558
$H_3P_2O_7^- + H_2P_2O_7^-)$[f]	49.8	5.41×10^{-6}	22.8 (313°)	559
$(H_4P_3O_{10}^- + H_3P_3O_{10}^-)$[e]	60	1.14×10^{-4}	. . . .	558
$(H_4P_3O_{10}^- + H_3P_3O_{10}^-)$[f]	49.0	2.69×10^{-5}	22.9 (313°)	559

[a] Corresponds to composition of transition state without regard for water, i.e., $H_5P_2O_7^+$ represents the transition state moiety corresponding to the reaction of $H_4P_2O_7$ and H_3O^+.

[b] Pseudo first-order constants at $(H_3O^+) = 1$ M.

[c] According to ref. 557, $H_4P_2O_7$ reacts somewhat more rapidly (with H_3O^+ or with H_2O) than $H_3P_2O_7^-$. The figure given is approximate for purposes of comparison.

[d] No detectable reaction at 0.1 M sodium hydroxide.

[e] Solutions (1%) of the appropriate $(CH_3)_4N^+$ salt plus 0.65 M $(CH_3)_4N^+Br^-$ adjusted to pH 1 and therefore containing a mixture of species. The ions thought to make the chief contribution to solution composition are listed as reactants. The discrepancies in rate constants listed in the table cannot be regarded as serious because of the variation in solution composition (and the known effect of solution composition on the rates).

[f] Probable composition of solution prepared by added excess hydrochloric acid to sodium pyrophosphate or sodium triphosphate.

biochemistry (e.g., ATP) attest to its possible significance. A summary of the hydrolysis rates of the various pyrophosphate ions and of some triphosphate ions is given in Table 2.15-6. Of the recent studies, only one[557] separated the over-all rates of hydrolysis into constants for the various ionic species present. Rate constants from the other investigations[558,559] are listed for probable reactant species.

[556] A. Kornberg, S. R. Kornberg, and E. S. Sims, *Biochim. et Biophys. Acta*, **20**, 215 (1956).

[557] D. O. Campbell and M. L. Kilpatrick, *J. Am. Chem. Soc.*, **76**, 893 (1954).

[558] J. R. Van Wazer, E. J. Griffith, and J. F. McCullough, *J. Am. Chem. Soc.*, **77**, 287 (1955).

[559] S. L. Friess, *J. Am. Chem. Soc.*, **74**, 4027 (1952).

2.15C-3. By analogy with the reactions of phosphate derivatives, some mechanistic possibilities for pyrophosphate hydrolysis may be written. Exchange of oxygen with H_2O^{18} has not been investigated, nor has the exchange of radioactive phosphate into pyrophosphate been studied. Presumably, the "good first-order kinetics" observed for the hydrolysis reaction preclude a large contribution from any reaction involving phosphate, but some might be expected on the basis of one of the possible mechanisms. The simplest pathway for hydrolysis is by displacement of phosphate by water [Eq. (2.208)]. The more negatively charged the pyrophosphate ion under attack, the less susceptible it would be to nucleophilic attack. In this context, the rate constant for the reaction of $H_3P_2O_7^-$ with water might be regarded as somewhat high, just as the monoanions of monoalkylphosphates hydrolyzed somewhat more rapidly than the neutral species. In analogy with the mechanism proposed in 2.15B for the reaction of the monoanions, Eq. (2.209) may be written, postulating the formation of metaphosphate ion. The latter can react with water to form phosphate or with phosphate to form pyrophosphate, and the latter process could be detected by the occurrence of exchange of radioactive phosphate into pyrophosphate [Eqs. (2.210) and (2.211)].

(2.208)

$$H_2O \rightarrow P \begin{matrix} OH \\ | \\ OH \end{matrix} \overset{H}{\underset{O}{}} P=O \begin{matrix} O^- \\ | \\ OH \end{matrix} \longrightarrow \overset{+}{H_2O}P=O \begin{matrix} OH \\ | \\ OH \end{matrix} + HOP=O \begin{matrix} O^- \\ | \\ OH \end{matrix}$$

(2.209)

$$^-O-P-O-P=O \longrightarrow ^-O-P + H_3PO_4$$

(2.210)

$$\bar{O}-P\overset{O}{\underset{O}{\lessgtr}} + H_2O \longrightarrow H_2PO_4^-$$

(2.211)

$$\bar{O}-P\overset{O}{\underset{O}{\lessgtr}} + H_3PO_4 \longrightarrow H_3P_2O_7^-$$

The situation for triphosphate is more complex, and aside from displacement reactions, which can occur on either the end or the central phosphorus atoms [Eqs. (2.212) and (2.213) indicate how H_2O^{18} might be used to distinguish these possibilities], either "metapyrophosphate" or metaphosphate might be formed [Eqs. (2.214) and (2.215)].

(2.212)
$$H_2O^{18} \rightarrow P\overset{OH}{\underset{OH}{\mid}}\overset{O}{\mid}O^+ - \overset{O}{\underset{O^-}{\mid\mid}}P - O - \overset{O}{\underset{OH}{\mid\mid}}P - OH \longrightarrow \overset{+}{H_2}O^{18}\,P(OH)_2 + HO\overset{O}{\underset{O^-}{\mid\mid}}P - O - \overset{O}{\underset{OH}{\mid\mid}}P - OH$$

(2.213)
$$H_2O^{18} \rightarrow \text{[cyclic P structure]} \longrightarrow \overset{+}{H_2}O^{18}\,\overset{O}{\underset{OH}{\mid\mid}}P - O\overset{O}{\underset{OH}{\mid\mid}}P - OH + H_2PO_4^-$$

(2.214)
$$O^- \rightarrow P\overset{O}{\underset{O_-}{\mid\mid}} - \overset{+}{O} - \overset{O}{\underset{OH}{\mid\mid}}P - O - \overset{O}{\underset{OH}{\mid\mid}}P - OH \longrightarrow PO_3^- + H_4P_2O_7$$

(2.215)
$$HO - \overset{O}{\underset{O}{\mid\mid}}P - O - \overset{H}{\underset{O^-}{\overset{O}{\mid\mid}}}P - O - \overset{O}{\underset{OH}{\mid\mid}}P - OH \longrightarrow H_3PO_4 + \,\overset{O}{\diagdown}P - O - \overset{O}{\underset{OH}{\mid\mid}}P - OH$$

It is thought that the oxygen exchange found for H_2O^{18} and phosphoric acid ($t_{1/2}$ ca. 720 sec in 18.3 F acid) is accomplished through formation and hydrolysis of pyrophosphoric acid, since the rate of exchange and the rate of hydrolysis are approximately equal in concentrated phosphoric acid.[560]

The sequence of compounds formed in hydrolysis of trimetaphosphimate[561] suggests the possibility of "polymetaphosphate" analogues as intermediates. One conversion might be interpreted as in Eq. (2.216) for illustrative purposes.

(2.216)

[Cyclic phosphimate structures with arrows: first ring → H^+ → second ring → third ring; then $+ H_2O$, $+ H^+$ downward; bottom row right to left: third ring → $-H^+$ → with $-H^+$ → ring]

[560] B. Keisch, J. W. Kennedy, and A. C. Wahl, *J. Am. Chem. Soc.*, **80**, 4778 (1958).
[561] O. T. Quimby, A. Narath, and F. H. Lohman, *J. Am. Chem. Soc.*, **82**, 1099 (1960).

2.15C-4. A considerable number of polyphosphates are important in biochemical reaction sequences, e.g., adenosine di- and triphosphates, uridine di- and triphosphates, etc. It is not known which chemical factors control the pathways open to these polyphosphates in reactions with nucleophilic reagents, although many of the possible modes of cleavage are apparently found in enzymatic reactions. The occurrence of higher polyphosphates, adenosine tetraphosphate[562,563] and adenosine pentaphosphate,[564] has been reported. The linearity of the polyphosphate chain in the tetraphosphate (AQP) seems assured, but no biological function has been found for it, and AQP does not replace ATP in enzymatic reactions.

To elucidate some of the factors involved in the reactions of pyrophosphates, tetrabenzyl pyrophosphate was solvolyzed in dry 1-propanol.[565] In the presence of highly hindered bases (tribenzylamine or $N,N,2,4$-tetramethylaniline) to reduce the catalytic effect of the acid produced by solvolysis, C—O cleavage is observed, forming benzyl n-propyl ether and tribenzyl pyrophosphate [Eq. (2.217)]. Less-hindered bases (2,6-lutidine or 2,4,6-collidine) attack phosphorus, with the probable forma-

$$(2.217)$$

tion of a reactive intermediate, as shown in Eqs. (2.218) and (2.219).

$$(2.218)$$

$$R_3N = base$$

$$(2.219)$$

[562] D. H. Marrian, *Biochim. et Biophys. Acta*, **13**, 278 (1954).
[563] I. Lieberman, *J. Am. Chem. Soc.*, **77**, 3373 (1955).
[564] J. Sacks, *Biochim. et Biophys. Acta*, **16**, 436 (1955).
[565] G. O. Dudek and F. H. Westheimer, *J. Am. Chem. Soc.*, **81**, 2641 (1959).

The reaction described in Eq. (2.217) is probably the initial step in the reaction of pyrophosphates with water. The half-lives for the series of tetraalkyl pyrophosphates $(RO)_2P(O)OP(O)(OR)_2$ have been found to be 1 hour $(R = CH_3)$, 8 hours $(R = CH_3CH_2—)$, 16 hours $(R = CH_3CH_2CH_2—)$, and 15 days $[R = (CH_3)_2CH—]$.[566] This trend is what would be expected for a bimolecular displacement by water with C—O cleavage. Further aspects of pyrophosphate ester reactions are considered in Sec. 2.15D on metal-ion catalysis.

2.15C-5. A crystalline enzyme can be isolated from yeast which specifically catalyzes the hydrolysis of pyrophosphate to phosphate in the presence of magnesium ion.[567] The enzyme does not catalyze the hydrolysis of alkyl pyrophosphates (ADP, ATP, thiamine PP, etc.) in the presence of magnesium ion but does so in the presence of zinc ion.[568] The concentration of magnesium required at pH 7.2 for maximum activity is *equal* to the concentration of pyrophosphate.

The enzyme catalyzes a rapid exchange of oxygen between H_2O^{18} and phosphate ion (unlike phosphatase, cf. page 249). The oxygen exchange reaction is some five hundred times faster than the reaction which exchanges P^{32}-phosphate into pyrophosphate.[569] It is therefore probable that an enzyme-phosphate compound is formed as an intermediate, according to Eqs. (2.220) and (2.221).[569] The enzyme-phos-

(2.220) $\quad\quad\quad HP_2O_7^{3-} + EH \leftrightarrows EPO_3^- + HOPO_3^- + H^+$

(2.221) $\quad\quad\quad EPO_3^- + H_2O \rightleftharpoons EH + HOPO_3^-$

phate compound is thought to possess a covalent bond between a group on the enzyme and the phosphorus,[569] but it is possible to write a mechanism which rationalizes the results using only ionic interactions between the phosphate and the enzyme. This mechanism (Fig. 2.79) postulates the formation of metaphosphate as an intermediate which can react with water to give phosphate, or with phosphate to form pyrophosphate. Magnesium ion is presumably important in arranging an appropriate geometry for the intermediates and transition states.

2.15C-6. The role of the pyrophosphate group per se in biochemical processes is best illustrated by its probable behavior in 3,3-dimethylallyl pyrophosphate and homologous pyrophosphates which serve as intermediates in the biosynthesis of squalene (cf. Sec. 1.8). Although the allylic pyrophosphate is reasonably stable in neutral solution, it is extremely sensitive to the presence of acid and is rapidly hydrolyzed

[566] A. D. F. Toy, *J. Am. Chem. Soc.*, **70**, 3882 (1948).

[567] M. Kunitz and P. W. Robbins, in "The Enzymes," vol. 5, chap. 11, Academic Press, Inc., New York, 1961.

[568] M. J. Schlesinger and M. J. Coon, *Biochim. et Biophys. Acta*, **41**, 30 (1960).

[569] M. Cohn, *J. Biol. Chem.*, **230**, 369 (1958).

under those conditions.[570]   We have seen that neutral glucose phosphate ionizes to a glucopyranosyl ion (pp. 233–235), and since anions function as leaving groups in a fashion roughly parallel to the acidity of the acid from which they are derived, we can expect that an allylic pyrophosphate

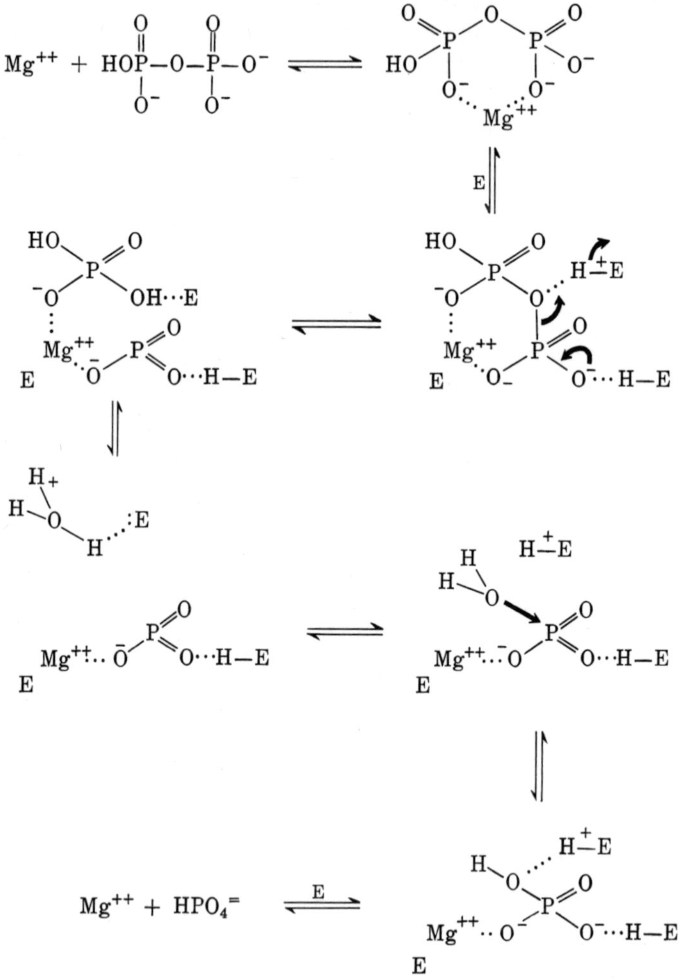

FIG. 2.79. Mechanism of pyrophosphatase action.

would ionize to an allylic carbonium ion.   Chemical evidence for two isomeric alcohols formed in acid hydrolysis of the relevant allylic pyrophosphates has been obtained, and constitutes support for the occurrence

[570] B. W. Agranoff, H. Eggerer, U. Henning, and F. Lynen, *J. Am. Chem. Soc.,* **81,** 1254 (1959).

of an allylic carbonium ion.[571] One may interpret the behavior of
allylic pyrophosphates as a simple illustration of the fact that it is more
difficult to withdraw a doubly negative ion from a positive center than
a singly negative ion (and, of course, still more difficult to remove a
triply negative ion). These points are illustrated in Eqs. (2.222) to
(2.224). Biological systems thus have evolved an extremely convenient

$$
(2.222) \quad
\underset{\substack{|\\ O^-}}{\overset{\substack{O\\ \|}}{ROP}}-O-\underset{\substack{|\\ O^-}}{\overset{\substack{O\\ \|}}{P}}-OH
\longrightarrow
R^+ \cdots \; {}^-O-\underset{\substack{|\\ O^-}}{\overset{\substack{O\\ \|}}{P}}-O-\underset{\substack{|\\ O^-}}{\overset{\substack{O\\ \|}}{P}}-OH
$$

$$
(2.223) \quad
\underset{\substack{|\\ O^-}}{\overset{\substack{O\\ \|}}{ROP}}-O-\underset{\substack{|\\ OH}}{\overset{\substack{O\\ \|}}{P}}-OH
\longrightarrow
R^+ \cdots \; {}^-O-\underset{\substack{|\\ O^-}}{\overset{\substack{O\\ \|}}{P}}-O-\underset{\substack{|\\ OH}}{\overset{\substack{O\\ \|}}{P}}-OH
$$

$$
(2.224) \quad
\underset{\substack{|\\ OH}}{\overset{\substack{O\\ \|}}{ROP}}-O-\underset{\substack{|\\ OH}}{\overset{\substack{O\\ \|}}{P}}-OH
\longrightarrow
R^+ \cdots \; {}^-O-\underset{\substack{|\\ OH}}{\overset{\substack{O\\ \|}}{P}}-O-\underset{\substack{|\\ OH}}{\overset{\substack{O\\ \|}}{P}}-OH
$$

method for transporting very reactive groups as far as may be necessary
without danger of unwanted hydrolysis reactions. The pyrophosphate
can be "activated" by neutralizing the charge with positive ions; it is
likely that the chief function of magnesium ion in promoting the reactions
of pyrophosphates is its ability to "neutralize" the negative charges of
the pyrophosphate.

The specificity of the biopolymerization of 3,3-dimethylallyl pyrophosphate with isopentenyl pyrophosphate argues against ionization
in the biological system. As pointed out in Sec. 1.8, a displacement
reaction is at least as likely[572] as ionization and is favored on the grounds
of specificity. One biological function of pyrophosphate is therefore to
act as a good leaving group in a bimolecular displacement reaction.

A similar displacement mechanism has been written for the enzyme-
catalyzed reaction of purines, pyrimidines, nicotinamide, etc., with
5-phosphoribosyl pyrophosphate (5-PRPP). However, the 5-phos-
phatomethyl group should hinder the approach of a nucleophile (see
Sec. 1.7) to the opposite side of the carbon bearing the pyrophosphate

[571] J. W. Cornforth and G. Popják, *Tetrahedron Letters No. 19*, 29–35 (1959).

[572] In the bimolecular displacement reaction, displacement of chloride ion by iodide
ion in acetone, 3,3-dimethylallyl chloride is approximately 2000 times as reactive as
1-propyl chloride.[573]

[573] E. L. Eliel, in "Steric Effects in Organic Chemistry," chap. 2, p. 84, John Wiley
& Sons, Inc., New York, 1956.

leaving group. Although displacements on the five-membered ring are appreciably faster than those on a six-membered ring, the factor is not really large (ca. 100 for iodide ion exchange with radioactive iodide).[574] Further, the factor which should hinder the approach of the nucleophile could favor the ionization of the pyrophosphate by electrostatic stabilization of the transition state, as proposed for the ionization of glucosyl phosphate (or the protonated glucoside, Fig. 2.77). For such ionization reactions, the five-membered ring is 50 times as reactive as *t*-butyl chloride, as comparison of the solvolysis rates in 80% ethanol of 1-methyl-1-chlorocyclopentane and *t*-butyl chloride demonstrates.[574] The ionization proposed for 5-PRPP is shown in Eq. (2.225). A precedent for

(2.225)

the stereochemistry indicated is found in the methanolysis of *O*-tetra-methylglucopyranosyl chloride (Fig. 2.74).

2.15C-7. Adenosine triphosphate (ATP) is one of the most important chemical entities in biochemical systems. The two main pathways followed by this molecule may be written[575] as in Eqs. (2.226) and (2.227). At least two reactions corresponding to Eq. (2.228) have also been observed.[576,577]

$$
\begin{array}{ll}
(2.226) & \text{ATP} + \text{RO}^{18}\text{H} \rightarrow \text{ADP} + \text{PO}_4^{18} {}^{---} \\
(2.227) & \text{ATP} + \text{RO}^{18}\text{H} \rightarrow \text{AMP}{-}\text{O}^{18} + \text{PP} \\
(2.228) & \text{APPP*} + \text{ROH} \rightarrow \text{AP} + \text{ROPP*} \\
& (\text{P*} = \text{P}^{32})
\end{array}
$$

The reactions of ATP can be divided mechanistically (and in a somewhat speculative manner) into three groups: (*a*) those involving displacement on phosphorus, with either the first or the terminal phosphorus

---

[574] Ref. 573, p. 123.

[575] P. S. Boyer and M. P. Stulberg, *Proc. Natl. Acad. Sci. U.S.*, **44**, 92 (1958).

[576] H. G. Khorana, J. F. Fernandes, and A. Kornberg, *J. Biol. Chem.*, **230**, 941 (1958).

[577] O. Forsander, quoted by M. Cohn, *J. Cellular Comp. Physiol.*, **54**, Suppl. 1, 22 (1959).

as the usual site of attack, (*b*) those involving displacement on carbon, and (*c*) those forming "hot," or "activated," intermediates. The pathways belonging to the three groups are illustrated in Fig. 2.80.

The "hot" intermediates are, with respect to the results that might be obtained in exchange experiments, equivalent to enzyme-phosphate compounds containing a covalent enzyme-phosphorus bond. They are

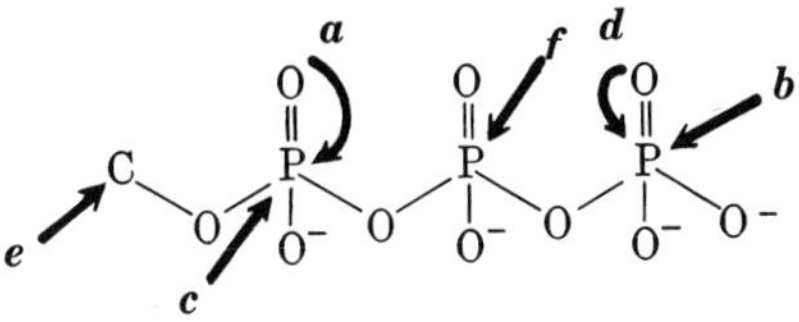

$\xrightarrow{\ a\ }$	"hot AMP" + PP	APS dinucleotides acyl AMP
$\xrightarrow{\ b\ }$	ADP + ROP	G-6-P
$\xrightarrow{\ c\ }$	AMPOR + P P	Polynucleotide
$\xrightarrow{\ d\ }$	"hot P" + ADP	PEP ATP hydrolysis by myosin (see text)
$\xrightarrow{\ e\ }$	Y – C + PP + P	S-Adenosyl methionine
$\xrightarrow{\ f\ }$	AMP + 5-PRPP	5-Phosphoribosyl pyrophosphate

Fig. 2.80. Pathways for reaction of ATP.

postulated as possibilities on the basis of the chemical proposals outlined earlier.[578,578a]

2.15C-8. The reaction of ATP with sulfate ion in the presence of sulfurylase[579] produces adenosine phosphosulfate. The low nucleophilicity of sulfate ion coupled with the repulsion expected between the doubly negative sulfate and the negatively charged ATP (even allowing

[578] Basically the same idea was expressed in somewhat different form by A. Todd, *J. Cellular Comp. Physiol.*, **54**, Suppl. 1, 27 (1959).

[578a] A bacterial enzyme which forms polymetaphosphate from ATP has been partially purified. A number of its properties, including the nonformation of ATP from ADP and polymetaphosphate,[578b] are consistent with metaphosphate as a "hot" intermediate.

[578b] A. Muhammed, *Biochim. et Biophys. Acta*, in press (1962).

[579] L. G. Wilson and R. S. Bandurski, *J. Biol. Chem.*, **233**, 975 (1958).

for the presence of the magnesium ion required for the reaction) leads to the suspicion that a displacement on phosphorus (path *c*) is *not* the route followed.   A mechanism for the formation of the phosphosulfate (APS) is shown in Fig. 2.81.   It is conceivable that dinucleotide forma-

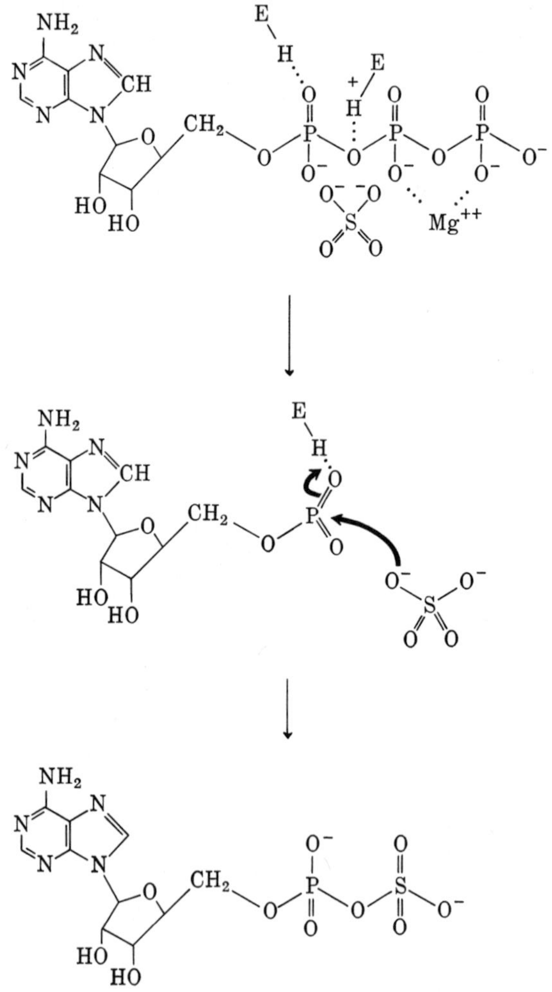

FIG. 2.81. Mechanism of APS formation.

tion (e.g., DPN) proceeds by the same pathway.   A less certain possibility is that of acyl adenylate formation, for which path *c* might be equally suitable.   The latter pathway is the obvious route.   Acetyl adenylate is apparently "enzyme-bound" and reacts further with CoASH to form acetyl ScoA.   The elaborate single complex proposed for the over-all reaction has been criticized and does not appear to offer an intellectual advantage over a sequence of two successive reactions, the first forming acetyl adenylate, the second giving acetyl ScoA.[580,581]

Another reaction in which one might suspect that a reasonably reactive intermediate might be involved is that of pyruvic acid with ATP to form phosphoenolpyruvic acid and ADP. If the reaction does not involve enolization of pyruvic acid prior to the formation of the oxygen-phosphorus bond, a good "acceptor" like metaphosphate could compensate for the relatively weak nucleophilicity of the carbonyl oxygen of pyruvic acid [Eq. (2.229)]. The enzyme might catalyze hydrogen exchange of phosphoenolpyruvic acid with the solvent.

(2.229)

Phosphoenolpyruvic acid can be formed in an enzymatic reaction through the reaction of the enolate anion of pyruvic acid with pyrophosphate ion. The enolate ion is the probable intermediate derived by the decarboxylation of the actual reactant, oxaloacetic acid.[582]

2.15C-9. The course of the hydrolysis of ATP by myosin ("purified muscle protein") is reported to differ according to the nature of the activating divalent ion. The over-all reaction of Eq. (2.230) introduces one atom of O^{18} from H_2O^{18} in the presence of calcium ion[583] but two to three atoms when magnesium ion is used.[584] There is no

(2.230) $APP{\}P + H_2O^{18} \rightarrow APP + PO^{18}$

oxygen exchange into inorganic phosphate or ATP,[583,584] and neither phosphate exchange nor ADP exchange into ATP.[583] A potential

[580] L. L. Ingraham and D. E. Green, *Science*, **128**, 310 (1958); **129**, 896 (1959).

[581] P. Berg, *Science*, **129**, 895 (1959).

[582] P. M. L. Siu, H. G. Wood, and R. L. Stjernholm, *J. Biol. Chem.*, **236**, PC 21 (1961).

[583] D. E. Koshland, Jr., Z. Budenstein, and A. Kowalsky, *J. Biol. Chem.*, **211**, 279 (1954).

[584] H. M. Levy and D. E. Koshland, Jr., *J. Am. Chem. Soc.*, **80**, 3164 (1958).

energy diagram along the reaction coordinate is shown in Fig. 2.82. (The additional complexities introduced by the enzyme are not indicated.)

Although it is tempting to imagine that a "hot P" (i.e., metaphosphate) intermediate is bound to the enzyme, such an intermediate would be an "enzyme-bound" form of phosphate which would not exchange

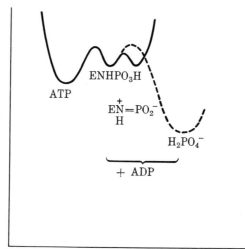

FIG. 2.82. Hydrolysis of ATP by myosin.

readily with phosphate of the solution. Precedents do exist for such failures to exchange (mevaldic acid, acetyl adenylate, etc.) but are usually found in cases in which the intermediate is converted into another molecule. It is probably more satisfactory in the present instance to postulate a covalent bond to phosphorus formed by an amino group. Exchange with oxygen of water without exchange with phosphate is then possible as shown in Eqs. (2.231) to (2.233).

$$(2.231) \qquad \text{E--NH}_2 + \underset{\text{H}}{\text{O}}-\underset{\underset{\text{O}^-}{|}}{\overset{\overset{\text{O}}{\|}}{\text{P}}}-\text{O}-\underset{\underset{\text{O}^-}{|}}{\overset{\overset{\text{O}}{\|}}{\text{P}}}-\text{O}-\underset{\underset{\text{O}^-}{|}}{\overset{\overset{\text{O}}{\|}}{\text{P}}}-\text{OAd} \longrightarrow \text{ENH}\overset{\overset{\text{O}}{\|}}{\underset{\underset{\text{O}^-}{|}}{\text{P}}}-\text{OH}$$
$$\text{Mg}^{++}$$

$$(2.232) \qquad \text{ENH}\overset{\overset{\text{O}}{\|}}{\underset{\underset{\text{O}^-}{|}}{\text{P}}}-\overset{+}{\text{OH}}_2 \underset{\text{+ H}_2\text{O}}{\overset{\text{- H}_2\text{O}}{\rightleftharpoons}} \text{E--}\underset{+}{\overset{\text{H}}{\text{N}}}=\text{P}\overset{\nearrow\text{O}}{\underset{\searrow\text{O}^-}{}}$$

$$(2.233) \qquad \text{ENH}\overset{\overset{\text{O}}{\|}}{\underset{\underset{\text{O}^-}{|}}{\text{P}}}-\text{OH} \longrightarrow \text{ENH}_2 + \text{H}_2\text{PO}_4^-$$

A conversion for which no straightforward mechanism is immediately obvious is that of methionine to S-adenosylmethionine catalyzed by an enzyme[585] in the presence of both magnesium and a monovalent ion like potassium, ammonium, or rubidium.[586] Both pyrophosphate and phosphate are produced, the latter arising from the terminal phosphorus of ATP. The reaction is shown in Eq. (2.234).

(2.234)

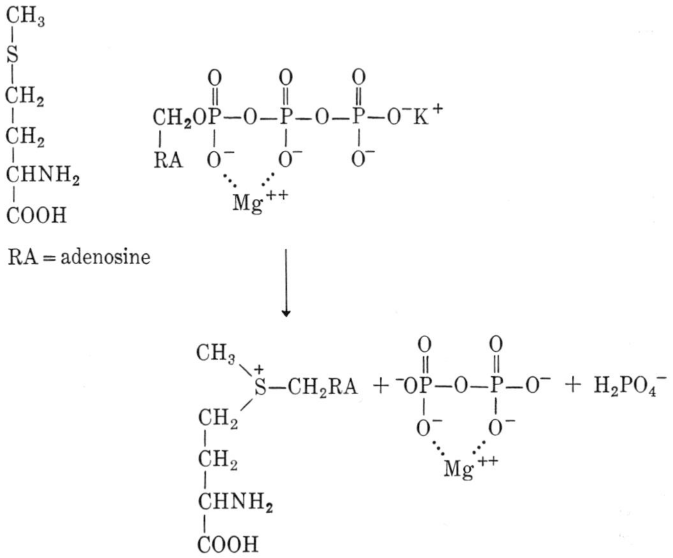

$$
\begin{array}{c}
CH_3 \\
| \\
S \\
| \\
CH_2 \\
| \\
CH_2 \\
| \\
CHNH_2 \\
| \\
COOH
\end{array}
\qquad
CH_2OP-O-P-O-P-O^-K^+
$$

RA = adenosine

$$
\begin{array}{c}
CH_3 \\
\diagdown_+ \\
\quad S-CH_2RA \; + \; ^-OP-O-P-O^- \; + \; H_2PO_4^- \\
CH_2 \diagup \\
| \\
CH_2 \\
| \\
CHNH_2 \\
| \\
COOH
\end{array}
$$

2.15D. Metal-ion Catalysis

Without doubt, metal ions exert a large, and often determining, influence over the reactions of phosphates and polyphosphates in both enzymatic and nonenzymatic reactions. The interpretation of the effects observed has thus far been possible only in the most general terms.

2.15D-1. The combination of the phosphate or pyrophosphate grouping with a metal ion varies with the nature of the cation and the ligand group. The stability constants for complex formation according to the reaction of Eq. (2.235) are listed for some cases of interest in Table 2.15-7. The *stability* of a complex with respect to *dissociation*

(2.235) $M^{+n} + L^{-y} \rightleftharpoons ML^{n-y}$
                         (L = ligand group)

depends on such factors as the relative solvation of M, L, and ML, the

[585] G. L. Cantoni and J. Durell, *J. Biol. Chem.*, **225**, 1033 (1957).
[586] S. H. Mudd and G. L. Cantoni, *J. Biol. Chem.*, **231**, 481 (1958).

ionic radius of M and the geometry of L, and the electron configuration of M. An inflexible stability order is not found even for a group of such closely related cations as calcium, magnesium, and strontium in complexes with a variety of ligands.[587]

Table 2.15-7. Stability Constants for Complexes[a,b,e]

$$K = \frac{[ML]}{[M][L]}$$

Ligand	Cation					
	K^+	Na^+	Li^+	Mg^{++}	Ca^{++}	Sr^{++}
HPO_4^-	3	4	5	76	50	33
$P_2O_7^{4-}$	6	10	240	250,000	1000	
$P_3O_{10}^{5-}$	25	44	740	680,000	90,000	
AMP^-	2	3	4	100	58	21
ADP^{3-}	6	7	14	1400	660	310
ATP^{4-}	11	14	38	10,000	5900	1100
$AQP^{5-\,c}$	19	27	80			
$P_2O_8^{4-\,d}$	10	10	22	2140		

[a] The original should be consulted for notations regarding ionic strength, comments on the measurements, and references.

[b] K is in units of liters/mole.

[c] AQP is adenosine tetraphosphate.

[d] $P_2O_8^{4-}$ is peroxydiphosphate ion.[588]

[e] Ref. 552.

For a reaction in which the ligand L is converted into two fragments J and K, and the moiety K remains coordinated to the cation available, the expression (2.236) may be written. The *reactivity* of a complex in

(2.236) $$ML^{n-y} \rightarrow J + MK^{n-y}$$

formation of products, as in Eq. (2.236), is determined by the height of the transition-energy barrier (i.e., by the activation free energy). In some cases, the height of the barrier may be a reflection of the stabilities of the products J and MK; comparison of two products formed in two parallel reactions MK and MK′ might indicate which reaction would be faster. Thus, stability constants for reactants cannot be used to predict catalytic effectiveness of cations. When we further consider that the reactant in the cases of particular interest is actually an enzyme-metal-ligand complex, the problem of evaluating the catalytic activity of a cation is seen to be quite difficult.

[587] H. M. N. H. Irving, "International Conference on Coordination Chemistry," *Chem. Soc. (London), Spec. Publ. No. 13*, p. 23, 1959.

[588] M. M. Crutchfield and J. O. Edwards, *J. Am. Chem. Soc.*, **82**, 3533 (1960).

2.15D-2. In various places throughout this book, we have stated that the chief function of the magnesium ion in catalyzing the enzymatic reactions of polyphosphates is to neutralize the negative charges of the polyphosphate and thus permit the approach of a nucleophile. Matters cannot be that straightforward, however. If simple chelation were sufficient to activate ATP for hydrolysis, we should not expect the alkyl triphosphate to survive the *milieu intérieur,* nor to exhibit great specificity in its reactions. Not only is ATP moderately stable in biological systems, but no spectacular increases in hydrolysis rate are noted at pH 8.5 to 8.8 in the presence of either calcium or magnesium.[589,590] Thus, the enzymes concerned with the reactions of ATP must provide some further chemical activation for the magnesium-ATP combination.

Some clues as to the nature of the additional activation are found in the results obtained for the calcium or magnesium-promoted reaction of tetrabenzylpyrophosphate in 1-propanol.[510,565] If the reaction described in Eq. (2.217) is carried out in the presence of magnesium ion, equal amounts of C—O and P—O cleavage are observed, in contrast to the C—O cleavage observed in the absence of the magnesium ion. The sterically hindered nature of the base used to neutralize the acid produced in the reaction argues against its participation either as a nucleophile or as a general base (removal of a proton from the 1-propanol in the transition state). An appropriate basic group on an enzyme could (*a*) increase the nucleophilicity of an attacking reagent XOH by the removal of a proton in the transition state and (*b*) direct the nucleophilic attack at a particular phosphorus atom of the ATP. A further point to be noted is that the metal-ion activation was observed in the case of a neutral pyrophosphate. The enzyme might add one or two protons[578] (or provide strong hydrogen bonding) to neutralize the charges remaining after complex formation of ATP with magnesium. The enzyme might also be concerned in controlling the kind of chelation within the enzyme-ATP-magnesium complex, the possibilities being chelation of the magnesium with the first and second phosphorus-oxygen bonds, with the second and third phosphorus-oxygen bonds, with all three such bonds, or with any of these plus the ribosyl oxygen of the adenosine moiety. The structures of the ATP-magnesium or ATP-calcium complexes in solution do *not* involve coordination of the adenine ring with the metal ion as shown by the lack of change in the chemical shift observed for the ring hydrogens in NMR spectra on metal-ion complexation.[591]

[589] L. B. Nanninga, *J. Phys. Chem.,* **61,** 1144 (1958).

[590] C. Liebecq and M. Jacquemotte-Louis, *Bull. soc. chim. biol.,* **40,** 759 (1958).

[591] G. G. Hammes, G. E. Maciel, and J. S. Waugh, *J. Am. Chem. Soc.,* **83,** 2394 (1961).

2.15D-3.   It was estimated that a combination of 2,6-lutidine and calcium ion reacted in 1-propanol with the tetrabenzylpyrophosphate to effect P—O cleavage about 100,000 times faster than found with a sterically hindered base in the absence of calcium ion.[510]   In those enzymatic cases in which an enzyme-phosphate compound might be involved (such as those indicated as "hot AMP" or "hot P" in Fig. 2.80), an appropriate nucleophilic group at the "active site" might be involved in the enzyme-catalyzed reactions of ATP.   Essentially the same proposal has been made previously on other grounds.[583]

The hydrolysis of the dianion, but not of the monoanion, of acetyl phosphate is accelerated by magnesium ion.[534]   Although a cyclic chelate of magnesium involving the carbonyl oxygen and a phosphorus oxygen was written as an intermediate,[534] it seems more likely that the magnesium ion was functioning simply to reduce the negative charge in the region of the phosphorus and thus increase its susceptibility to nucleophilic attack.   (The direction of cleavage, P—O or C—O, was not experimentally determined.)   Barium-ion catalysis of phosphate ester hydrolyses favors P—O cleavage over C—O cleavage.[502]   Calcium ion does *not* catalyze the hydrolysis of ethylene phosphate under alkaline conditions,[484] in contrast to its effectiveness in reactions of tetrabenzylpyrophosphate. Accelerations of hydrolysis rates have been noted for cerium(III) and lanthanum(III) ions[487,592] with certain phosphate esters.   It is reported that mercuric ion effects instantaneous hydrolysis of vinyl phosphates (vinyl phosphate, phosphoenolpyruvic acid).[593,594]   Hydrolysis rates of certain anticholinesterases (e.g., diisopropyl phosphorofluoridate) are markedly accelerated by cupric ion.[472]

Further study of metal-ion catalysis of the reactions of phosphates and polyphosphates is both necessary and desirable on the chemical as well as the biochemical level.   It may be important, for example, that the rate of combination of ADP and ATP with calcium ion is ca. 10^2 times greater than that for magnesium.[595]   A noteworthy series of reactions of ATP with certain nucleophiles, catalyzed by divalent metal ions, has been reported.   In the presence of calcium ion, at concentrations for which ATP is largely complexed (1:1), ATP and phosphate react to form ADP and pyrophosphate[596] [Eq. (2.237)].

$$(2.237) \qquad\qquad \text{ATP} + \text{P} \xrightarrow{\text{Ca}^{+2}} \text{ADP} + \text{PP}$$

[592] E. Bamann and W. D. Mütterlein, *Chem. Ber.*, **91**, 471, 1322 (1958).

[593] E. Baer, L. J. Ciplyauskas, and T. Visser, *J. Biol. Chem.*, **234**, 1 (1960).

[594] G. Schmidt, B. Ottenstein, W. A. Spencer, K. Keck, R. Blietz, J. Papas, D. Porter, M. L. Levin, and S. J. Thannhauser, *A.M.A. J. Diseases Children*, **97**, 691 (1959).

[595] M. Eigen and G. G. Hammes, *J. Am. Chem. Soc.*, **82**, 5952 (1960); **83**, 2786 (1961).

[596] J. M. Lowenstein, *Biochem. J.*, **70**, 222 (1958).

Monovalent cations, especially potassium ion, increase the amount of pyrophosphate formed in a given time.[597] Carboxylate anions (e.g., acetate) apparently react with ATP to form acyl phosphates, detected by conversion to the hydroxamic acid. The most active catalyst for the latter reaction is beryllium ion, which is rather ineffective for the reaction of Eq. (2.237).[598] The major obstacle to a more detailed interpretation of these interesting reactions is the paucity of information on the actual species present in the reaction mixtures.

[597] J. M. Lowenstein, *Biochem. J.*, **75,** 269 (1960).
[598] J. M. Lowenstein and M. N. Schatz, *J. Biol. Chem.*, **236,** 305 (1961).

PART 3

PHYSICAL PATTERNS

3.0. PROBLEMS

Some of the most important materials present in biological systems act primarily by virtue of their physical properties rather than by taking part in chemical transformations. This does not mean that their chemical properties are not significant in determining their biological activity, but simply that a useful focus of attention is the physical behavior of these materials. The purpose of this section is to mention briefly some of the important problems and to discuss one (the "active site" problem) at some length.

The chief component of the *milieu intérieur* of biological systems is water. The small size of the water molecule and its strong tendency to participate in intermolecular interactions, chiefly through hydrogen bonds, complicate the properties of aqueous media. Liquid water behaves as if it consisted of a highly structured component in addition to monomeric water molecules. The existence of gas "hydrates" (water clathrates of, for example, krypton) led to a proposal that the structured water is a fairly definite arrangement of 20 water molecules in a pentagonal dodecahedron;[1] a statistical-thermodynamic treatment on the basis of water in two states gives a satisfactory representation of the pressure-volume-temperature properties of water over limited ranges of temperature and pressure.[2]

---

[1] L. Pauling, in "Hydrogen Bonding," ed. by D. Hadzi, p. 1, Pergamon Press, London, 1959; cf. also L. Pauling, "Nature of the Chemical Bond," 3d ed., p. 472, Cornell University Press, Ithaca, N.Y., 1960.

[2] H. S. Frank and A. S. Quist, *J. Chem. Phys.*, **34**, 604 (1961); cf. also H. S. Frank and W.-Y. Wen, *Discussions Faraday Soc.*, **24**, 133 (1957).

Ions and polar groups as well as nonpolar groups interact with water. These groups modify the structure of the water; the range of influence of ions has been estimated experimentally in one case as approximately 5 Å (for alkylammonium ions).[3] Nonpolar groups cause the water molecules near them to become more strongly hydrogen-bonded to one another than in pure water, giving rise to an abnormally high heat capacity.[2]

Many of the important biopolymers (enzymes and other proteins, DNA, glycogen, phospholipids, etc.) exist in an aqueous medium. The three factors mentioned above, moderate-sized groups of water molecules, influence of charged groups on water (the sphere of this influence is referred to elsewhere in this book as the *cybotactic region*[4]), and structural change (or changes) induced by nonpolar groups, must all play some part in determining the physical properties of the biopolymers. A simplified attempt to rationalize "many aspects of protein behavior" in aqueous solution in terms related to water structure has appeared.[5] Further, the effect of water structure may be important for understanding rate processes (like enzyme-substrate combination) which appear to be diffusion-controlled.

Protein structure is being attacked in a number of ways on different levels.[5a] The *primary* structure or amino acid sequence has been elucidated for a small number of "easily" characterizable proteins: insulin, ribonuclease, and the protein component of tobacco mosaic virus. The *secondary* structure, or regular folding of the primary chain, is approached through measurements of optical rotatory dispersion and determinations of the numbers of hydrogens which exchange slowly with deuterium oxide. The former measurement depends upon the fact that the helices which constitute one major type of secondary structure (pleated sheets are another) are themselves optically active. The slow hydrogen exchange is presumably related to the greater difficulty in replacing hydrogens in hydrogen bonds which stabilize the helices than those which are hydrogen bonded to water. There are discrepancies in the extent of helical structure indicated by the two methods which may arise from either (*a*) the occurrence of left-handed helices in addition to the expected right-handed helices or (*b*) the presence of difficultly exchangeable hydrogens which are associated with structures other than intrahelical hydrogen bonds.[5b] The *tertiary* structure of the protein arises from a tendency for many long chains to fold back on themselves,

[3] D. H. Everett, *Discussions Faraday Soc.*, **24**, 220 (1957).

[4] E. M. Kosower, *J. Am. Chem. Soc.*, **80**, 3253 (1958).

[5] I. M. Klotz, *Science*, **128**, 815 (1958).

[5a] Cf. the review by E. Katchalski and I. Z. Steinberg, *Ann. Rev. Phys. Chem.*, **12**, 433 (1961).

[5b] E. R. Blout, C. de Loze, and A. A. Sadourian, *J. Am. Chem. Soc.*, **83**, 1895 (1961).

with stabilization arising from interhelical hydrogen bonds, disulfide linkages, "hydrophobic bonds,"[6] and ionic interactions.[7-10]

Additional physical and chemical problems of major importance exist in the areas of DNA modification ("mutagenesis"),[11,12] DNA sequence (the genetic code), and transport processes (movement of metabolites through cell walls, establishment of differential in potassium and sodium concentrations within the nerve cell), to mention only a few for which some approaches at the molecular level can be imagined.

3.1. THE "ACTIVE SITE"

It's hard and it's hard, ain't it hard,
To love one that never did love you.
It's hard and it's hard, ain't it hard, great God,
To love one that never will be true.
*Woody Guthrie**

Enzyme proteins catalyze many reactions of relatively small molecules. The large size of the enzyme molecules requires that only a relatively small portion be in "direct contact" with the substrate molecules. The small portion thus involved is called the "active site."

3.1A. Definition

The "active site" may be defined as consisting of those arrangements of functional groups, peptide linkages, and hydrophobic regions which belong to the enzyme protein and which are *directly* involved in the construction of the transition state (or states) for the chemical transformation (or transformations) catalyzed by the enzyme. A number of qualifications are necessary; they are listed below.

[6] "Hydrophobic" bond is a loose term useful for describing the juxtaposition of nonpolar portions of the protein molecule produced by the expulsion of these nonpolar portions from the structure-forming water region.

[7] K. U. Linderstrøm-Lang and J. A. Schellman, in "The Enzymes," vol. 1, chap. 10, Academic Press, Inc., New York, 1959.

[8] P. D. Boyer, Protein Structure and Function, *Brookhaven Symposia in Biol.,* No. 13, BNL 608 (C-30), p. 1, 1960.

[9] I. M. Klotz, in ref. 8, p. 25.

[10] H. A. Scheraga, in ref. 8, p. 71.

[11] E. Bautz and E. Freese, *Proc. Natl. Acad. Sci. U.S.,* **46,** 1585 (1960).

[12] S. Brenner, L. Barnett, F. H. C. Crick, and A. Orgel, *J. Mol. Biol.,* **3,** 121 (1961).

* "Hard, Ain't It Hard." Words and music by Woody Guthrie. Copyright 1952 by Ludlow Music, Inc., New York, N.Y. Used by permission.

1. The definition is *minimal;* if a large protein molecule is required for the maintenance of a special relationship between two functional groups, most of it is not considered part of the active site. The need to specify portions of the protein molecule relatively distant from the substrate in the transition state will depend on the way in which these distant portions are found to participate in the enzyme-catalyzed reaction.

2. Hydration is unspecified except as dictated by the requirements of the reaction under consideration.

3. Coenzymes are considered as parts of the enzyme for the purposes of the definition given above.

4. The *minimal* description sought in the definition should permit important features of enzyme-catalyzed reactions to be explained (or specified) without necessarily providing profound insight into enzymatic catalysis.

5. *Direct* involvement is here defined as *contact* with the substrate in the transition state without regard for a limited number of water molecules which may intervene.

3.1B. Properties of the "Active Site"

3.1B-1. Nature of enzymatic catalysis. *a. Presumed Analogies with Nonenzymatic Organic Reactions.* An ester hydrolysis catalyzed by an enzyme can obviously be compared to nonenzymatic ester hydrolysis. The over-all reactions are the same. Difficulties arise, however, if the analogies are extended to intermediates and mechanisms. For example, imidazole catalyzes the hydrolysis of *p*-nitrophenyl acetate with the formation of an intermediate, acetylimidazole (Sec. 2.7, page 132). Chymotrypsin hydrolyzes the same acetate with the formation of an acylchymotrypsin, but it is known that the acetyl group is attached to the oxygen of the hydroxyl group of serine. Thus, for very similar reactions in enzymatic and nonenzymatic hydrolysis, *the pathways are different.* It is even more problematical that a close resemblance exists between the mechanisms of these two hydrolyses, and yet it is necessary to have such a relationship in order to make meaningful comparisons of the rates of enzymatic and nonenzymatic reactions. These considerations are quite apart from the intrinsic difficulty in comparing such rates (see below).

These objectives do not mean that a search for useful model (nonenzymatic) reactions should be abandoned, but they suggest that the comparisons be made carefully. Three degrees of appropriateness can be distinguished for model reactions.

(1) *Duplication of the transformation.* Certain enzymatic reactions have no good counterpart in a nonenzymatic reaction. Reduction of

carbonyl compounds by DPNH is a particular example. It is desirable to discover model reactions which bear *some* resemblance to the one catalyzed by the enzyme so as to obtain some notions about the kind of factors which affect the process. Thus, reduction of thiobenzophenone by 1-benzyl-1,4-dihydronicotinamide is a successful model by this criterion (see Sec. 2.13F).

(2) *Parallelism.* If a model reaction resembles an enzymatic reaction to a reasonable degree, it may be useful in evaluating details of substrate behavior. Thus, the use of a series of imidazoles or a series of varied nucleophiles as catalysts for ester hydrolysis reveals how the carbonyl group is susceptible to nucleophilic reagents (see Sec. 2.7).

(3) *Congruency.* When there is good reason to believe that the model reaction is *very much* like the enzymatic reaction, it might be labeled congruent. The decomposition of hydrogen peroxide by the triethylenetetramine complex of ferric ion seems quite similar to the process catalyzed by the enzyme catalase, even though the detailed mechanism for catalase action is not known.[13] The catalytic activity of thiazolium betaines formed by the loss of the 2-proton appears to be a congruent model for thiamine pyrophosphate-enzyme-catalyzed reactions.[14]

One kind of study which has been useful at the *parallel* level of appropriateness is that in which the compounds under investigation contain the moiety to be acted upon (e.g., an ester group) and a functional group which might function in a catalytic fashion. The most striking model of this class is the γ-(4-imidazolyl)-butyrate ester of *p*-nitrophenol (see Sec. 2.7). The reactions observed belong in the class known as "neighboring-group" reactions. The advantage of such models is that they permit fairly straightforward comparisons between the enzyme-catalyzed reaction rates and those of the model, both as first-order constants. A less satisfactory method of comparing rates is to calculate the concentration of "catalytic" reagent in a bimolecular model reaction which would produce the same rate as the enzyme acting upon a given substrate.[15] The physical significance of the "concentration for equivalent rate" is not clear, but may be useful for indicating the effectiveness of an enzyme in a semiquantitative manner. One must respect the convention regarding the units chosen for the bimolecular rate constants (e.g., 1 mole^{-1} sec.$^{-1}$).

b. Sources of the Enzymatic Rate Advantage. For a number of enzymatic reactions, the lower limit of the rate of combination of the enzyme

[13] R. C. Jarnagin and J. H. Wang, *J. Am. Chem. Soc.*, **80**, 6477 (1958); J. H. Wang, *J. Am. Chem. Soc.*, **77**, 4715 (1955).

[14] R. Breslow, *J. Am. Chem. Soc.*, **79**, 1762 (1957); R. Breslow, *J. Am. Chem. Soc.*, **80**, 3719 (1958); R. Breslow and E. McNelis, *J. Am. Chem. Soc.*, **81**, 3080 (1959).

[15] M. L. Bender, *Chem. Revs.*, **60**, 88 (1960).

with the substrate derived from steady-state kinetic data approaches within one or two orders of magnitude of the value derived from the theory of diffusion-controlled encounters[16-18] [Eq. (3.1)] in which D_1 and D_2 are the diffusion coefficients for substrate and enzyme, respectively, and R_{12} is the reaction radius. The lower limits for the combination

$$(3.1) \qquad\qquad k = \frac{2\pi N_{Av}}{1000} R_{12}(D_1 + D_2)$$
$$(N_{Av} = \text{Avogadro number})$$

rates are obtainable from a general formulation of an enzyme-catalyzed interconversion of two compounds involving an arbitrary number of intermediates.[19,20]   A modification of Eq. (3.1) by a factor f to allow for electrostatic interactions between the enzyme protein and the substrate in the case of fumarase gave qualitative agreement between the theory and the experiment.[21]

Regardless of how we account for the rearrangements subsequent to enzyme-substrate combination (that is, for the catalysis of the chemical transformation), it is clear that one of the important features of enzymatic catalysis is the high affinity of the substrate for the enzyme "active site." The low activation energy for the combination process implies that only weak bonds are formed or broken. Beyond some general suggestions as to topological and charge matching, no efforts have been devoted to explaining the combination process. The entropy advantage of chelation (less negative ΔS than a "corresponding" nonchelating reaction) has been estimated[21a] and is presumably a contributing factor in enzyme-substrate combination processes after an initial interaction is present. Unless the functional groups at the "active site" play the major role in the combination process, it is unlikely that the present approaches to the investigation of the "active site" will elucidate any features of the combination process. However, the "direct approach" outlined in Sec. 3.1C-3 should be of aid in this regard.

The following paragraphs will develop some of the possible factors that contribute to the effectiveness of the enzyme in catalyzing the chemical transformation without considering further the advantages conferred by the rapid formation of the enzyme-substrate complex.

[16] M. V. Smoluchowski, *Z. physik. Chem.* (*Leipzig*), **92**, 129 (1917).

[17] P. Debye, *Trans. Electrochem. Soc.*, **82**, 265 (1942).

[18] R. A. Alberty and G. G. Hammes, *J. Phys. Chem.*, **62**, 154 (1958).

[19] L. Peller and R. A. Alberty, *J. Am. Chem. Soc.*, **81**, 5907 (1959).

[20] L. Peller and R. A. Alberty, "Progress in Reaction Kinetics," Pergamon Press, London, 1961.

[21] G. G. Hammes and R. A. Alberty, *J. Phys. Chem.*, **63**, 274 (1959).

[21a] F. H. Westheimer and L. L. Ingraham, *J. Phys. Chem.*, **60**, 1668 (1956).

(1) *Electrostatic effects.* The attraction or repulsion between charges located a few atomic diameters apart is of a magnitude [Eq. (3.2)] that

$$(3.2) \quad E \text{ (in kcal/mole)} = 333 \frac{q_1 q_2 \text{ (in fractions of a unit charge)}}{Dr \text{ (in Å)}}$$

would seriously affect ground or transition state free energies, and thus the rates of reactions. Although electrostatic effects on equilibria have been evaluated in a reasonable empirical way (K_1 and K_2 for dicarboxylic acids, etc.[22]), it is more difficult to find a pure electrostatic effect on a reaction rate. The "distant attack" favored by chromium(II) on certain cobalt(III) derivatives with π-electron-containing ligands[23] is presumably favored by the lesser repulsion between the positively charged ions at a great distance as compared with approach to the coordination sphere immediately around the ions.

A rather small increase in the rate of hydrolysis of *o*-nitrophenyl hydrogen oxalate caused by 2-aminopyridine in the pH range 3 to 6 has been interpreted as a large rate effect caused by 2-aminopyridinium ion. The latter ion supposedly aids in the formation of an especially favorable transition state through electrostatic interaction of a positive and negative charge[24] [Eq. (3.3)].

(3.3)

(2) *Concertedness.* If the replacement of X in the primary halide, RX, by Y, a nucleophilic agent, is considered, we might write the reaction as a *concerted displacement* reaction (S_N2), or as a two-step reaction, ionization to a carbonium ion and anion, followed by combination of the carbonium ion with Y (S_N1) [Eqs. (3.4) to (3.6)].

$$(3.4) \qquad\qquad Y + RX \rightarrow YR + X$$
$$(3.5) \qquad\qquad RX \rightarrow R^+ + X$$
$$(3.6) \qquad\qquad Y + R^+ \rightarrow RY$$

In the absence of special effects (neighboring groups, strain relief, etc.),

[22] J. G. Kirkwood and F. H. Westheimer, *J. Chem. Phys.*, **6**, 506, 513 (1938).
[23] D. K. Sebera and H. Taube, *J. Am. Chem. Soc.*, **83**, 1785 (1961).
[24] M. L. Bender and Y.-L. Chow, *J. Am. Chem. Soc.*, **81**, 3929 (1959).

the ionization pathway will require considerably more energy than the displacement pathway. In this case, the concerted pathway has been lowered in relation to ionization by the contribution of the partial bond Y----R to the transition state, R----X.

It is likely that enzymes favor a particular pathway by avoiding the formation of highly unstable intermediates when it is possible by a concerted atom transfer to reduce the activation free energy. Thus, DPNH does not yield hydride ion, but rather is induced to transfer hydrogen to the carbonyl bond to be reduced. Concertedness, then, only favors a reaction relative to another reaction, and is not necessarily a required feature of enzymic catalysis.

A well-known example of a reaction in which concerted atom transfers apparently occur is that of the mutarotation of α-D-2,3,4,6-O-tetramethylglucose with 2-pyridone as catalyst.[25] The surprising aspect of this catalysis is the effectiveness of the 2-pyridone even though it is a rather weak base and a rather weak acid. The rate comparisons reported are rather difficult to evaluate because of the inherent difficulty in comparing a first-order rate constant (for the mutarotation reaction of the complex of 2-pyridone with the glucose) with a third-order rate constant for the reaction of the same glucose with pyridine and phenol.[26] The reaction of the 2-pyridone with tetramethylglucose is said to be the first example of "polyfunctional catalysis"[25] and is often quoted as a good model for enzymatic catalysis [Eq. (3.7)]. The mechanism illustrated is

that of the literature,[25] but it should be noted that an alternative formulation, in which an intermediate oxonium ion occurs, is also possible.

(3) *Correct stereochemical arrangements.* Many reactions occur through transition states which are rather narrowly defined in a stereochemical sense. Bimolecular elimination reactions (and the reverse addition reactions) are favored by a transition state in which the leaving group (X) is *trans* to the other group being removed (Y) [Eq. (3.8)]. It is likely that "orientation" of the substrate (when necessary) is achieved through the enzyme-substrate combination step, with a much higher binding constant for the appropriate rotational (or other) form than any

[25] C. G. Swain and J. F. Brown, Jr., *J. Am. Chem. Soc.*, **74**, 2538 (1952).
[26] C. G. Swain and J. F. Brown, Jr., *J. Am. Chem. Soc.*, **74**, 2534 (1952).

other conformational isomer, even if the appropriate form is not the most stable isomer in aqueous solution.

$$(3.8) \qquad \overset{X}{\underset{\diagup}{\diagdown}}C-C\overset{\diagup}{\underset{\diagdown}{}} \longrightarrow \;>C=C< \; + \; XY$$

(4) *"Local concentration" effect.* Combination of the reactants with the enzyme produces a high "local concentration" (or "propinquity") of these molecules. There is little doubt that some enzymatic rate advantage is derived from this source, but other factors are important.

(5) *Electron transport.* In certain cases, as, for example, that of cytochrome c, no obvious means for electron transport to another molecule (or from another molecule) exists in view of the probability that the heme-iron combination is "buried" within the protein molecule, and therefore inaccessible to potential electron-transfer agents. If the only route to the next reactant is through the protein, why not electron transfer through the peptide linkages?

One suggestion along these lines was that the protein could serve as a semiconductor.[27] The energy gap is, however, far too large to make such a proposal realistic (see Sec. 1.4 for discussion). Another alternative, however, is suggested by the discovery of oxidation-reduction reactions which occur through conjugated systems.[23] While adequate verification of the possibility still remains to be accomplished, the exciting finding that cobalt(III) combined with poly-L-glutamic acid is reduced more rapidly by chromium(II) than model compounds, and that the rapid reaction may be associated with helical secondary structure in the polymer, implies that electron transport through at least one peptide linkage may indeed occur[28] (see complete discussion in Sec. 2.12). The nonheme iron-protein combination which functions in electron transport could be another example of such electron transport.[29]

(6) *Miscellaneous possibilities.* *Activation by distortion* is a general term to cover a whole variety of suggested enzymatic mechanisms.[30] It is imagined that certain vibrational modes of the protein-substrate combination lead to a substrate in a "distorted" form (i.e., with stretched bonds, bent bonds . . .) and that the substrate thus is made more reactive. Another idea is to "distort" a portion of the enzyme. The "distorted" enzyme is somehow more reactive toward the substrate,

[27] A. Szent-Györgyi, *Science,* **93,** 609 (1941).

[28] K. D. Kopple, R. R. Miller, and T. C. Muller, *Proc. 1st Intern. Symposium on Polyamino Acids,* Madison, Wis., June, 1961.

[29] H. Beinert and W. Lee, *Biochem. Biophys. Res. Comm.* **5,** 40 (1961).

[30] Cf. R. Lumry, Chapter 4, Volume I, "The Enzymes," Academic Press, Inc., New York, 1959.

perhaps by releasing its strain energy in causing the substrate to react. A related proposal suggests that reactive groups exist at the active site (thioesters, oxazolines, thiazolines . . .) and that these are responsible for enzymatic activity. No evidence concerning the role of these factors in enzyme action is available, and it is difficult to see how such evidence might be obtained in the present state of knowledge about enzymes.

The "induced fit" hypothesis[31] suggests that the substrate produces the "active site" by an "ingathering" of the appropriate groups, i.e., by causing a comformational change in the protein on formation of the enzyme-substrate complex. This hypothesis, which was introduced to explain enzyme specificity, does not appear to be easily verifiable, and should be regarded as an *ad hoc* notion which expresses in one way what might easily be due to a variety of factors. It offers no further insight into why enzymes are efficient at enzyme-substrate combination than "classical" (i.e., lock and key) theories. There is meager evidence in favor of changes in properties upon combination of substrates (including coenzymes) with enzymes, but it is not certain that these should be interpreted as changes in conformation.[32] In addition, even if these changes were easily ascribed to conformational changes, it remains to be shown that these changes occur at the "active site" and not elsewhere in the protein molecule.

3.1B-2. Exchange criteria. A valuable technique for investigating mechanism is based on the use of isotopically labeled reactants. Many enzymes catalyze the exchange of certain atoms (or groups) of a substrate; speculations about mechanism can take place within well-defined limits. In other cases, exchange is not observed at all or only to a limited extent. It is important to realize that mechanistic conclusions *do not follow unequivocally* from all exchange results.

a. Exchange of Hydrogen with Water. If an enzyme catalyzes exchange of a hydrogen with water, it is a fair assumption that the hydrogen being exchanged was removed from the substrate as a proton. However, the converse is not true.

Intramolecular hydrogen rearrangement is observed in the glyoxalase-catalyzed conversion of methylglyoxal to lactic acid. A congruent model for the transformation using hydroxide ion or 2-diethylaminoethanethiol as catalyst also transfers hydrogen from the first carbon to the second in an intramolecular fashion in deuterium oxide solvent (see Sec. 2.3). It can then be concluded from the lack of hydrogen exchange with the solvent that a *hydride* ion was transferred.

[31] D. E. Koshland, Jr., in "The Enzymes," vol. 1, chap. 7, Academic Press, Inc., New York, 1959.

[32] Cf. G. Szabolcsi and E. Biszku, *Biochim. et Biophys. Acta,* **48,** 335 (1961).

In the conversion of isocitric acid to citric acid, the elements of water undergo the rearrangement depicted in Eq. (3.9). By analogy with many organic reactions, and especially hydration of double bonds, it seems highly unlikely that the hydrogen moves as anything but a proton.

(3.9)

Yet deuterium is introduced only partially from the solvent.[33] The lack of complete hydrogen exchange with the solvent does not imply thereby that a hydride-ion migration has occurred but only that the hydrogen is relatively inaccessible to the solvent. The fact that exchange does occur rules out a *purely* intramolecular rearrangement.[34]

The enzyme-catalyzed rearrangement of 5-androsten-3,17-dione to 4-androsten-3,17-dione (see discussion, Sec. 2.3) occurs without exchange of hydrogen with solvent. In this case, many precedents and analogies exist for the removal of a hydrogen as a proton [Eq. (3.10)] and few for its removal as a hydride ion. We must conclude that the lack of

(3.10)

hydrogen exchange simply means that the proton is inaccessible to the solvent, and further, that the atom which transfers the proton has no other hydrogen attached.

Occasionally, exchange of an enolizable proton will not occur in an expected case like that of isocitric dehydrogenase and α-ketoglutaric acid until what we might call an "irrelevant" coenzyme has been added, which in the case cited is TPNH. We can only conclude that the "active site" for enolization requires the presence of TPNH.

In examples for which no good analogy is available, such as that of the enzyme–vitamin B_{12}–catalyzed rearrangement of 1,2-propanediol to propionaldehyde, the lack of hydrogen exchange[35] with the solvent does not provide any reliable indication as to whether a proton or a hydride ion is the best approximation for the nature of the hydrogen being transferred.

b. Identity of an Intermediate. If an isotopically labeled molecule which is thought to be an intermediate in a particular transformation is

[33] J. F. Speyer and S. R. Dickman, *J. Biol. Chem.*, **220**, 193 (1956).
[34] See ref. 17, Sec. 1.2-1.
[35] A. M. Brownstein and R. H. Abeles, *J. Biol. Chem.*, **236**, 1199 (1961).

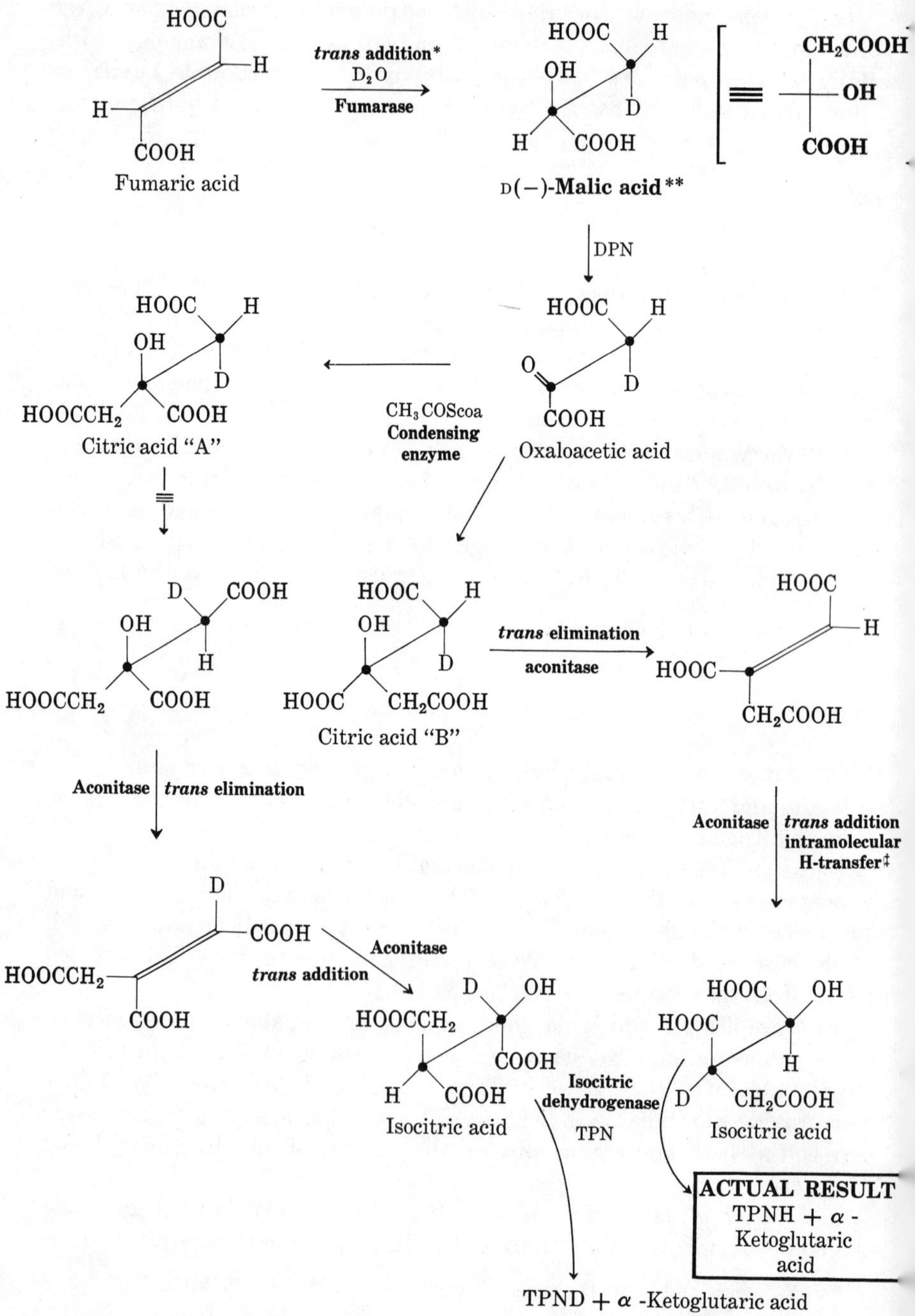

FIG. 3.0. Conversion of D(−)-malic acid to d-isocitric acid.
Footnotes for Fig. 3.0 appear at bottom of page 285.

added to a system containing the enzyme and the substrate, evidence for the role of the labeled molecule as an intermediate is provided by the appearance of the label in the product. If the label does not appear, or appears only to a limited extent, it does not follow that the molecule in question was not an intermediate.

The reduction of hydroxymethylglutaryl coA to mevalonic acid only involves added mevaldic acid to a limited extent, even though the aldehyde is a "natural" intermediate in the conversion of the acyl coA grouping to a primary alcohol. The participation of mevaldic acid can be definitely shown, however, and it must be concluded that "enzyme-bound" mevaldic acid does not exchange readily with added mevaldic acid [Eq. (3.11)].[36]

In a similar manner, the failure to incorporate added acrylic acid into succinic acid in the presence of methylmalonic acid and an enzyme system containing methylmalonyl coA isomerase does not *prove* that acrylic acid is not involved as an "enzyme-bound" intermediate in the transformation.[37]

(3.11)

$$\underset{\underset{OH}{|}}{\overset{\overset{CH_3}{|}}{HOOCCH_2CCH_2COScoA}} \xrightarrow{ESH} \underset{\underset{OH}{|}}{\overset{\overset{CH_3}{|}}{HOOCCH_2C-CH_2COSE}} \xrightarrow{TPNH} \underset{\underset{H}{|}}{\overset{\overset{OH}{|}}{\text{---}C-SE}}$$

$$\text{---}CH_2OH \xleftarrow{TPNH} \underset{HSE}{\text{---}CHO}$$

Mevalonic acid	"Bound" mevaldic acid

Other cases to which the same stricture may be applied include the formation of aminoacyl adenylates and oxaloacetic acid in the formation of pyruvic acid from malic acid.[38]

[36] J. Brodie and J. A. Porter, *Biochem. Biophys. Research Comm.*, **3**, 173 (1960).
[37] R. W. Swick, *Federation Proc.*, **20**, 80 (1961). Cf. *Proc. Natl. Acad. Sci. U.S.*, February, 1962.
[38] W. J. Rutter and H. A. Lardy, *J. Biol. Chem.*, **233**, 374 (1958).

* Established by O. Gawron and T. P. Fondy, *J. Am. Chem. Soc.*, **81**, 6333 (1959), and F. A. L. Anet, *J. Am. Chem. Soc.*, **82**, 994 (1960). See Sec. 2.5, Fig. 2.70.

** Written according to the Fischer convention; cf. L. F. Fieser and M. Fieser, "Organic Chemistry," 3d ed., p. 263, D. C. Heath and Company, Boston, 1956.

† Supported by O. Gawron, A. J. Glaid III, A. LoMonte, and S. Gary, *J. Am. Chem. Soc.*, **80**, 5856 (1958).

‡ J. F. Speyer and S. R. Dickman, *J. Biol. Chem.*, **220**, 193 (1956).

§ S. England, *J. Biol. Chem.*, **235**, 1510 (1960).

3.1B-3. Stereospecificity. Most enzymatic reactions exhibit a considerable degree of stereospecificity. The structure of the "active site" must be more precisely defined than would be expected simply on the basis of proper geometry for certain functional groups, because the stereochemistry at an atom not involved in a given transformation nevertheless maintains a precise relationship to the reaction center. An excellent example of the kind of stereospecific reactions which are to be found in biochemical systems is shown in Fig. 3.0 for the conversion of D(−)-malic acid to d-isocitric acid.[39]

It may be noted that a symmetric molecule, citric acid, participates in the reactions of Fig. 3.0 in an asymmetric manner, because the transition states from the enzyme–citric acid complex are asymmetric.[40] Hydrolysis of the symmetric molecule, diethyl-β-acetamidoglutarate, can be effected in an asymmetric manner by α-chymotrypsin for the same reason.[41]

Stereospecific reduction of a molecule as simple as acetaldehyde also occurs and can be demonstrated with the use of deuterium as tracer (see Sec. 2.13A). In this reaction, the enzyme is able to fix the relative orientation of two groups as similar in size as methyl and hydrogen.

The stereospecific aspect of enzyme action requires that the "active site" be considerably greater in extent than would be required for interaction at a reaction center. Even a molecule as small as fumaric acid can represent a rectangular prism (including van der Waal's radii) of ca. $9 \times 4 \times 4$ Å. If portions of two helical sections of the enzyme, fumarase, are in "direct" contact with such a prism, at least twelve amino acids represent the minimum number of components of the active site (based on an α-helix of 5.4 Å pitch with 3.6 amino acid residues per turn[42]).

3.1C. "Mapping" the Active Site

The ideal method for "mapping" the active site would be an X-ray diffraction analysis of the enzyme-substrate complex in solution. However, the low concentration of the enzyme-substrate complex and the tremendous difficulties in X-ray diffraction analysis of solutions make the ideal method scarcely realizable. In certain cases (e.g., that of hemoglobin), X-ray analysis of the crystals offers a method for determining the "active site" (i.e., for oxygen transport),[43] but there is some doubt that

---

[39] S. Englard, *J. Biol. Chem.*, **235**, 1510 (1960).

[40] A. G. Ogston, *Nature*, **162**, 963 (1948).

[41] S. G. Cohen and E. Khedouri, *J. Am. Chem. Soc.*, **83**, 1093 (1961).

[42] G. C. Pimentel and A. L. McClellan, "The Hydrogen Bond," p. 313, W. H. Freeman and Co., San Francisco, 1960.

[43] M. F. Perutz, in ref. 8, p. 165.

the conformations of the protein in the crystal would be fully indicative of the conformation(s) appropriate for the "active site."

Current approaches to the problem are to identify as far as possible the *functional groups* which participate in the chemical transformation. With one exception, identification of these groups has depended upon indirect methods, based upon a correlation of enzyme activity with a chemical change in the environment. The changes utilized are formation of covalent enzyme-substrate compounds (*direct!*), formation of inactive enzyme-inhibitor complexes, pH changes, photoöxidation, and limited reaction with group-specific reagents.

A new *"direct approach"* to the "mapping" of the "active site" is outlined in Sec. 3.1C-3.

3.1C-1. The choice of functional groups. The number of possible functional groups, even including possible unknown and labile combinations within the enzyme molecules, is comparatively small since the number of naturally occurring amino acids which constitute the enzyme proteins is fairly small. A list of the functional groups is given in Table 3.1-1.

A relatively fertile field of chemical investigation is a systematic study of how the inclusion of a functional group in a polypeptide of controlled composition and helix-random coil ratio affects the properties of the functional group.

3.1C-2. Methods of study of "active sites." One technique which may prove to be quite useful but which has not yet been applied to many cases is that of ultraviolet and visible spectroscopic examination of enzyme-coenzyme complexes or of enzyme-substrate compounds, followed by a detailed examination of expected environmental and structural effects upon the electronic transition being observed. An analysis of the effect of alcohol dehydrogenase on the spectrum of DPNH led to some conclusions about a functional group present at the active site, and thus to a mechanism for the DPN-ethanol reaction (see Sec. 2.13G). The study of cinnamoylchymotrypsin suggested the conclusion that the acyl group was bonded to oxygen (presumably serine) and not to nitrogen.[44]

a. Covalent Intermediates. The best indication that a functional group is located in an "active site" is the isolation of peptide degradation product containing a portion of the substrate covalently bonded to the group. The conclusion that this indication is correct is predicated on the assumptions that the covalent compound is a result of the interaction of the enzyme "active site" with the substrate and not the product of a rearrangement step subsequent to the enzymatic catalysis, and that the

[44] M. L. Bender, Paper presented at the Reaction Mechanisms Conference, Princeton, N.J., September, 1960.

TABLE 3.1-1. FUNCTIONAL GROUPS AT "ACTIVE SITES"

Group	Amino acid	Evidence	Ref.
—CH₂OH	Serine	Inhibition of hydrolytic activity of α-chymotrypsin by diisopropyl phosphorofluoridate (DFP) results in a phosphoenzyme which can be degraded to a polypeptide containing a phosphoserine (i.e., serine phosphate)	45
CHOH	Hydroxy-proline	Present in collagen, which is a structural protein. No indications of presence at "active sites"	
—COOH	Aspartic acid Glutamic acid	Either of these acids has been found next to serine phosphate in polypeptides isolated from a number of phosphoenzymes prepared with DFP. The significance of their presence next to serine is not known	46
$\underset{\underset{H}{\overset{\displaystyle}{N}}}{\overset{\displaystyle N}{}}$	Histidine	Loss of activity for a number of enzymes seems to parallel destruction of histidine by photo-öxidation, by chemical destruction, or by salt formation (with H⁺)	47
—NH₂	(ε-)Lysine	Inferred from the DPNH-ADH spectrum. Combined with pyridoxal in phosphorylase. Loss of ribonuclease activity connected with reaction of lysine with 2,4-DNFP[b]	a, 48
—SH	Cysteine	Inhibition of enzyme activity by reagents which react with thiol groups, e.g., PCMB, IAA.[c] An argument against the "masking" of thiol groups through thiazoline ring formation is based on the relatively low rate of ring-opening observed for 2-methylthiazoline (ref. 49)	
—NHCNH₂ $\overset{\displaystyle N}{\underset{H}{\parallel}}$	Arginine		
—⟨benzene⟩OH	Tyrosine		
⟨indole⟩	Tryptophan	Possibly responsible for a long-wavelength band observed in the DPN-TPD[d] complex, originally termed a charge-transfer band (ref. 50) and ascribed to tryptophan by experiments with models	51

[a] Sec. 2.13G.

[b] 2,4-Dinitrofluorobenzene.

[c] p-Chloromercuribenzoic acid, iodoacetic acid.

[d] Triosephosphate dehydrogenase.

[45] E. F. Jansen, M. D. F. Nutting, and A. K. Balls, *J. Biol. Chem.*, **179,** 201 (1949).

[46] P. D. Boyer, *Ann. Rev. Biochem.*, **29,** 1 (1960).

[47] E. A. Barnard and W. D. Stein, *Advances in Enzymol.*, **20,** 51 (1958).

[48] M. Halmann, in ref. 8, p. 131.

[49] R. B. Martin, S. Lowey, E. L. Elson, and J. T. Edsall, *J. Am. Chem. Soc.*, **81,** 5089 (1959).

[50] E. M. Kosower, *J. Am. Chem. Soc.*, **78,** 3497 (1956).

[51] G. Cilento, *J. Biol. Chem.*, **236,** 907 (1961).

degradation of the enzyme does not produce any further change in the covalent bond arrangements within the polypeptide linkages.

The covalent intermediates can be isolated from the reaction of an enzyme with its substrate, as in the case of phosphoglucomutase and glucose-1-phosphate, or by reaction of the enzyme with a "quasi-substrate"[52,52a] like diisopropyl phosphorofluoridate (DFP). The covalent intermediate formed from diphenyl phosphorochloridate and α-chymotrypsin also provides evidence that a second nucleophilic group is located very close to the serine by its further rapid formation of one molecule of phenol per molecule of inhibited enzyme (see Sec. 2.7).[53]

b. Inhibitors. Useful inhibitor molecules are those which resemble "true" substrates to some extent and which can form an enzyme-substrate complex but not undergo further reaction. It is presumed that inhibitor binding as measured directly or kinetically reflects affinities between enzyme functional (or other) groups and corresponding portions of the inhibitor molecule.

Although inhibitors are useful in delineating certain gross aspects of the "active site," they are intrinsically incapable of providing very precise information about the "active site." Thus, studies of inhibitors were applied to the design of antidotes for anticholinesterases, and presumably might be useful in other problems of drug design in which it was necessary to affect the activity of a particular enzyme. A careful investigation of some competitive inhibitors of fumarase gave some information about possible arrangements of hydrogen-bonding groups at the "active site" but also demonstrated that such parameters as the pH-inhibition profile for the enzyme-inhibitor complex were different from those for the enzyme-substrate complex, even though the groups involved in the dissociation had not changed.[54]

A substrate for the enzyme α-chymotrypsin, α-N-acetyl-L-phenyl-alaninamide, has a Michaelis constant K_s of 31×10^{-3} M, while the competitive inhibitor, α-N-acetyl-L-phenylalaninamidoxime, yields an inhibition constant K_i of 30×10^{-3} M.[55] The failure of an amidoxime to hydrolyze at the same site as an analogous amide and hydroxamic acid might reflect an aspect of the enzyme mechanism, but not one that is easily defined.

c. pH-rate Profiles. It is common practice to take the bell-shaped pH–enzyme activity curves observed for many enzymatic reactions and derive from these the dissociation constants for the two functional

[52] D. E. Koshland, *Advances in Enzymol.*, **22**, 45 (1960).

[52a] Cf. Sec. 1.1, ref. 4.

[53] W. Lee and J. H. Turnbull, *Experientia*, **17**, 360 (1961).

[54] P. W. Wigler and R. A. Alberty, *J. Am. Chem. Soc.*, **82**, 5482 (1960).

[55] R. E. Peterson and C. Niemann, *Biochim. et Biophys. Acta*, **48**, 331 (1961).

groups which are supposedly involved in the action of the "active site." There are, however, objections to this procedure, and it is a matter of some importance that conclusions derived from pH-activity curves be regarded as tentative hypotheses.

Consider the acid-base equilibria in Eqs. (3.12) and (3.13), in which, for the sake of the argument, we assume that the base B is the functional group of the enzyme E. We further assume that the combination of the substrate S and the enzyme is favored by groups other than the basic group.

$$\text{(3.12)} \qquad \text{H}_3\text{O}^+_{aq} + \text{B}_{aq} \rightleftharpoons \text{BH}^+_{aq} + \text{H}_2\text{O}$$
$$\text{(3.13)} \qquad \text{H}_3\text{O}^+_{aq} + \text{E} \cdot \text{S}_{aq} \rightleftharpoons \text{EH}^+\text{S}_{aq} + \text{H}_2\text{O}$$

If, as will often be the case, S contains a negative charge (fumarate ion, for example), the equilibrium constant for Eq. (3.12) will not be the same as that for Eq. (3.11). It is easily possible that the difference will be several orders of magnitude. An example of this effect is found in the dissociation constants for fumarase-inhibitor complexes,[54] given in Table 3.1-2.

TABLE 3.1-2. DISSOCIATION CONSTANTS FOR FUMARASE-INHIBITOR COMPLEXES[a,d]

Complex	pK_a	pK_b
Free enzyme	6.3	6.9
Succinate-enzyme complex	6.5	7.5
D-Tartrate-enzyme complex	6.9	7.8
L-Tartrate-enzyme complex	7.4	7.5
meso-Tartrate-enzyme complex	5.7	7.1

[a] Determined at 25°C in 0.01 ionic strength "tris"[b] buffer with "L-malate" (i.e., D(−)-malate by the Fischer convention) as substrate by plotting Φ^c against pH.
[b] Tris(hydroxymethyl)aminomethane.
[c]
$$\Phi = \frac{K_I V_S [1 + (\text{H}^+)/K_{\overline{\text{HS}}}]}{K_S (E)_0 [1 + (\text{H}^+)/K_{\text{HI}}]} \text{ sec}^{-1}.$$

[d] Ref. 54.

The presence of one or more charged groups close to the functional group at the "active site" can have a considerable effect on the observed dissociation constants, and can be observed in such molecules as simple aliphatic dicarboxylic acids.[22] An equilibrium prior to the rate-determining step will have an effect upon the observed pK_a based on pH-activity curves.[56]

Two other points should be mentioned in connection with pH-activity

[56] T. C. Bruice and G. L. Schmir, *J. Am. Chem. Soc.*, **81**, 4552 (1959).

results.   First, a completely different interpretation of the bell-shaped curves obtained by plotting pH against activity has been given, based on the interaction of the fluctuating protein charge with the substrate dipole.[57]   Although this interpretation has been criticized as not representing the experimental situation quantitatively,[58] it does seem possible that such "fluctuation interactions" make some contribution to the over-all enzyme-substrate interaction and therefore must be taken into account in any interpretation of the effect of pH.   The second point concerns the location of the protonated basic group (or of the deprotonation).   There is no guarantee that the gain (or loss) of a proton takes place at the "active site," and not at some other location, in which the presence (or absence) of a proton serves to allow an enzymatically active protein to "form."

In summary, although interpretation of pH–enzyme activity curves offers a seductively simple method for the identification of functional groups at the "active site," modest use of such information is urged until its value can be established by other methods.

d. "Destruction" versus Activity Correlations.   A general criticism which can be leveled at all methods which attempt to identify functional groups at the "active site" by a correlation of their destruction with enzyme activity is that there is little direct evidence that these functional groups participate in the enzymatic reaction.   Even the sophisticated approach of using *rates* of destruction does not provide evidence that the amino acids which are being destroyed actually have anything to do with the catalytic action of the enzyme.[59,60]   The two principal destructive methods used have been methylene blue–sensitized photoöxidation and the use of a limited amount of amino acid reagent (e.g., 2,4-dinitrofluorobenzene for amino groups).

3.1C-3. "Direct" Approaches.   A very simple idea is the starting point for "direct" approaches to the problem of the "active site." If what we want to know is the structure of the enzyme portion of the "active site," then it would be desirable to trap this arrangement (see the definition) as it acts upon the substrate.   We should then decompose our substrate in the enzyme-substrate complex in such a way as to mark the "active site" for later identification.   This information would be combined with sequence determinations so that a three-dimensional picture of the enzyme-substrate complex can be constructed.

[57] J. G. Kirkwood, *Discussions Faraday Soc.*, **20**, 78 (1955).

[58] K. J. Laidler, *Discussions Faraday Soc.*, **20**, 254 (1955).

[59] W. J. Ray, Jr., J. J. Ruscia, and D. E. Koshland, Jr., *J. Am. Chem. Soc.*, **82**, 4739 (1960).

[60] W. J. Ray, Jr., H. G. Latham, Jr., M. Katsoulis, and D. E. Koshland, Jr., *J. Am. Chem. Soc.*, **82**, 4743 (1960).

An enzyme-substrate compound is a better initial choice than an enzyme-substrate complex because it avoids the difficulty of distinguishing between substrate combined to the enzyme and substrate in solution. Chymotrypsin seems to offer many advantages as an initial choice: (a) low molecular weight, (b) much progress toward sequence determination, and (c) possibility of preparing an acyl enzyme. The acyl enzyme should be susceptible to an outside reagent which produces one or more reactive entities capable of reacting more or less indiscriminately with amino acids of the "active site." A compound which fits these requirements is an azo compound which can be photolyzed to give free radicals. Thus, a possible choice for initial substrate is the p-nitrophenyl ester of methyl azocarboxylic acid. Formation of the acyl enzyme can be followed by the production of p-nitrophenol, while the acyl enzyme should be susceptible to photolysis. The affected amino acids should appear in abnormal positions in amino acid analysis[61] or might be labeled with tritium by the addition of a suitable hydrogen-atom donor to the photolysis medium.

The photolytic reduction of an o-nitro group attached to a 4-phenyl group in a 1,4-dihydropyridine[62] suggests that the photolysis of DPNH-enzyme complexes might lead to modification of the "active site," perhaps by the route shown in Eq. (3.14).

$$(3.14)$$

Although the "direct" approach to the "active site" is certainly laborious, it appears to offer a reasonably unequivocal method for discovering the nature of the "active site." It might not be long afterward that explanations for enzyme action may be possible. We wish to find out the precise and detailed mechanisms of enzyme action as they occur in nature, so that eventually we may be able to correlate the information on enzymatic mechanisms with genetic analysis and other microscopic and macroscopic biological phenomena.

[61] D. H. Spackmann, W. H. Stein, and S. Moore, Anal. Chem., 30, 1190 (1958).
[62] J. A. Berson and E. Brown, J. Am. Chem. Soc., 77, 447 (1955).

NAME INDEX

293

SUBJECT INDEX